The NHS—
A Kaleidoscope of Care—
Conflicts of Service
and Business Values

The NHS—
A Kaleidoscope of
Care—Conflicts of
Service and Business
Values

Tony Kember and Gordon Macpherson

The Nuffield Provincial Hospitals Trust

Published by the
Nuffield Provincial Hospitals Trust
59 New Cavendish Street, London W1M 7RD

ISBN 0 900574 87 9

Designed by Bernard Crossland

PRINTED IN GREAT BRITAIN BY
BURGESS (ABINGDON) LTD
THAMES VIEW, ABINGDON
OXFORDSHIRE

CONTENTS

ABOUT THE AUTHORS

Tony Kember, MA, MHSM, Dip HSM, CBIM

Tony Kember left Oxford in 1956, joined the NHS as an Administrative Trainee and was promoted on his first day. He held two posts of Hospital Secretary before becoming Deputy House Governor of Westminster Hospital. He studied computing and hospital management in the USA in 1967 and was subsequently seconded to Management Consultants, McKinseys. He was Group Secretary to Hillingdon Hospital Management Committee, a field-testing site for the 1974 Reorganisation, before being appointed Administrator of the Kensington and Chelsea and Westminster Area Health Authority. He was appointed Regional General Manager of South-west Thames in 1983. He was Secretary to the Regional Chairmen's Group for eight years and Chairman of RGMs for three. In 1989 he was transferred to the Department of Health as Communications Adviser until his retirement in 1992. He is Chairman of the Disabled Living Foundation. He believes in the NHS.

Gordon Macpherson, MB, BS(London)

Gordon Macpherson was educated at McGill University, Montreal and St. Thomas's Hospital Medical School, where he qualified MB BS in 1955. After a house job at St. Thomas's he worked in the Royal Air Force Burns Unit, entering general practice in 1959. In 1964 he joined the staff of the British Medical Association, where he was secretary to its planning unit. Moving to the British Medical Journal in 1970, Gordon Macpherson was from 1976 until 1990 Deputy Editor, when his prime responsibilities were writing on the NHS and medico-politics. On his retirement he was made a vice-president of the Association. Since retiring he has been a freelance writer on medical affairs, also editing Black's Medical Dictionary.

ACKNOWLEDGEMENTS

We are most grateful to the Nuffield Provincial Hospitals Trust for their invitation to write this commentary of the fast changing health scene and particularly to Walter Holland for his ideas, support and encouragement. We would also like to thank Heather Lodge for her assistance in supplying substantial source material. Finally, we are grateful to Mr Simon Hildrey for help with editing and to Yvonne Smith and Hannah Armah for their secretarial support.

1

INTRODUCTION

———— ◆ ————

"For forms of government let fools contest,
Whate'er is best administered is best."
ALEXANDER POPE.

The past 14 years have seen the most dramatic and profound changes in the provision of social and welfare services in the United Kingdom since 1945, encapsulating both philosophy and policy. Even the upheaval caused by the introduction of the NHS in 1948 may not have been as great because it followed a gradual alteration in the way health services were delivered, funded and provided during the second world war.

The writing of this book arose from the belief that it was important to provide a contemporary account of some of the events and changes that have taken place over the past 14 years. Admittedly, it has been written without the benefit of historical hindsight and without knowing what the result of the various policies and reforms will be, leading either to the improvement of health or to the deterioration in the quality of service. As a result this book can only serve as an ephemeral account. It has, however, been written by two individuals who have been closely involved with the developments and observation of the NHS, offering an illuminating and important view of both the reforms and the personalities who have been involved over this time, while also serving as an historical account.

The changes that have occurred over the past 14 years are chronicled in this book. They include reforms of the provision of services, changes in attitudes towards the service and, in particular, alterations in the working practices of those providing the services. These reforms are only just beginning to make an impact and we will have to wait and see whether the hopes of some or the fears of others on this sea change will be realised.

The NHS was the first tax funded health service, as distinct from insurance coverage, for the whole population. It was established in 1948 as part of a broad commitment in the postwar era to social welfare measures, a commitment which crossed class and party lines. The NHS was designed to be comprehensive in provision and universal in population coverage and all health services were to be free of charge at the point of use. The intention was to integrate, plan and distribute services more effectively, and to provide equality of access to health care.

It was expected that the cost of the NHS would be met by the increase in productivity resulting from the improvements in the health of the population, with the consequence that the health service would effectively pay for itself. Naturally, this has never been the case. Costs have risen inexorably, owing to improvements in technology, methods of treatment, changes in demography and because of the increased expectations of the population and the health professions. Every government since the establishment of the Guillebaud Committee inquiry into NHS finance in 1956[1] has attempted to limit the rise in costs.

In the 1950s governments concentrated upon upgrading medical care throughout the country, with the capital programme being limited and largely devoted to replacing worn-out buildings at existing acute hospitals. In the 1960s and 1970s funds were directed towards hospital construction and upgrading technology. But the implementation of the hospital construction programme was hampered by insufficient capital to realise its objectives and, despite some achievements, it came under increasing criticism by the late 1960s. From the mid-1970s onwards the financial situation of the NHS worsened, reflecting the overall performance of the British economy. There was the oil shock of 1973 followed by nearly a decade of 'stagflation'. This end to growth, and with it the end to associated increases in tax revenues, forced central governments across northern Europe to rein in public spending sharply. As a consequence, the objectives of health care systems were to increase productivity and efficiency. In Britain, the NHS, however, remained largely sheltered from the effects of the economic recession for at least the first three years of the 1974–79 Labour government. Current spending (in volume terms) continued to increase, with the initial pressure for reductions being placed on the capital budget for building.

Other factors combined with the economic constraints to

give a perception that the health service was facing severe
problems. Britain's population was ageing, with the consequence that the demands upon the NHS were increasing and
simply to maintain the existing level of services, while accom-
modating these extra demands, required a one per cent
increase (in real terms) in the NHS budget every year. There
were the demands made by pressure groups on behalf of
specific client groups. More important, however, was the increasing emphasis placed on achieving the original 1948 aim of
an equitable geographical distribution of resources. The principle of incremental resource allocation was consequently
replaced by differential resource allocation according to need.
The report of the Resource Allocation Working Party (RAWP)
in 1976[2] led to the introduction of a formula for the allocation
of the hospital and community health services budget in England, the purpose of which was to provide equal access to
health care for equal need. This entailed the RAWP formula
setting each regional health authority in England an equitable
target or a fair share of financial resources in proportion to the
weighted regional populations to produce the RAWP target
for each region to which existing allocations would gradually
be moved. There were separate formulae and targets for revenue and capital. In 1976 it was envisaged that redistribution
could largely be achieved by differential growth within 10
years. However, the pace at which allocations were shifted
towards targets was still to be determined by ministers.

By the end of the 1970s the NHS had reached a crossroads in
its development. On the one hand demands for new resources
continued to grow unabated but on the other hand the government remained financially constrained by the economic
legacies of the 1970s, in particular by the consequences of having expanded public sector spending during a period of
overall economic stagnation.

These new problems were, paradoxically, the result of previous successes and the raised expectations of the public.
Growth of the health sector and an expansion in the aims of
health policy to incorporate health promotion, community
care and rationalisation led to an increase in inequitable access
to health care and a rise in health care costs.

Of course, the UK has not been alone in facing these challenges. In most developed countries the demand for health

care exceeds the supply of resources. In response, politicians have implemented user charges, reformed the financing and management of the health service, and introduced competition between hospitals.

On the election of the Conservative party in 1979 public expenditure was immediately targeted in an effort to reduce the rate of inflation and the national debt. As far as the NHS was concerned the government tried to limit the rise in costs, increase efficiency, introduce management and structural reforms, and encourage other methods of provision, such as the private and voluntary sectors.

In looking at the founding principles of the NHS in 1948 no one would claim that all, or indeed any, of the criteria were fully satisfied by the NHS as it stood 40 years later. Although equality of access, comprehensiveness and free services at the point of delivery were still strong features of the NHS other characteristics have emerged over the past decade, including effectiveness, efficiency, quality, choice and consumerism, which may counteract many of the positive developments of the past 40 years.

Potentially the most damaging consequence of the reforms, however, has been the breakdown in relations between the government and the professions and between managers and the professions. This latter development has been exacerbated by the apparent introduction of a hierarchical system of management from the centre to the unit. Whereas in the past there have always been routine problems, the breakdown in relationships that occurred between 1986 and 1991 were more prolonged and severe than any other since the foundation of the NHS. In addition, Andrew Wall, the ex-district general manager of Bath, argued in the Health Service Journal that "They [managers] have every reason for conforming. No one wants to lose their job during a recession, when they can't sell their house, can't get their children into the schools of their choice. The current climate is breeding thoroughly unconfident managers! A service that conforms to that extent will be second class in terms of ideas and innovation. It will be typified—and already is—by rhetoric masquerading as truth."[3]

When the NHS was founded the British Medical Association and doctors, while supportive of the NHS in principle, were opposed to the way it was implemented and yet have now become its staunchest defenders. The concern shown by the health professions about the introduction of the market has been one of the most important of the numerous changes that have occurred as a result of the introduction of the health reforms. This is a cause of optimism since it is evidence of the doctors' determination to ensure that the patients will not unduly suffer as a result of the reforms.

When scientific findings and breakthroughs were comparatively rare scientists and researchers were looked upon with awe and their pronouncements were heeded by most. Now, with scientists being plentiful and the number of findings increasing rapidly, it is of interest to see how disregarded their views and opinions are, along with the advice of all other experts and academics, compared to those of others in government. It is that, perhaps, which is most likely to cause a breakdown in the health service in the future. It is the neglect of education, the lack of concern with the maintenance of science in the health service and the apparent inability of those in government to devote their energies to supporting researchers in the less recognised fields of research as opposed to the glamorous areas, such as nuclear physics or molecular biology, which could well prove to have the most damaging effect upon the long-term future of our health service. Linked to this is the fact that the market reforms are based upon demand and, therefore, as the health service is increasingly constrained by resources it is possible that only those services that earn cash will be provided. People with genuine needs may suffer as a result. It is this which is of the greatest concern to those of us who are involved with the health service. This is compounded by the unwillingness of the government or any other group to set out precisely the future priorities for the NHS and to decide what can be funded by the State in the future. This, of course, raises important ethical and philosophical issues which will not be covered here.

Over the past 40 years one of the most dramatic changes has been the improvement in the quality and standards of care provided by, and through, general practice. It is unfortunate that in trying to split the provision of services from the purchasing of services the logical division between primary and secondary care has not been made and that primary care is no longer considered to be the major purchaser of secondary care services. If the logic had been adhered to and groups of general practitioners had been collected together as in the Health Maintenance Organisations in the United States then perhaps a more appropriate method of dividing the purchaser and provider roles might have been achieved. Whether this will result from the proliferation and random development of fundholding is arguable, but the competition between fund-holders and purchasing authorities or consortia is undoubtedly one that needs to be watched. A further problem has been, and will continue to be, that people often make purchasing decisions based upon the quantity rather than the quality of service that they receive. This dilemma has yet to be resolved.

With the increase in the complexity and cost of treatment it is not surprising that in recent times the NHS has become increasingly concerned with prevention, usually based on the belief that through the introduction of preventive methods costs will be kept down in the future. The fallacy of this has been exposed on many occasions, although it is to be welcomed that prevention has become something which is now considered appropriate rather than abstruse.

For the first time the government through a white paper in 1992, 'The health of the nation',[4] actually decided upon five major areas where services should be provided through a variety of different agencies in order to improve the health of the nation. These included cardiovascular disease, mental illness and accidents. This is to be welcomed but it is, however, unfortunate that these initiatives have not been accompanied by additional funding, nor a precise strategy for future policy. The government has, of course, also failed to provide the essential initiatives needed to curb the use of tobacco, probably the most important preventable cause of death.

What is, however, of most concern to those of us involved in the health service is the recent decline in morale and the obvious deterioration in some of our services over time. In the past the United Kingdom could justly argue that improvements were continually being made and that many countries were envious of our health service. Now, although we still have an excellent and relatively equitable service in contrast to that provided in some countries, such as the United States where at least 15% and probably 30% of the population are unable to receive appropriate health care, we do appear to be slipping. While indicators, such as the infant mortality rate and the avoidable mortality rate within the European Community, showed us to be ranked first for many years this is no longer the case. While the NHS has long been regarded as one of the best value for money health services in the world this situation may not continue for long. There are growing concerns that the market reforms implemented under the Conservative governments will militate against the development of new technologies and techniques, will make planning of scarce resources and the health service in general even harder, will make the provision of health care more uneven, and will lead to a decline in the quality of treatment as achieving budgetary targets assumes paramount importance.

The purpose of this book is to provide an account of the health reforms since the late 1970s. We have concentrated our account on England but recognise that there are differences in Wales, Scotland and Northern Ireland. It is important to appreciate that what this book has tried to do is to provide an account of the significant events, to try to interpret these at one point in time and, perhaps more importantly, that this has been done concurrently with a major reform programme being implemented. But while the attempt can only be judged as incomplete and partial it should provide an impression of events while they are fresh in people's minds.

REFERENCES

1. Guillebaud Committee (1956). *Report of the committee of inquiry into the cost of the National Health Service*. Cmnd 9663. London: HMSO.

2. Sharing Resources for Health in England (1976). *Report of the resource allocation working party*. London: HMSO.

3. Davies P (1992). The truth, the whole truth. . . . *Health Service J* 102 (5327): 17.

4. Department of Health (1991). *The health of the nation*. Cm 1523. London: HMSO.

THE 1982 REORGANISATION—
SLIMMING DOWN

◆

INTRODUCTION

The report of the Royal Commission on the NHS, published as
Command Paper 7615 in July 1979,[1] was the first comprehensive review of the service for nearly a quarter of a century,
since the Guillebaud Committee reported in 1956.[2] It found
that the 1974 reorganisation had had the noble objective of
seeking to integrate all health services for patients in the hospitals and the community into one administration. The then
Secretary of State, Sir Keith Joseph, had planned a unified
structure in which the area health authority (AHA) could provide comprehensive health care for a given population living
in a defined geographical location and, where possible, coterminosity of health and local authority boundaries could offer
significant advantages for collaboration in planning the delivery and continuity of health care.

The Royal Commission reported that serious faults had
emerged in the implementation of this concept. In addition,
there had been widespread industrial action during the 'winter of discontent', which caused the public to be concerned and
adversely affected the morale of NHS staff. It summed up its
criticisms as:

> "too many tiers,
> too many administrators in all disciplines,
> failure to take quick decisions,
> money wasted."

The new Tory government's response was to accept the basic criticisms and the majority of the recommendations. It
published its 'Patients first'[3] consultative paper in December
1979 with the intention of streamlining the services in such a
way as to "avoid wholesale upheaval" and "minimise turbulence." It proposed to tackle these problems through:

(a) the strengthening of management arrangements at the local level with greater delegation of responsibility to those in the hospital and community services;

(b) simplification of the structure of the service in England by the removal of the area tier in most of the country and the establishment of district health authorities;

(c) simplification of the professional advisory machinery so that the views of clinical doctors, nurses and the other professions would be heard by the health authorities; and

(d) simplification of the planning system in such a way as to ensure that regional plans were fully sensitive to district needs.

The new authorities were to manage districts "natural in terms of social geography and health care" (the catchment area of the major hospitals, the size and range of facilities, and the links with local government) with "maximum devolution to hospitals and community services at local level" and a clearer definition of personal responsibility amongst members of the management team. The hospital administrator would be accountable for "all non-clinical support services rather than district level managers." The mission was to seek greater devolution and clearer personal accountability to achieve the best value for money as an ever increasing share of public funds was spent on health care. These three objectives remained constant over the next decade and were at the heart of the general management revolution of the mid-1980s.

SIMPLIFICATION AND DELEGATION

In the 1974 reorganisation the prime task and objective had been unification. In the 1982 changes the prime objective was simplification. The white paper on NHS reorganisation,[4] issued in August 1982, was about administration not treatment and care, "but the purpose behind these changes proposed is a better, more sensitive service to the public." Under the 1974 plan a single service was to have been achieved through the unification of the NHS administration (family practitioner services, community health services, the school health service and hospitals) as part of the government's wider programme of administrative reform. Below the department and regions a single new statutory level was established and "since each area health authority will service the same population within the same boundaries as its matching local authority, the purpose will be that formal divisions between health, education and the personal social services will be bridged by the arrangements for collaboration. There will in effect be parallel organisations with links between them." Emphasis was placed on making the new integrated health structure coterminous with local authorities, working effectively through systems of planning and collaboration.

The planning function was exercised at three levels—the area, region and department. "The central department will settle national health policies, objectives and priorities; the regional health authorities will have a regional planning responsibility that will include settling priorities when there are competing claims between areas. But the fundamental unit in the planning process will be the area. AHAs' plans for the communities within the area—the districts—will strongly influence the way in which local, regional and national priorities are carried into effect in the area, and how they are harmonised with local authority plans."[4]

Health care planning teams were established by the AHAs' district management teams "to plan services to meet particular groups of needs, such as services for the elderly, children and the mentally ill and mentally handicapped."[4] In theory, multidisciplinary teams of professionals would look at various aspects of need and determine future requirements. The reports from these teams would be integrated and costed at the district and area level within the overall policies operating throughout the region. It was to be a bottom-up approach—a rational and comprehensive, if elaborate, planning system, which at its inception was warmly welcomed by doctors, nurses and other professionals.

One of the main problems that emerged was the lack of any long-term financial strategy which might have constrained professional enthusiasm. As a result, expensive plans were devised at all levels of the service despite the country's economic problems at the time of the oil crisis. They naturally stood less chance of being implemented as the rate of inflation rapidly increased, cash limits were introduced and the RAWP methodology was developed. Delays in the implementation of health care plans led to professional disenchantment and gave planning a bad name.

The Joint Working Party on collaboration between the NHS

and local government submitted its report in 1973.[5,6] There was a statutory duty to collaborate and a statutory requirement was placed on area health authorities and corresponding local authorities to set up joint consultative committees (JCCs). It was common for there to be:

(a) "In each metropolitan district a single committee covering environmental health, personal social services, education and other functions in respect of which health and local authorities collaborate. It would represent on the local authority side the metropolitan district council"; and

(b) "In each non-metropolitan county one committee for education and personal social services representing on the local authority side the county council; and another linked by common membership and collaboration between officers for environmental health, which would include representatives of all the local authority district councils and of the county council. Other arrangements for collaboration between the area health authorities and the local authorities could be brought under whichever level of consultative committee was appropriate." Thus a number of joint committees were established, which included a large number of representatives from the two sides, and were supported by joint teams of officers.

"The function of these committees would be to examine jointly the needs of each area, the plans of the two sets of authorities for meeting those needs and the progress made towards meeting them; and to *advise* on both the planning and the operation of the services in matters of common concern." From the outset formal machinery was established for resolving disputes! These committees could only advise as the final executive decisions rested with separate statutory bodies. On the social services side JCCs were expected to pay particular attention to the problems of collaboration at district level, and to ensure that good working relationships were not impaired by organisational divisions that were bound to exist. In the large county councils this often presented special problems where the Director of Social Services was reluctant to delegate authority to his 'area officers', who day-to-day worked closely with health managers and professionals at district level, and where final decisions on additional resources through joint financing were reserved for county hall.

The success of the machinery for collaboration largely depended on mutual trust and credibility. It worked well where the local authority representatives on the AHA were knowledgeable, powerful and influential, where they carried authority within the council, and where they gained the confidence of AHA colleagues. It was also successful where the AHA staff were sensitive to local authority sensibilities (the reorganisation was not *an NHS hospital take-over*) and where close, effective working relationships were achieved at local level, with a genuine sharing of information and services with mutual benefit. Where all of these conditions applied some of the hopes and expectations of the working party were fully realised. In many parts of the country, however, effective collaboration and trust remained illusory. Parallel organisations did not unite. This, taken together with the complex system for planning and joint planning, meant that much good work was achieved but with insufficient benefit for the people it was intended to serve, and it thus failed to justify the huge investment of time, staff and money. By 1982, therefore, the government's key task was the simplification of the management and structure, planning and collaboration.

The 1974 reorganisation had caused such a radical structural change and such staff upheaval in an NHS which had developed a complacent attitude to its own tried and tested traditions that the service was reluctant to embark on a second round. On this occasion the government's first objective was to simplify the structure. Perhaps understandably its second aim was to achieve the change in such a way as to minimise turbulence. This was no doubt a praiseworthy intention but unfortunately the latter consideration was allowed to influence the former and in some ways created a more complex organisation and yet further problems.

The future structure of statutory authorities (DHAs) was to be based on the existing pattern of health districts, whose definition owed more to chance and history than to logic or the health needs of local communities. In 1974 health districts had been determined by joint liaison committees. These committees consisted of representatives of both health and local authorities and their recommendations, often taken by majority vote, resulted in most districts being determined not just by general health requirements but also by acute hospital considerations. Prior to 1982 an opportunity presented itself to decide conclusively on a genuinely new pattern of local health authorities, with new roles, new levels of delegated authority, and with new and close relationships with clearly defined communities. That opportunity was missed because of the very strict timetables set for introducing the changes and in the interests of minimising turbulence.

Within one decade the NHS had been exposed to a frantic programme of change. In 1976 the Royal Commission was set up and eventually reported in July 1979.[1] The government's response was embodied in the consultation document 'Patients first', published in December of that year, which declared that its proposals had to be implemented by April 1982. The NHS was to be turned upside down for a second time in eight years.

Health Circular HC (80) 8 set the tight timetable: recommendations on the establishment of DHAs to the Department of Health by February 1981; the Secretary of State "promised" to take decisions by the end of May and to appoint chairmen to the new authorities by the end of June; RHAs would make their appointments of members of DHAs by the end of September, who in turn would appoint their chief officers by the end of November.[7] This timetable would enable the new health authorities to operate for three to four months in shadow form before assuming responsibility on 1st April 1982. This ambitious programme depended on three things—the skill and speed with which RHAs undertook their analysis and appraisal of the options; the manner in which they carried out and responded to the process of consultation with all interested parties; and ministers' ability to keep to their commitments as demanded by the tight timetable. Even though RHAs met their deadlines ministerial decisions were often delayed because of representations from local MPs and perceived weaknesses in the consultation process. As a result decisions were taken hurriedly late in the day and the time spent operating in shadow form was shorter than was hoped.

THE ESTABLISHMENT OF DISTRICT
HEALTH AUTHORITIES

The government has always shown a love-hate relationship with the regions. A consequence of its policy of seeking greater devolution to the local operational level has been a concern that the regional tier is an expensive and comparatively unproductive level of organisation. The difficulty faced by each administration has been that RHAs are the only effective change agents at their disposal. Repeatedly, therefore, in 1982, 1984 and 1989 the regions were called upon to plan and implement major change at a time when their own role was under review and when their long-term future was implicitly at risk. It appeared that at best RHAs might prove to be a necessary evil.

In planning the 1982 changes ministers, particularly Sir Gerard Vaughan, emphasised that there would be a review of the RHA function once the new structure had had time to settle. It was his intention that the review (which with the passage of time and ministers never formally took place) would focus in particular on management costs. The declared intention was to make significant management savings through the elimination of the area tier and a reduction in management costs of 10% nationally on a revised formula to be applied differentially across regions. If large savings in administration could be achieved through the elimination of the area tier what might be accomplished by cutting out the regional bureaucracy? For the time being, however, RHAs had a lot to do. They were exhorted by HC(80)8 to set about the task of restructuring and during the inevitable period of instability and uncertainty they were required to:

(a) ensure continuity in the standard of patients' services provided in the hospital and the community throughout the transitional period (do the sick no harm);

(b) minimise the turbulence to staff caused by the changes (avoid the 1974 system of musical chairs);

(c) leave the future DHAs as much discretion as possible to determine their own management arrangements (keep faith with devolution); and

(d) ensure the continuation of adequate systems of financial control (meet one of the Treasury's main concerns).

In recommending the new DHAs, RHAs had to apply several criteria, which often conflicted with one another, against the overriding principle that "ministers expect that unless there are powerful reasons to the contrary, new DHAs should follow the boundaries of existing districts, or single district areas."[6,7]

The key criteria were:

(a) social geography: "As far as possible districts should be coherent in terms of social geography taking due account of settlement and transport patterns, and boundaries should not cut through localities with well established community identities";

(b) the catchment area of major hospitals: "The health district should, whenever possible, include the majority of the population who looked to its main hospitals";

(c) size and range of facilities: "The districts should not be too small to support the range of services normally associated with the district general hospital. This suggests that most districts would have a population of 200,000 or over, although a few might be below 150,000. The district should not be so large as to have so many hospitals and other health service facilities and activities as to require an intermediate tier of management, or to make staff feel remote from the authority. Very few districts should have populations of over 500,000";

(d) links with local government: "The need for good working relationships between district health authorities and local authorities responsible for social services, education and housing is important and will become increasingly so as primary health care and community services for the elderly, mentally handicapped and mentally ill develop. Where a geographical identity can be achieved it should be. If this is not possible it would be desirable that boundaries of two or more health authorities should be coterminous with the boundary of a social services or education authority or both"; and

(e) management costs: The advantages of smaller health authorities in terms of simplified decision making and close communications with both staff and the community had to be weighed against the costs which every new health authority generated. A large number of DHAs would place greater constraints upon the future management structures within those authorities in order to meet the overall 10% target reduction in management costs which was required.

The problem of balancing the criteria was summed up in Appendix 1 of HC (80) 8, which dealt with the future of London: "no one criterion taken by itself could produce satisfactory results; whatever solution emerges will represent a balance between several criteria and as the problems will vary from place to place the emphasis on the different criteria will also vary."[7] Specifically on London the advice was: "where a match with whole boroughs proves impracticable, efforts should be made to establish new DHAs' boundaries from a combination of whole social services divisions of adjacent boroughs. In some cases a solution may be found only after negotiating an adjustment to the boundaries of social services divisions."

In summary, existing districts were used as a starting point and their future viability was related to local authority boundaries, catchment areas, social geography and teaching needs. Other considerations included flexibility for planning in the future, the turbulence caused by the proposals, the remoteness of a DHA from its population, whether an intermediate tier of management would be required, and whether the proposals would as a consequence, but not as an objective, contribute to the declared aim of reducing management costs overall. There were two obvious and significant areas of conflict. First, in the relationship between the needs of acute and community services. Although the freedom of GPs to refer patients across DHA boundaries was paramount, administrative boundaries were particularly important for community and priority services. Second, although by replacing AHAs and their health districts with only one level, the smaller DHAs, the total number of teams of officers (administrators generating management costs) would be reduced, the larger number of health authorities would bring with them fixed additional costs.

IMPLICATIONS AND RESULTS

By April 1982 the 90 AHAs had been abolished and replaced by 201 new District Health Authorities (DHAs)—nine in Wales and 192 in England (subsequently 190 by 1989 following two amalgamations). The Family Practitioner Committees (FPCs) became increasingly separate bodies from the main line of NHS administration and, under the 1984 Health and Social Security Act,[8] became independent health authorities in their own right. These developments reflected the fact that the NHS had still not secured the full administrative integration of general practitioners, whose FPCs' boundaries and finances now emerged entirely independent of DHAs.

Between 1974 and 1982 strenuous efforts had been made throughout the service not only to unify its structure and management at area level but also to integrate services on that basis. Area based services had been developed extensively and often brought benefits in both cost and quality through economies of scale. With a doubling of the number of health authorities and with the intention of devolving as much decision making as possible to district level these services and economies were put at risk. To minimise disruption area services continued to be managed centrally in the short-term, and it was for the DHAs to decide at a later date the extent to which these services should continue to be managed on an agency basis and the extent to which they should be split and run as separate district services.

The options were for:

(a) each DHA to manage its own services (politically desirable but expensive devolution);

(b) one DHA to act as the agent for two or more created from within one former area (cheap but requiring trust);

(c) DHAs to form consortia to run the services jointly (difficulty of ensuring fair shares for all); and

(d) the RHA temporarily or permanently to manage a common service within parameters set in consultation with the DHAs for whom that service would be provided. This was the least favoured option.

In most instances reason prevailed. For example, county ambulance services were managed by one district on behalf of the area and supply services were maintained where benefit accrued from unified purchasing arrangements. However, for many services which had been run on an area basis the new district health authorities were anxious to do their own thing. For example, DHAs wanted to manage their own financial services, split their area works departments, run their own nursing schools, stand alone as planning authorities, and break-up any area-wide planning service. The break-up and fragmentation of integrated area managed services was intended to achieve devolution, often at a significant cost in terms of duplication, and to feed the ambitions of 'district self-sufficiency'. Where DHAs took over health districts that were very small, had boundaries determined primarily by history, or where there was a reluctance to accept the benefits generated by unifying services on an area basis, the perceived advantages of devolving policy and decision making closer to the community and patients were outweighed by the implications of breaking up area based services and the complexity involved in joint planning and collaborating with local authorities. In some cases changes were made simply for changes sake.

In the consultation which took place over the establishment of DHAs local authorities were particularly concerned about the difficulties of creating satisfactory collaborative arrangements. They often expressed the view that one of the key advantages from the 1974 reorganisation had been the opportunities it had presented for face-to-face discussion between local and health authority members and officers on an area basis and with coterminosity. They pointed out:

(a) the dangers of no coterminosity between the DHA and the local authority in a high proportion of cases;

(b) the perceived complexity and inadequacy of local authority representation on DHAs, especially in 'overlap' areas;

(c) the loss of the recently formed joint consultative machinery covering AHAs. A district based machinery would be extremely complex and expensive in terms of administrative support;

(d) the advantages of unified medical and nursing advice which they had been receiving from a small number of named professionals employed by the AHAs;

(e) those individuals should remain and be formally adopted as the DHAs' advisers; and

(f) some of the area managed services had proved of benefit to the local authority and might be split up to their own disadvantage.

In noting these concerns RHAs generally recognised the importance of maintaining not only informal day-to-day contacts with doctors, nurses, officers of the DHAs and their local authority counterparts but also the necessity of maintaining or recreating some effective formal joint consultative machinery. Generally speaking the following principles were accepted:

(a) the 'proper officer' responsibilities should continue to be provided by named specialists in community medicine (SCMs), who were appointed jointly by local and health authorities. This applied to child health services and liaison with social services, and meant that there could continue to be one specialist in community medicine for each county or London borough with the responsibility of maintaining a common policy for all the DHAs within the appropriate area. The SCMs were given appointments with each DHA and acted on its behalf in dealing with their county council or London borough. Similarly, appropriate links were established for nursing support; and

(b) there had to be mutual agreement by all parties for the establishment of consultative machinery for the purposes of joint strategic planning, joint funding and joint financing. Such arrangements would cover one or more DHAs as local circumstances dictated, but generally had to provide for the co-ordination of service planning over an area which paid particular reference to local authority boundaries. In some places it was a county based joint consultative committee (JCC) with health authority representatives from all the DHAs within the county. In other cases there were separate arrangements between DHAs and parts of, or the whole of, the county council.

Other collaborative machinery with the universities was also affected. The number of university liaison committees increased; the number of health authority members tended to increase, as each DHA that undertook a significant proportion of medical student training had the right to be represented; DHAs sought representation on medical and dental school councils; and the Dean or his representative had the right to attend meetings of the district management team, which managed the main centres of teaching. In all cases the principles of representation and involvement in decision making, which affected both medical education and health service management, meant that from April 1982 the arrangements were bound to become more complex as the number of health authorities grew.

This increase created by the reorganisation also had implications for communications, roles and relationships. Clearly, the Department of Health now had to communicate with twice as many health authorities, though admittedly often still through the 14 RHAs. The RHAs themselves had to relate to twice as many new authorities and had to rethink policies which had been based on area services and where many clinical services had been planned on a multi-district basis.

The 'power' balance shifted with the reorganisation. AHAs employing a large work force and spending many millions of pounds could exert individually and collectively great pressure on the RHA. The smaller district health authorities individually carried less weight and were often vulnerable to the principle of divide and rule. For example, in the allocation of resources it was one thing to involve all DHAs in the formulation of the policy for redistribution but it was another for them to combine sufficiently to challenge the RHAs' preferred option.

The Secretary of State for Health had been able to hold regular meetings with the chairmen of the 90 AHAs. He was less likely to be able to establish meaningful relationships with more than double that number of chairmen. As he distanced himself from the district chairmen so he grew closer to, and relied increasingly on, regional chairmen. Although the determining principle in the formation of the district tier had been the devolution of authority to the local level there was an increasing expectation that RHAs would have a stronger clinical policy planning function because DHAs were too small to plan and maintain comprehensive health services.

From 1982 the health service would be very different. The cost of dismantling area services proved to be high. The savings and improvements in greater efficiency derived from simplifying management structures and teams were illusory. The regional role, still to be reviewed, was intended to be one where the RHA 'stood back', devolved and allowed districts to run their own show. Former regional or multi-district services were to continue only where they met the stated needs of the constituent DHAs. Districts were to aim for autonomy. In practice, districts were small and comparatively weak in political terms. They relied on each other and relied on the RHA to solve inter-district conflict and rivalry. The aim had been greater devolution, which was partly achieved. The result, however, that had not been expected was a strengthening of the role of the regions. In reviewing the objectives of ministerial policy in 1979:

(a) 'Patients first'[3] had sought to strengthen management arrangements at the local hospital level. Devolved authority to districts had been achieved but the devolution of authority from districts to the hospital and community service level, where most staff were employed and where most patients were treated, was still limited and varied tremendously;

(b) 'Patients first' had called for a simplification of the structure and this had been achieved by the removal of the area tier;

(c) 'Patients first' had sought the simplification of the professional advisory machinery and although DHAs had brought representation of professionals onto local health authorities the medical committees at hospitals, districts and regions in reality had little impact on day-to-day operational clinical policies or practices. 'Patients first' had promised a comprehensive review of professional advisory machinery which never took place; and

(d) 'Patients first' had also looked for a simplification of the planning system in a way which would ensure that regional plans were fully sensitive to district needs. Undoubtedly, RHAs went out of their way to involve and consult district authorities in the development of clinical and management policies. Districts, perhaps understandably, were inward looking, jealous of interference from outside and progressively searched for 'self-sufficiency', which meant some duplication and wasteful replication of services. 'District needs' continued to be determined in part by agencies outside the district.

In 1979 the Royal Commission on the National Health Service criticised "too many tiers, too many administrators in all disciplines, failure to take quick decisions, money wasted."[1] From 1982 onwards one tier of authority had been removed but the large number of 'administrators' actually increased as the new DHAs sought to do their own thing. The failure to take quick decisions had been tackled in part because issues requiring decisions were no longer referred up the ladder beyond district level. But the real issue was the extent of genuine delegation of authority from district to unit. Whether money continued to be wasted related as much as anything to the beguiling concept of district self-sufficiency and to the loss of large numbers of senior officers, who took advantage of early retirement, the cost of which was five times greater than the department's estimate and attracted condemnation from the Public Accounts Committee.

REFERENCES

1. *Report of the Royal Commission on the National Health Service* (1979). Cmnd 7615. London: HMSO.

2. Guillebaud Committee (1956). *Report of the committee of inquiry into the cost of the National Health Service*. Cmnd 9663. London: HMSO.

3. Department of Health and Social Security, Welsh Office (1979). *Patients first: consultative paper on the structure and management of the National Health Service in England and Wales*. London: HMSO.

4. Department of Health and Social Security (1972). *National Health Service reorganisation: England*. Cmnd 5055. London: HMSO.

5. Department of Health and Social Security (1973). *Working Party on Collaboration between the National Health Service and local government: report on its activities to the end of 1972*. London: HMSO.

6. Department of Health and Social Security (1973). *Working Party on Collaboration between the National Health Service and local government: report on its activities from January to July 1973.* London: HMSO.

7. Department of Health and Social Security (1980). *Health service development, structure and management.* HC80(8).

8. *Health and Social Security Act* (1984). London: HMSO.

GENERAL MANAGEMENT— THE MANAGEMENT INQUIRY AND THE GRIFFITHS REPORT

INTRODUCTION

The Griffiths report was sent to the Secretary of State for Health on 6th October 1983[1] and was the latest in a long series of government inspired reports, which had sought to influence and improve the organisation and management of the NHS:

(a) *the Bradbeer report* in 1954 was on the internal administration for hospitals[2];

(b) *the Guillebaud report* in 1956 was on the cost of the National Health Service, a recurring theme[3];

(c) *the Hospital plan for England and Wales* was prepared in 1962 and implemented during the 1970s[4];

(d) *the Lycett Green report* in 1963 was on the recruitment, training and promotion of administrative and clerical staff in the hospital service[5];

(e) *the Farquharson-Lang report* in 1966 was on the administrative practice of hospital boards in Scotland[6];

(f) *the Salmon report* in 1966 was on the senior nursing staff structure and the elimination of the matron[7];

(g) *the Cog-Wheel report* in 1967 on the organisation of medical work in hospitals was a cog-wheel which would never actually go round[8];

(h) *the Hunter report* in 1972 was on medical administrators[9]; and

(i) *the Grey Book* in 1972 was on management arrangements for the reorganised National Health Service[10].

These nine reports were written over a period of 20 years in a continuous attempt to improve the organisation and management of hospitals and the health service in general. Throughout there had been a fundamental assumption that management of the health service was inevitably a multi-disciplinary activity. Even as late as 1979 in 'Patients first',[11] the consultative paper on the structure and management of the NHS in England and Wales, the multi-disciplinary management team was endorsed and the concept of the chief executive dismissed. "The government has rejected the proposition that each authority (health district) should appoint a chief executive responsible for all the authority's staff. It believes that such an appointment would not be compatible with the professional independence required by the wide range of staff employed in the service. Instead, each authority should appoint a team to co-ordinate all the health service activities of the district."

In 1982 the new district health authorities were still to be managed by management teams. In February 1983 the Prime Minister asked Roy Griffiths, deputy chairman of J. Sainsbury plc, a large supermarket chain, to conduct his management inquiry and less than a year later the concept of a general manager with personal responsibility and accountability for all the services provided by the authority had become respectable. This was a sudden shift in the government approach to managing the service and reflected the Griffiths' team view. "We have been told that the NHS is different from business in management terms . . . these differences can be greatly overstated. The clear similarities between NHS management and business management are much more important."

MANAGEMENT ARRANGEMENTS AND THE GREY BOOK

It is worth emphasising the administrative chaos of the late 1970s. The implementation of the Reorganisation Act in 1973[12] had resulted in a scramble for jobs despite the best endeavours of the National Staff Committee, which was set up to reduce staff 'turbulence'. The higher up the hierarchy the wider the scope for influence and the better paid jobs. This meant that competent and ambitious administrators running local hospitals sought to leap frog the district and gravitate to the area health authority, leaving behind at the unit level a second or third in command. The doctors in teaching hospitals were the most vociferous in complaining that their house governor had gone to the area health authority, his deputy to the district and the office boy was left to run the multi-million pound business and, more importantly, to deal with their problems of professional politics! It was clearly detrimental for the NHS if the limited management talent available gravitated away from the hot end of the business—the cutting edge of clinical care. It worked against the objective of devolution as in these circumstances it was all too easy to pass the buck up the chain of command. There were numerous stories, which frequently received national publicity, of simple management decisions that were required to resolve day-to-day issues in hospitals being referred to the district and even to the area authority, causing delay, frustration and inefficiency.

The authorities themselves had a membership based on representation (a doctor, a nurse and local authority representatives). They usually took routine decisions and gave little strategic direction. There was often too little delegation and their Chief Officer was reduced to the status of 'secretary' with limited power (the ear of the Chairman) and little opportunity to exercise delegated discretion. It is not surprising that many administrators were constantly looking over their shoulders for some superior officer to carry the can.

Much of the blame for the magnitude of the administrative disruption lay with the Grey Book.[10] It was inflexible, it increased administrative complexity through an extension of functional management and ensured that decisions had to be taken by 'consensus'. It offered a single-bullet solution to management arrangements throughout the service at district, area and regional level. The Grey Book prescribed precisely the management arrangements in the representative membership of the management team (district management team/area team of officers/regional team of officers) and the relationships between the different levels. Almost the same arrangements had to apply in an area whether it be a single district coterminous with its local authority or a multi-district, multi-teaching hospital and multi-London borough enterprise. This lack of flexibility to respond to different local needs was a recipe for disaster and its weaknesses were manifest almost as soon as its recommendations had been implemented.

The Social Services Department at Brunel University had advised the government on management arrangements and had contributed the most to the Grey Book. In studies of other large organisations it had discovered the principle that professionals are best managed by professionals but believed that in the NHS some professionals (the doctors) could simply not be managed at all. The application of this principle led to the ludicrous and extravagant development of functional management and to a situation where the AHA appointed senior professionals as managers, who were frequently inappropriate for the job. In some places even chiropodists and speech therapists, who were in short supply, were appointed as area managers to manage a handful of other professionals. They ought to have been treating patients but spent an increasing proportion of their time on administration, learning to plan and manage with other area officers and all the time becoming ever more removed from their patients.

[All effective managers employ consultation and consensus.] The problem with the reorganisation of the NHS was the way it was interpreted. The argument was that the NHS was a large multi-professional organisation where major decisions affecting patient care should be taken in close consultation with the doctors, nurses and other staff. The more these decisions were shared the greater the commitment would be to carry them out and the more likely that they would always take into account the patient's best interests. So far so good. In many parts of the NHS this requirement for complete consensus/agreement worked well. This was often due to the skill and personality of an individual—usually the administrator. As well as running administrative and support services (the porters, the cooks and the cleaners) he was also charged: *are there no female administrators?*

(a) as co-ordinator with responsibility for managing the business of the team, bringing issues forward for decision-making and seeking to resolve differences of opinion; and

(b) as secretary he had the responsibility for managing the business of the authority, preparing the agenda and papers, and identifying issues which needed authority decisions.

One of the greatest difficulties in making consensus work was in persuading the doctors on the management team (consultants and GPs) to co-operate. To what extent could they or would they be able to speak for and give the commitment of their colleagues? Throughout the service at all levels the medical advisory machinery was cumbersome and slow and often run by doctors with inadequate administrative support. A group secretary of a hospital management committee who had dinner with the chairman of the medical committee to discuss the agenda before the meeting (usually held in the evenings to suit the GPs) was a rarity. The doctors usually argued at length and decided little which had a significant effect upon local management. They preferred to tackle 'the administration' individually in their ward or department rather than take advantage of their considerable potential power by coming to a consensus agreement and having the internal discipline to enforce it. It is not surprising, therefore, that the consultant member of the team often felt powerless. His advice should have had a crucial influence on local management decisions but too often he was seen as the representative of ill-disciplined warring factions. The GP member was no better off as most of his colleagues felt that the management team had no influence whatsoever on their practices and its credibility could only come from improving day-to-day operations, such as the early sending of discharge letters informing them of their patients' return home from hospital. The problem of medical representation and the need to simplify the medical advisory machinery was a priority in 'Patients first', but failed, and the need to involve doctors more in the management process was to become a key feature of the general management function in the mid-1980s.

Although it was expected that the doctor would be the natural leader it was the administrator who was usually in the best position and had the best training to undertake the central role of providing leadership to the team and overcoming professional jealousies. In many cases, however, through poor training, lack of experience and determination, this central role was not fulfilled by him nor any other member of the team (what determined the outcome of deliberations was the lowest common factor). Decisions were delayed, the organisation lacked leadership and direction, staff motivation was adversely affected and patients' services suffered. It became obvious both within the service and to the public at large that the NHS was not being efficiently managed and that opportunities were being missed to maximise the use of available resources.

BETTER MANAGEMENT AND VALUE FOR MONEY

On coming to office in 1979 one of the government's prime and continuing objectives was to gain increasing value for money as the cost of the NHS grew as a proportion of public sector expenditure. Long before they introduced general management they could legitimately claim to have sown the seeds for the more effective use of resources which could prosper in the more positive climate and performance driven culture of general management.

By the summer of 1984 there had been a bewildering number of central initiatives, many of which were resisted by managers and authorities who were sceptical of the centre's ability to understand the complex and multi-professional environment in which NHS management operated. These initiatives were often seen as interference and simplistic solutions to complex problems, and were regarded as being aimed at political advantage rather than trying to develop the service itself. Nevertheless, they were significant initiatives which together had an important impact on management attitudes over time and created a more positive approach to using and managing resources.

The removal of AHAs shortened the lines of communication and decision making. A range of statistical indicators of performance were being developed and made available to help local managers assess how well they were doing compared with others. Information needs had been reviewed and improved systems were being developed following the report of a committee under the chairmanship of Mrs Edith Körner,[13] the vice-Chairman of South Western RHA. Manpower monitoring had been introduced and manpower limits had been decided upon personally by ministers, admittedly in a somewhat arbitrary way. The Prime Minister had asked Sir Derrick Rayner of Marks & Spencer to head a team investigating central departments with the intention of reducing the size of the civil service, which was a major objective of government policy. The Rayner scrutiny method had subsequently been transferred to the NHS from Whitehall. Value for money audit programmes had been started and a system of management cost limits had been introduced, the cost being broadly defined as the total staff at regions and districts—the much maligned administrators. All RHAs were required to reduce their cost levels to a maximum given percentage of total spending. Comparisons are clearly difficult but this percentage of some 4.5% was very low if compared to local government administrative costs or the management costs of health services in other countries.

Other initiatives included: the establishment of a NHS training authority; a review of the flow of health circulars from the department to the health authorities; the development of management budgets using several pilot projects; and a study of family practitioner committees' administration.

During this period ministers had also taken the decision to make family practitioner committees separate and directly accountable to them, by-passing their local health authorities. Between 1948 and 1974 executive councils were statutory bodies charged with administering contracts of medical and dental general practitioners, pharmacists and opticians. GPs had won independent contractor status from Aneurin Bevan and jealously guarded it. In 1974 these councils were succeeded by family practitioner committees, which had become part of the area health authority organisation with the objective of assisting collaboration between primary and secondary care. Ministers viewed the new decision to make these committees accountable to them directly as a management improvement, whereas the rest of the service thought it was a step in the wrong direction. This was, first, because the Department of Health could not adequately monitor and control the performance of 90 FPCs and, second, in the interest of continuity of care for the patient it was important that the primary care services should be planned, managed and integrated with secondary care at the local level.

It is true to say that a substantial number of government initiatives to improve the management of the service were introduced over a comparatively short space of time in the early 1980s. It is also true that many of them were regarded as interference in day-to-day operational management and were resisted by authorities, members and managers. Nevertheless, these initiatives changed attitudes, made genuine savings, and prepared fertile soil for the growth of the general management culture. Ministers were encouraged in 1983 when the Prime Minister's adviser, Roy Griffiths, reviewed NHS management. He endorsed these initiatives and recommended extending cost improvement programmes, bringing proper budgetary control under a management accountant down to unit level, and developing the role of clinicians in management.[1]

COMPETITIVE TENDERING

Competitive tendering was one of the most significant steps forward in the drive for greater efficiency savings. Under this stringent policy set out in health circular HC(83) 18[14] all health authorities were required to test the cost-effectiveness of all cleaning, catering and laundering services by seeking competitive tenders within a rigid timescale. Independent professional expertise was said to be available without charge from the Department of Health's domestic services management branch, its catering and dietetics branch and its laundry engineers! RHAs had to submit by February 1984 a timed programme for implementation and then produce frequent reports for the department on its progress. "Where exceptionally a district's programme holds out no early prospect of a tendering exercise, then the region should supply with its summary a full explanation of the failure to make progress."[14] In many cases this was the first time that NHS management had specified precisely what levels of services it required and for the first time looked critically at the use of manpower in support services. It is not surprising that ministers took a personal interest in the results.

It is worth noting that the hospital building programme of the 1960s was getting under way in the 1970s. New district general hospitals were intended to centralise services and lead to the closure of small and uneconomic units, resulting in major savings. But the revenue consequences of capital schemes (RCCS) and the extra running costs of the new hospitals were traditionally met by the DHSS. This meant that there were no incentives in the planning process to seek the economic use of staff, who account for 75% of all costs. The new hospitals, therefore, had small wards for better patient privacy and large areas of circulation space. They may have been comfortable, well appointed, well equipped and attractive but they were certainly not cheaper to heat, light and staff. New was better but was also proving to be more expensive. Competitive tendering might help to tackle one aspect of this development.

In the case of domestic staff, particularly, their pay had always been poor, even in comparison with local authority workers. The quality of staff was, therefore, often poor and staff rotas were developed to provide staff with a living wage through overtime payments rather than to get the job done efficiently, quickly and cheaply. There was also a view that in hospitals the domestic staff not only did the cleaning but also relieved the nurses of some 'non-nursing duties' and played an interactive role with patients in the wards, which did much for both patient and staff morale.

The success of competitive tendering depended largely on the manager's skill in defining the specification and the availability of commercial tenderers, their understanding of the NHS environment, and the motivation of health authorities and their staff. It was a process aimed at reducing staff levels and therefore was bound to incur union opposition. It was surprising, however, that although NUPE and COHSE publicly criticised the policy and the way it was carried out, arguing that it was evidence of the government's intentions to privatise the NHS, local opposition varied from place to place, was often low key and had the effect of delaying the programme rather than disrupting the service. The government's industrial relations legislation had not only beaten the miners' strike but had had repercussions for the NHS, of which the majority of staff were members of no fewer than 47 unions and staff associations!

Specifications in the first round of tendering were generally poor and inadequate, which caused additional items to be added after the tender had been let and, therefore, generated extra costs and reduced the planned savings. Problems in defining the quality of service required were also significant.

Several commercial organisations offered cleaning services and, therefore, provided genuine competition. A number of companies were interested in the hospital laundry contracts. However, only a very few looked for a profit from tackling the 24 hour low-cost catering service in a range of acute, mental illness, mental handicapped and elderly units. Recent developments in centralising services had complicated the position. Some hospitals had installed a 'cook chill' system and some had planned other major capital investments.

With its likely effects on NHS motivation many authorities opposed the policy on 'political' grounds. Some felt that the extra workload falling on management could not be justified. Some were concerned about the formal position if there was a strike or the company failed. Progress was initially slow, par-

ticularly in Scotland. The policy was, however, close to ministers' hearts as they expected large savings to result from it. The
Minister of State himself became personally committed to implementing the programme across the whole country and
within the fixed timescale. RHAs had to inform senior civil
servants in the department if it looked as though a district
health authority would accept an in-house tender which was
not the lowest bid. In some cases ministers rang the regional
chairman and the district chairman to ensure that the cheapest
option was taken. Initially, commercial companies offered
'loss leader' tenders to get into the market but after the first
round of tenders prices were jacked up, thus reducing the
initial levels of savings.

The way in which the policy was implemented by direct
ministerial interference in day-to-day operational decisions
taken at unit level, at a time when the government was profess-
ing the aim of greater devolution, caused considerable anger
throughout the service. The policy itself, however, had a number of major benefits. Managers became accustomed to
specifying their service needs with some accuracy, manpower
levels were significantly reduced, particularly amongst domestic staff, and many millions of pounds were saved which
could be diverted to improve patient care.

COST IMPROVEMENT PROGRAMMES

The pressure for efficiency savings continued in the early 1980s
in response to criticisms about inadequate expenditure growth
for the hospital and community health services (HCHS). Arguments were developed which identified the extra costs of
coping with the rising tide of need. Was it a one per cent
increase in expenditure which was required to simply stand
still by accounting for the inevitable rise in costs resulting from
medical and technical advances and demographic changes?
Anything above one per cent might be genuine growth.

The sums raised by greater efficiency were added to expenditure figures provided by the DHSS in its submissions to the
House of Commons Social Services Committee. Health authorities were set specific targets for efficiency savings of £30
million and £39 million for years 1981–2 and 1982–3 respectively, representing about a half of one per cent of total

revenue allocations. In the event £29 million and £25.5 million were reported, which was below target but still represented very significant savings. As time went on, however, it appeared that not all the reported savings resulted from the more efficient use of resources. Transfers from capital accounts; delays in implementing the planned preventive maintenance programmes, resulting in a further deterioration in hospital fabric; deferred developments, with the associated disadvantageous impact on professional morale; the use of savings from previous years; 'revenue from land sales'; and increased income (income generation programmes) were all reported as 'savings'. The DHSS decided in 1984/85 to introduce a new approach to targeting savings, which was intended to place greater discipline on health authorities.

The cost improvement programme (CIP) was introduced in HC 84 (2)[15], which defined cost improvements as:

"Measures which are aimed at releasing cash or manpower used in providing a service by getting the same service output for a smaller input of resources; or improving productivity by getting a higher output for the same input or a less than proportionate increase in input."

Under the CIP system no formal top-down targets were set. In theory, the level of savings would be identified at local discretion. However, each district and region was expected to incorporate a 'satisfactory' CIP within its short-term (two years) planning programme. Success in meeting the objectives set out in the short-term programme was one of the main subjects covered by the annual accountability review of performance.

The circular HC 84 (2) required all health authorities to initiate these programmes to release cash savings which would be retained by them for reinvestment in patient care. The concept was a good one and was welcomed by professionals as it allowed the savings on 'administration', always an 'Aunt Sally', to be ploughed back into services for patients. In the first couple of years cash savings were released and were devoted to services at the bedside.

In 1984/5 and 1985/6 these programmes yielded some 1.1% and 1.4% respectively of the total amount of current spending. Clearly, local CIPs were a very important source of 'additional funding'. There were, however, concerns that some of the 'savings' were in fact service reductions. The National Audit Office[16] reported that "at some district health authorities there was evidence that the focus was on saving costs without necessarily any matching improvement in efficiency."

For example, some emphasis had been placed on setting lower budgets and expecting individual managers to remain within them. In such cases it was not always clear whether savings had been made without corresponding reductions in the standard of health care provided. Although reductions in the length of stay, earlier discharge and increasing day cases for minor surgery all showed improvements in the cost weighted index of activity, the professionals wanted to know whether this was the same as improvements in quantity and quality of care? These and other doubts had an adverse effect on professional motivation. The doctors, in particular, were concerned about the deterioration in service quality. CIPs were intended to generate extra cash for patient care. Was it proving to be a means of cutting corners and having an adverse effect on their patients' lot?

Concerns were also expressed about the attitude of the Treasury to these additional funds. Was the Treasury making less generous growth allocations available because of expected savings from CIPs? Were the savings generated, therefore, not genuinely 'additional'? A major problem also arose over Whitley Council pay agreements and review body awards. Government policy came to require the NHS to meet part of the additional pay bill from CIP savings. The perceived underfunding of the pay bill, which arose from nationally negotiated and agreed levels, got CIPs a bad name. When doctors were told that part of their review body award was to be met from their local savings they argued that CIP savings which went to patient care through their salaries was not in fact extra care but simply better pay for existing levels of care. CIPs soon lost credibility and the support of doctors and nurses.

THE GRIFFITHS REPORT

It was against a background of increasing political and public concern that the Prime Minister, Mrs Thatcher, sought the help of her personal adviser Roy Griffiths, on the possibility of introducing business principles into the NHS to make it more managerially effective.

Griffiths began his task knowing little about the structure and operations of the NHS. He had relatives who worked in the service and their experience led him to start with a strong conviction that management could succeed if it had not only the respect of the professions but also their active participation. Managers and doctors had to get together and work in a new partnership.

He underestimated the complexity of the service and the magnitude of his task, and what started out as a one or two day a week secondment for a couple of months soon became a full-time commitment. Griffiths was helped by 'three wise men' on his inquiry team—Michael Betts, British Telecom board member; Jim Blyth, Finance Director of United Biscuits; and Sir Brian Bailey, Chairman of Television South and the Health Education Council. This constituted two successful businessmen and a former chairman of a regional health authority with a union background. Cliff Graham, who was a free thinking civil servant, led a small team to support them.

Griffiths had been invited to undertake the inquiry in February 1983 and six months later he offered the Secretary of State for Health his report.[1] His report was, unusually, in the form of a letter, written in his own down-to-earth style. It was short and offered very much a personal prescription for curing the NHS managements' ills. The last sentence in the letter stressed the urgency—"the point is that action is now badly needed and the health service can ill afford to indulge in any lengthy self-imposed Hamlet-like soliloquy as a precursor or alternative to the required action." This was too much to hope for. In fact, the DHSS offered it for consultation and then thought long and hard before issuing its implementation circular on the 4th June 1984.[17] The then Permanent Secretary admitted privately that the circular had gone through some 14 drafts—rather more than the average! The Hamlet soliloquy had taken nine months.

The first critics of the NHS Management Inquiry report said that it concentrated mostly on acute hospital management rather than on all NHS management, with references to community and cinderella services being added only as an after-thought. Although there was some evidence for these criticisms it should be remembered that over 70% of all expenditure on health goes into the hospital and community health services. If the report was aimed at achieving better value for money and better quality of care, improvements in the management of those huge resources would be a very significant step forward.

THE CHALLENGE

Griffiths wrote that "businessmen have a keen sense of how well they are looking after their customers. Whether the NHS is meeting the needs of the patient and the community, and can prove that it is doing so, is open to question." He boasted that every Monday he received reports on the relative success of all Sainsbury's supermarkets and paid regular but unannounced visits to keep managers on their toes. In the NHS there was no continuous evaluation of performance against clearly stated criteria and little measurement of improved health. What was the service achieving for a huge investment of public funds? What was needed was better planning, implementation and control of performance through a general management process; a real measurement of output against clearly stated objectives; and controlled budgets, particularly at the unit/shopfloor level. In time this would secure the best deal for patients, the best value for the taxpayer and the best motivation for staff. This was the central aim of the report. Over the succeeding 10 years the development of general management has produced much of value, not least of which has been the shift from measuring performance by the costs of non-clinical support services towards the concept of health outcomes as measures of success.

Griffiths also believed that if his recommendations gained ministerial approval the following benefits would result:

(a) "demonstrable leadership to capitalise on the existing high levels of dedication and expertise among NHS staff of all disciplines;

(b) a constant search for major change and cost improvement;

(c) better motivation of staff through incentives, rewards and sanctions;

(d) professional functions would be more effectively geared into the overall objectives and responsibilities of the general management process (the development of clinical directorates); and

(e) the extent and process of consultation would be simplified."

A decade later there is plenty of evidence that there has been a revolution in the management culture in the NHS and the development of a new leadership style which is progressively delivering these benefits.

The government concluded that the central recommendation of the report—the establishment of the general management function—together with better management training, particularly for doctors and nurses, would be a powerful new means of delivering their consistent long-term objectives of greater devolution, stronger personal accountability and value for money. The long awaited Circular HC (84) 13[17] was issued on the 4th June 1984 with a covering letter from Mr Fowler, addressed to the chairmen of regions, districts and special health authorities. It called upon them to take "personal responsibility for ensuring the necessary action is taken to establish the general management function." The new general managers were to be held personally responsible and accountable for their performance in future. Mr Fowler intended to treat authority chairmen in the same way. The statutory accountability of authorities to the Secretary of State for Health would be expressed more and more through the personal responsibility of chairmen. This innovation provided a 'political' chain of command: Secretary of State for Health, regional chairmen and district chairmen. As it was never announced but simply evolved as a method of communicating with the NHS it often caused confusion and consternation among members of health authorities. The authorities themselves were accountable in law but it appeared that only their chairmen were instructed on what was required and held personally accountable for the performance of the authority as a whole.

MANAGEMENT AND POLITICS AT THE CENTRE

Griffiths's first target was the centre—the civil service. Civil servants had to improve their own understanding of management if they were to lead the management of the NHS. "We believe that a small, strong general management body is necessary at the centre (*and that is almost all that is necessary at the centre*) for the management of the NHS." Challenging words: time would show that the civil service culture, backed by hundreds of years of tradition, was made of stronger stuff. The Secretary of State for Health accepted the need to develop a clearer strategic management role in Whitehall. As far as possible the aim would be to separate that role from the 'political' role of the civil service in supporting ministers and developing their policies. The logic was that the Department of Health, led by its First Permanent Secretary, would deal with the politics and policies, while the new management arm of the department, the NHS Management Board, chaired by a Second Permanent Secretary, would manage the NHS and ensure that those policies were implemented. The Management Board would need to gain credibility in the eyes of the NHS by delegating to the service and yet retain accountability and control. It was hoped that the board would reduce civil service interference in operational NHS affairs and limit the constant change of priority and direction. In recent years health authorities had been called upon to deliver a range of new priorities. At one count no fewer than 47 emerged from all corners of the DHSS and created the flavour of the month syndrome, with NHS management not knowing which way to turn.

The report also called for the establishment of a Health Services Supervisory Board to advise the Secretary of State for Health, to give strategic direction to the NHS, to approve resource allocation and to monitor performance. It was to be chaired by the Secretary of State and its members would include the Minister, Permanent Secretary, Chief Medical Officer and Chairman of the Management Board. It would have non-executive members with general management experience in business to introduce a new element and new thinking into policy formulation. The recommendations for membership of the board did not include the Chief Nursing Officer (CNO) (the statutory woman and nurse). The Supervisory Board was established in the Spring of 1984 amid an intensive campaign in the professional press about valuing the nursing input into health care and soon afterwards included the CNO as a full member.

The problem with the concept of the Supervisory Board was that responsibility to Parliament for the entire NHS and the huge expenditure of public funds lay solely with the Secretary of State for Health. The board could only offer advice. The impact of the board, therefore, depended upon the attitude of the minister of the day.

WHITEHALL ATTEMPTS TO 'DOMESTICATE GRIFFITHS'

It was rumoured that from the start there was a determination shared by ministers and civil servants to 'domesticate Griffiths'. It was in both their interests to keep the board at arms length but to give it the appearance of being consulted on policy issues. In reality, throughout its brief life the board played no obvious role in influencing major policy, such as the allocation of resources which was at the heart of serious public and political debate.

To give it greater credibility the membership of the board was expanded to include NHS representatives: a President of a Royal College, Sir Raymond Hoffenberg, and a Regional Health Authority Chairman, Sir Donald Wilson. But its public image remained vague and NHS managers complained that they knew nothing of its work and failed to recognise any strategic policy outcomes. Significantly, when the NHS got into extreme difficulty in 1988 with public criticism and concern over the shortage of funds, closure of beds, and children in Birmingham allegedly dying after operations had been postponed because of a lack of available facilities, it appeared that the Supervisory Board had no part to play and was in fact not even meeting on a regular basis. When in January 1988 Mrs Thatcher suddenly announced her decision to review the NHS and its funding on the Panorama programme it was an embarrassment to the board, and for that matter to the whole of the department who were taken by surprise. The Supervisory Board had failed. It was soon replaced by the Policy Board, which had a different membership but similar terms of reference and constitution.

Did the NHS have higher expectations for the Management Board? NHS management was sceptical. How can the centre 'manage' a multi-billion pound business under the day-to-day control of 200 statutory bodies? Had the civil service got any understanding of management? Would ministers ever allow the board to act with real delegated authority? But the NHS was also hopeful. Would there be less interference and greater devolution from the centre? Would the board pull away from the 'clammy' hand of control of the civil service (after all, government pressure had reduced manpower at the DHSS headquarters over the previous five years by around 20%, which was a very encouraging sign)? Would the board's consultation with the NHS be real, influence departmental thinking and be reflected in policy? Would its Chairman, a senior and experienced manager, be an ally against the old enemy? The board was to give leadership, control performance and achieve consistency and drive. Its members were to be drawn from business, the civil service and the NHS. Was this a first opportunity for NHS management to get in on the act?

Much would depend on the strength of personality and the new thinking of the Chairman, whom Griffiths thought "to achieve credibility would almost certainly have to come from outside the NHS and civil service!" He did. It was Victor Page, the former Chief Executive of the National Freight Corporation, a man well known to Mr Fowler and Mr Clarke, who during the same period had been Secretary of State and Minister for Transport respectively. The key question was whether he was strong enough to resist his old masters. The answer proved to be no. Mr Page, who was given the status of Second Permanent Secretary, arrived believing that he would have delegated authority, the freedom to act independently of ministers and manage the NHS as he wished. He soon became bewildered by the civil service culture and sophistication, discovered that he was out of his depth in the world of politics and suddenly resigned. The next day the First Permanent Secretary was admitted to hospital. Ministers were embarrassed. To lose one permanent secretary was bad luck. To lose two was most unfortunate.

Mr Page was succeeded by Len Peach of IBM, who had previously held the other key appointment on the Management Board, that of Personnel Director. In that role his main responsibilities had been to deal with the review bodies and Whitley Council's pay negotiations, provide incentives through remuneration systems, stimulate management training (including clinicians), review appointment procedures and manpower levels, and introduce performance appraisal and career development from the unit to the centre.

Mr Peach set out to bridge the culture gap between the

Department of Health and the NHS. He soon established good relations with personnel officers throughout the service and began to improve their role, status and pay. His main claim to fame was the introduction of individual performance review (IPR). Under this system every general manager was set annual targets and their achievement was reviewed by superiors 12 months later, when they were awarded performance pay. In general, the system had strong support in the NHS but criticism arose over the 'parent' and 'grandparent' roles. For unit managers the district manager, his immediate superior, was the 'parent' but the 'grandparent' was the regional general manager, who had wider scope for influencing management development and career opportunities. The district chairman was thus bypassed. District chairmen could not see why one of their own staff who was appointed by and accountable to the district should be assessed by a regional manager.

Similarly, regional chairmen were concerned that their own RGM would have to have his rating and performance pay fixed by the Chief Executive of the Management Board. Whoever fixes your pay has your close attention and allegiance. Did this new move toll the knell for chairmen? If the Chairman and Chief Executive of the Management Board were to ensure implementation of government policy he could now do so through regional, district and unit general managers by setting annual objectives and monitoring their achievement through IPR. In time the Chairman of the Management Board also led the accountability review process, replacing a minister, much to the concern of regional chairmen, who were convinced that they were being marginalised. By assessing personal performance through IPR and health authority performance through the review system a strong line of management accountability was created from top to bottom. This was to provide the means for delivering the reforms over the next few years.

THE APPOINTMENT OF GENERAL MANAGERS IN THE NHS

Major mistakes were made in the process of establishing the general management function. The Secretary of State for Health set an 18 months timescale for the 'identification' and appointment of general managers throughout the service. The process started in the summer of 1984 with HC (84) 13[17] and had to be completed down to, and including, unit level by the end of 1985. The policy was "intended to give authorities the *maximum freedom* to develop proposals which best suited local requirements, while enabling ministers to *monitor* their arrangements." So far so good. But the procedures, which were complex, detailed and bureaucratic, reserved for the centre the final decision on the appointment of all authority general managers.

It was a cascading process. RHAs and DHAs had to submit:

(a) "a statement on how it was proposed to establish the function;

(b) a job description for the general manager;

(c) proposals for identifying the general manager; and

(d) the name of the preferred candidate to allow the Secretary of State for Health to perform his role of monitoring health authorities."

Annex C of the circular gave assurances that the Secretary of State for Health "will not be attempting to take over the role of the authority" in appointing the Chief Officer directly accountable to it, nor "to standardise job descriptions to a national pattern" (as in the disastrous Grey Book).[10] The explanation or excuse was that ministers wished to be satisfied that the job descriptions "accorded with the Secretary of State's management changes within the DHSS, that any additional costs did not affect direct patient care and that the general manager identified had the capacity to undertake the general management function."

Decisions on the suitability of large numbers of candidates were to be taken centrally by ministers or, equally disturbingly, by civil servants whose knowledge of them was highly variable and who might wish to settle old scores. Chairmen, administrators and professional organisations objected but ministers were adamant. Cynics suspected a master plan. It was politically imperative that among the successful general managers there was a representative proportion of outsiders (from business, industry and the armed services) and the professions (especially doctors and nurses) to prevent it appearing as a take-over by administrators. Some believed that the candidates, if possible, ought to be 'one of us'—a bad start. So much for general management meaning greater devolution.

CHAIRMEN AND THE ACCOUNTABILITY REVIEW SYSTEM

The chairmen of district health authorities were conscious of the fact that they were individually appointed by and personally accountable to the Secretary of State for Health. Mr Patrick Jenkin had previously sought to bind AHA chairmen to him by holding meetings three times a year in comparatively large groups. This had failed to satisfy their wish for a personal and meaningful relationship. Although DHAs were subordinate authorities to RHAs, district chairmen were reluctant to be subordinate to regional chairmen.

On his appointment as Secretary of State for Health and Social Services Mr Fowler took a strong personal interest in strengthening his relationships at regional level and in helping to increase the authority which the regional chairmen were able to exercise over district chairmen. Mr Fowler, together with Sir Gordon Roberts, the Chairman of Regional Chairmen and of the Oxford RHA, devised the concept of the 'health cabinet' consisting of ministers and the 14 RHA chairmen, most of whom had been appointed by a Conservative Secretary of State. This cabinet would discuss new policy and review performance. For the Secretary of State for Health and Social Services it would provide a means of putting pressure on district health authorities to achieve the desired outcomes. For RHA chairmen it strengthened their control over their regions and brought them into closer contact with emerging policy. Gradually, ministers sought to use RHA chairmen as willing tools for getting a grip on policy implementation and for minimising 'political' opposition through their close relationships with local MPs. Some critics of these trends felt that the chairmen had become too dependent on political sustenance.

Ministers had for some time also been concerned about the National Association of Health Authorities (NAHA). They felt it could legitimately provide a platform for advice but that it too often expressed vociferous criticism of government policy. They were determined not to give it the authority and credibility it sought as the organisation representing the interests of DHAs. It is significant that a very high percentage of district health authorities and family practitioner committees were members of NAHA. Not all regions were, however, and RHA chairmen found that their strengthening relationship with ministers was a more effective means of influence. So as regional chairmen grew closer to ministers district chairmen saw the gap between them and the centre widen.

Ministers' policy of getting closer to regional chairmen had a number of difficult consequences. First, it was the authority and not the chairmen which was accountable in law. Second, it was one thing for the Secretary of State for Health and Social Services to instruct the chairmen but it was quite another for the chairmen to be able to persuade their authorities to toe the line and deliver. In a number of cases constitutional difficulties arose. Members felt that they were simply invited to become rubber stamps and the general manager found that he was serving three masters—his chairman, his authority and, progressively, the Chief Executive of the Management Board in the DHSS.

The strengthening of personal ties with regional chairmen increased through the accountability review system. This was an annual process whereby a minister met the chairman of the RHA, his general manager and some other senior managers, including the treasurer, to set objectives for the coming 12 months and to review past performance. The review meeting was followed by a letter from the Secretary of State setting out what had been agreed and what was required, and these letters were placed in the House of Commons Library. It was then for the regional chairmen and general managers to gain the agreement of the RHAs to what had been agreed and to ensure its implementation through a similar process at district level. Regional chairmen then had an annual meeting with each of their district chairmen and district general managers, when a similar process of objective setting and appraisal took place. The intention was to develop a structure whereby clear priorities were established in the centre and were translated at regional and district level into operational targets for achievement within 12 months.

There were significant difficulties with timing, the size of regions and the number of districts. First, it was understandable that because of the pressure of parliamentary duties ministers could not make themselves available to complete the 14 reviews within a few weeks, which would have been ideal as all regions would understand their priorities at the same time and it would be implemented over the same time period. Second, there were difficulties with the district reviews, in which the numbers involved varied from eight in Oxford to 22 in the West Midlands. It was difficult, if not meaningless, to address the same priorities with the same regional guidance in one district at the beginning of the financial year and in the last district some six months later, by which time the original assumptions on budget allocation, expenditure, workload forecasts, levels of Whitley pay settlements and expectations of cost savings had radically changed. For these reasons and because of the difficulty of agreeing objective data for measuring progress critics would say that appraisals were made more often on personal prejudice rather than on factual measurement and that the system degenerated into a time consuming merry-go-round. But to be more positive, for the first time since 1948 there was a determined effort by the centre to be clear about policy objectives and to convey these face-to-face in simple communications to the field via regions and districts. The health service is exceedingly large and complex. Ministers had always experienced difficulty in explaining to the Public Accounts Committee, the Social Services Select Committee or, for that matter, the Treasury exactly how resources had been utilised and what they had got for their money. The accountability review system gained in respect throughout government and the NHS as a positive and useful means of trying to influence directly the changing patterns of health care at the operational level. Unfortunately, in time ministers lost interest and handed over the reviews to the Chief Executive, who was then able to exert increasing influence not only on managers but also on chairmen!

Objective setting for health authorities had to be intimately interwoven with objective setting for general managers. A manager's performance was related to the achievement of the objectives which the authority had been set by the superior body. The strong relationship between general managers at different levels and the IPR system created links in the management chain which bypassed the traditional lines of statutory authorities. Later, the parallel lines of command—Secretary of State, RHA and DHA chairmen and, separately, that of general managers—brought irritation, particularly to regional chairmen, who felt that they were being marginalised as the real line of authority was driven through the general management function by the Chief Executive at the DHSS's headquarters at Richmond House.

CONCLUSION

Governments in the 1970s pursued a concept of a unified administration and integration of health services through collaboration in the interests of continuity of care. They did it through central prescription. The Grey Book, with its rigid management arrangements, was too prescriptive for implementation and was the NHS equivalent of painting by numbers. The prescription to appoint certain managers and only those managers and to follow detailed planning procedures equated to management by numbers. As the 1980s progressed lessons were to be learnt from the mistakes of the 1974 reorganisation. There was to be greater devolution with as many decisions as possible being taken at local level, better value for money with regions and districts setting their own targets for improved efficiency and maximising the input into direct services for patients, and stronger accountability to the centre for performance through improved management.

Nearly 10 years later it is difficult to exaggerate the contribution made by the Griffiths report. Management has become more self-confident, innovative, imaginative, open and frank in its dealings with staff and with the public. It is loyal to the centre but also to the ideals of the service and proud of its achievements, without suffering complacency. By the time the Thatcher initiated reforms were announced in 1989, reforms which were aimed at changing the very culture of the entire NHS—consisting of 200 authorities, 800 general managers and 1,000,000 staff—the general management function had matured sufficiently to enable ministers to have confidence that such a daunting enterprise could be tackled towards the end of Parliament's elected term. They had confidence that there would be a smooth take-off and that general managers with improved communications and relationships with their staff would gain from them a high level of commitment and achieve an identity of purpose which would deliver a new style of service, be more efficient and provide a better quality of care, and a service more responsive to patients' needs in the 1990s.

REFERENCES

1. Griffiths report (1983). *NHS management inquiry*. London: DHSS.
2. Report by a committee of the central health services council (1954). *The internal administration of hospitals*. London: HMSO.
3. *Report of the committee of inquiry into the cost of the National Health Service* (1956). London: HMSO.
4. *A hospital plan for England and Wales* (1962). London: HMSO.
5. *Report of the committee of inquiry into the recruitment, training and promotion of administrative and clerical staff in the hospital service* (1963). London: HMSO.
6. Report by a committee of the Scottish Health Services Council (1966). *Administrative practice of hospital boards in Scotland*. Edinburgh: HMSO.
7. Report by a committee of the Ministry of Health and the Scottish Home and Health Department (1966). *Senior nursing staff structure*. London: HMSO.
8. *First report of the joint working party on the organisation of medical work in hospitals* (1967). London: HMSO.
9. *Report of the working party on medical administrators* (1972). London: HMSO.
10. *Management arrangements for the reorganised National Health Service* (1972). London: HMSO.
11. Department of Health and Social Security, Welsh Office (1979). *Patients first: consultative paper on the structure and management of the National Health Service in England and Wales*. London: HMSO.
12. *Reorganisation Act* (1973). London: DHSS.
13. Report of the National Health Service/Department of Health and Social Security steering group on health services information (1982). *First report of the steering group on health services information*. London: HMSO.
14. Department of Health and Social Security (1983). *Competitive tendering in the provision of domestic, catering and laundry services*. HC 83 (18).
15. Department of Health and Social Security (1984). *Resource distribution for 1984–85: service priorities, manpower and planning*. HC 84 (2).
16. National Audit Office (1986). *Value for money developments in the National Health Service: report of the Comptroller and Auditor General*. House of Commons paper 212. London: HMSO.
17. Department of Health and Social Security (1984). *Implementation of the NHS management inquiry report*. HC 84 (13).

4

PRIMARY CARE

———— ◆ ————

INTRODUCTION

The primary care services entered the 1980s in surprisingly good shape despite the financial restraints, structural changes, and staff unrest that had affected the NHS during the previous decade. This may have in part been due to their relative independence as a sector in which the contractors providing medical, dental, pharmaceutical and ophthalmic services in effect operated as small businesses, insulated to some extent from the complex organisation and staffing of the hospital services. Furthermore, unlike hospitals primary care, as a demand led service, had never been cash limited by the Treasury. This, coupled with the relative financial freedom and the universal accessibility of the primary care services, had helped to cushion the public from the consequences of the troubles in the hospital service in the 1970s. Public opinion surveys showed the esteem in which the public held family doctors. Their regular face to face contact with patients, 90% of health problems were dealt with by general practitioners, gave them a potentially powerful voice in the NHS and politicians were wary of this influence. Even so, while the 1980s saw little let up in the financial and organisational pressures on the hospital services the decade was also to prove unsettling and challenging for primary care.

In 1979 the Royal Commission on the NHS had found that primary care services were "generally provided to a good standard."[1] Nevertheless, it called for closer working relations and teamwork between the professions, improved training and continuing education for general medical practitioners, better practice premises and more training for practice staff—all commendable proposals that few general practitioners would have quarrelled with. Perhaps the most encouraging sign for general practice, however, was that many medical students were making it their first choice of career. This recruiting surge was in marked contrast to the mid-1960s when more doctors were leaving than entering general practice and a crisis of confidence in this branch of medicine had developed. The pool system of remuneration, by which a fixed sum of money was allocated annually to general medical practitioners and paid out largely via a capitation fee and thus based on how many patients were on a doctor's list, was seriously discredited. The system favoured those doctors with large lists and low expenses and there was little incentive to improve standards of care. Doctors who spent money on supporting staff and good premises were penalised with lower incomes. Quantity and not quality was the main criterion for the payment of GPs.

Many general practitioners, especially those in urban areas, had little professional contact with hospitals and were rarely seen on postgraduate courses. There was almost no training for general practice during the undergraduate course or when a doctor first graduated. A newly registered doctor could enter practice straight away regardless of his lack of experience. Not surprisingly, general practice was seen by students as a career option that was inferior to that of becoming a consultant. The financial and professional frustrations of general practitioners exploded in 1964 and confronted the incoming Labour government with a major crisis in the NHS as doctors threatened to pull out en masse from NHS family doctoring.

To stem the haemorrhage of doctors and rescue general practice from precipitous decline the then Labour government and the profession negotiated the introduction of the Charter for the Family Doctor Service.[2] The charter abolished the pool system of remuneration and reduced the proportion of income from capitation fees. It introduced partial direct reimbursement for the cost of staff and premises, access to loan capital to improve premises, financial inducements to form group practices, allowances for vocational and postgraduate training, and financial recognition for out of hours work. The charter aimed to increase recruitment to general practice and reduce the size of general practitioners' lists to a maximum of 2,000.

Over the next two decades the number of general practitioners rose steadily to over 33,000 in Great Britain in 1990, the majority of whom practised in groups from premises which had improved immeasurably since 1966 and were supported by many more skilled staff. Stimulated by the Royal Commission on Medical Education[3] and by the profession itself, vocational training for general practice became compulsory in

1982 and postgraduate training the norm. Although list sizes
had fallen to under 2,000 on average the scope of services
provided had greatly increased, links with hospital services
much strengthened, and most practices ran clinics and appointment systems. So all in all it was not surprising that
general practitioners wanted these achievements given some
further recognition.

CHARTER FOR 1980s REJECTED

A few months before the Royal Commission reported in 1979
the BMA's General Medical Services Committee (GMSC),
which represents all general practitioners in the NHS, published a new charter for general practice which set out
objectives for the 1980s.[4] It called for more investment and
more doctors in primary care, improved vocational training,
development of medical audit, more information on activity,
an extension of services provided by GPs, a more work sensitive contract, and better income for doctors. The charter also
suggested ways of improving services for environmentally
and socially deprived areas. However, little progress was
made over the next five years in negotiating the second charter
with a government determined to contain public spending
and which was gestating its own plans for reforming general
practice.

In 1980 consultation and planning continued for the management reorganisation of the health service, the
implementation of which was set for 1982. The government's
aims were to reduce bureaucracy, to improve local responsiveness and to increase value for money. The reorganisation
mainly affected the hospital service but there were implications for primary care in the abolition of area health authorities
and increased autonomy for units. The Royal Commission on
the NHS had proposed that in England and Wales the family
practitioner committees, which were then responsible for running the contracts with practitioners and had some links with
district health authorities, should be abolished and their responsibilities transferred to district health authorities, as was
already the case in Scotland. The government rejected this
advice and decided to keep the committees, eventually legis-
lating in 1985 for them to be established as authorities in their

own right, independent of district health authorities. This
pleased the contractor professions in England and Wales who
had feared an erosion of their valued independent status if
primary care was run by district health authorities. However,
the family health services authorities, which succeeded family
practitioner committees, were streamlined and given greater
management powers in 1991—not what the doctor ordered.

Responsibility for primary health care services was split between several statutory agencies. Family practitioner
committees were responsible for administering arrangements
for the services provided by family doctors, dentists, pharmacists and opticians. Health authorities were responsible for
community health services provided by community doctors,
dentists, nurses, midwives, health visitors and other paramedical professions, and local authorities looked after personal
social services. Collaboration between these agencies varied
and the government wanted to encourage it where it was weak
since clearly this was an area where overlap of and gaps in
services could be costly, confusing and detrimental to patients.
The 1980s were to see the government act to achieve greater
integration within primary care and between it and hospital
and community care.

OPEN-ENDED FINANCIAL COMMITMENT

One government objective for the 1980s was to devolve management responsibility in the NHS to as close to the patient as
possible: the other half of the equation was accountability upwards. A vital aspect of that accountability was financial and
it was no secret that the Treasury viewed with concern the
government's open-ended financial commitment to family
practitioner services. Charges for some prescriptions, dental
care and spectacles made only marginal contributions to a
budget for family practitioner services that in England in 1983–
4 amounted to 23% of a total NHS budget of over £13 billion.[5]
The justification given that these services were demand led
and that its practitioners acted as gatekeepers to expensive
hospital care and were therefore a cost-effective investment
had to some extent protected them from the increasingly strict
budgetary constraints imposed on the rest of the NHS, for
which cash limits had been introduced in 1976. But the govern-

ment was determined to contain costs and in July 1982 the
Department of Health announced the appointment of a firm of
financial consultants, Binder Hamlyn, to study the feasibility
of applying cash limits to family practitioner services.[6] The
terms of reference were:

"To examine and review the arrangements for forecasting and control of
expenditure in the family practitioner services, including the possibility of
operating a cash limit on part or all of the expenditure either separately or in
conjunction with the hospital and community health services, and to make
recommendations compatible with the contractual status of the professions,
the structure of the health services and the present nature and extent of the
clinical services provided."

This proved to be a starting gun for the series of changes that
the government was to impose on primary care. The comprehensive brief was not, however, matched by the public
outcome. Although the inquiry was completed by 1982, the
department did not issue the report. Did the consultants conclude that cash limits were not feasible if patients were to
continue to have open access to their family doctors 24 hours
a day, 365 days a year? Or did they conclude that limits were
possible but despite that the government failed to grasp the
nettle because it feared the GPs' political clout? Whatever the
report's conclusions, however, the contents no doubt proved
of value to the Health Departments in planning subsequent
changes.

The setting up of the Binder Hamlyn inquiry prompted the
GMSC to commission one of its own and financial consultants
Cooper Lybrand and Associates, who had made an unsuccessful bid for the Department of Health contract, were asked to
study the financing of general medical services in England and
Wales. In 1983 the GMSC issued 'The cost effectiveness of
general practice' as a discussion document,[7] an abridged version of a larger unpublished report. Although positive about
the potential of general practice there were no crisp conclusions on cash limits one way or the other. Instead, the authors
set out to compare the provision of certain services within
general practice with similar ones in the hospital sector, a
difficult task given the lack of information on the cost of individual services in the NHS. The report suggested that general
practice was cost-effective and provided arguments for extending its scope. The GMSC announced that it would use the

report as a basis for its response to any proposals "which may emerge from the department's inquiry." That low key response and the government's silence on cash limits reflected the complexity of the contractors' payment systems and how the resources of primary care were used, as well as the paucity of financial information in the NHS.

In 1983 one informed independent observer interpreted the contractual position of general practitioners, and by implication family doctoring's cost-effectiveness, in more robust terms. Pointing to figures showing a fall in the average annual number of general practitioner consultations in Britain over the history of the NHS, Rudolph Klein argued that the incentive to general practitioners in the NHS was to minimise their work. "Given that earnings are not related to the services performed, the general practitioner has an incentive to maximise his or her leisure rather than to maximise medical activity."[8] This comment was a portent of what the government would soon be demanding of general practitioners.

Klein's view was not shared by family doctors. As a riposte to what the GPs' leaders saw as increasing control over how independent contractors fulfilled their responsibilities to the community and the dentists', pharmacists', opticians' and doctors' experience of a tightened rein on their professional activities, the GMSC published 'General practice: a British success' in 1983.[9] After listing what general practice had to offer the community—continuity of care; a wide range of skills; fully trained staff in an economical setting; readily accessible and locally available services; personal care in familiar surroundings; progressive standards of service with a high level of accountability; and flexibility—it went on to promise support for initiatives to improve co-ordination and integration in the NHS. The report also called for an expansion of general practice with an increase in funding and manpower to enable this to happen. In a sense this document and the 1979 charter formed the profession's 'green paper' for the development of general practice in the 1980s which, taken with the Royal College of General Practitioners' drive for improved quality and dedication, showed the profession's leaders taking a positive approach to the changes that many doctors realised were coming.

DISPUTES ON DEPUTISING AND DRUGS

Meanwhile, in the shape of the Griffiths report[10] the government had already taken the next step in its campaign to improve management, efficiency and accountability in the NHS. Before Griffiths' proposals became operational, however, general practice was to suffer two brisk assaults on its traditional practices. December 1983 saw Kenneth Clarke, then Minister of State for Health, issue proposals for tighter controls on the use of deputising services by family doctors.[11] The public was becoming anxious about the standards of deputising services. There was also parliamentary and professional concern about the overuse and misuse of these services by some doctors. Even so, the profession was upset that the changes could restrict the availability of the services and reduce its monitoring role of them (though commercially operated the services were overseen by local professional committees). But what particularly angered the GMSC was the Minister's announcement of the proposals without having gone through the traditional informal consultations with the profession, which had previously been a preliminary to any change affecting the health professions. This was a sign of the tougher stance that ministers were prepared to take to change the NHS. Not only were the Tories less respectful of 'experts' than previous governments but they were also determined to curb the power of the unions, whether these represented doctors or miners. In the public dispute that followed the government's initiative the Minister gave some ground to the profession on practicalities but not on principles. More importantly, the government had shown that it was prepared to tackle the profession head on in a way that none of its predecessors had succeeded in doing.

Almost a year later health ministers repeated these tactics, this time on the emotive issue of prescribing, telling Parliament in November 1984 that from 1st April 1985 the government would limit the range of drugs available for prescription on the NHS.[12] Once again there had been no preliminary soundings of the profession—or at least not its elected representatives. A list of banned drugs was prepared covering "medicines prescribed mainly for the relief of symptoms caused by minor and self-limiting ailments," as well as certain tranquillisers and sedatives. The aim was to save money on the rising drug bill—the annual target saving being over £100 million.

The profession was particularly piqued because it had been willing to accept the earlier Greenfield report on generic prescribing[13] but had not received a positive response from the government since discussing the report in 1983. Doctors were also highly critical of the contents of the list of banned drugs, which they saw as being hastily prepared and with seemingly little professional advice. Another public dispute occurred, with the difference this time being that the profession felt that it was defending a principle, clinical freedom, and was likely to attract the public support that had been absent in the dispute over deputising services. As it turned out the public was not greatly moved, even though the arguments about the limited list were vigorously rehearsed in the media, in Parliament, and in the professional journals. Even the Royal College of General Practitioners, normally wary of entering medicopolitics, was moved to protest after it had polled its membership on the proposals.[14] While most doctors accepted that restraints on prescribing were necessary many believed that the method chosen and the manner of its presentation were wrong.

Once again the government offered practical amendments but stuck to the original principle and in April 1985 the new scheme was introduced. It settled down with remarkably little trouble and has since been extended, with ministers chalking up another advance in their campaign to constrain NHS expenditure, to improve cost-effectiveness and to make health professionals more accountable. As important was the fact that they had once again shown their determination to act in the face of vigorous professional opposition. It was a further pointer to the setbacks that doctors were to experience during the second half of the 1980s.

VALUE FOR MONEY AND AN AGENDA FOR REFORM

Throughout the 1980s the health professions had argued as vigorously as the opposition parties and health unions for more resources for the NHS. In fact, the government provided extra resources, though never sufficient for its critics, but at the same time reinforced its demands for greater efficiency and value for money. The hospital service was the biggest target, with competitive tendering for support services and income generation schemes being introduced. But primary care was not immune and cost-effectiveness and income generation were behind a rise in dental charges (1985), the ending of the opticians' monopoly on the supply of spectacles (1984), and the removal of restrictions on opticians advertising (1985). A new and what the government hoped was a more cost-effective contract for pharmacists was also negotiated in the mid-1980s and introduced in 1988.

The government's first big initiative on primary care, however, was the publication on 21st April 1986 of its consultation document, 'Primary health care: an agenda for discussion'.[15] This agenda, which Mr Norman Fowler, the Secretary of State for Health, had been gestating for so long, covered all aspects of primary care and was, as he claimed, the first official comprehensive review since 1948. The message was clear, "our primary health care services are good but could be better still. The government believes there is scope for improving the quality, effectiveness and value for money which patients and the nation get from them."

The government's key objectives were:

(a) to make services more responsive to the consumer;

(b) to raise standards of care;

(c) to promote health and to prevent illness;

(d) to give patients the widest range of choice in obtaining high quality primary care services;

(e) to improve value for money; and

(f) to enable clearer priorities to be set for family practitioner services in relation to the rest of the health service.

To achieve these objectives in the general medical services the discussion document made several suggestions, including a 'good practice allowance' to encourage and reward the highest standards of performance. This allowance, favoured by some senior members of the RCGP but viewed with scepticism by many doctors and outright anger by the GMSC, could, it was argued, be linked to such factors as personal availability to patients, provision of a wide range of services, including

preventive activities for which targets might be set, and at-
tendance at recognised postgraduate education courses. It was
also suggested that doctors should be assessed (by other doctors) for the allowance. Professional opposition, however, to
this idea was so strong that it did not appear in the subsequent
white paper, 'Promoting better health',[16] although the objective permeated the proposed changes to the doctors' contract.

The discussion document attributed the genesis of this allowance to the RCGP and this provoked some friction between
the college and the GMSC, which had suspicions that the college was usurping the committee's traditional representative
function by discussing with the DHSS, albeit informally, matters that affected GPs' terms and conditions of service. In the
event, the college's own members repudiated their leaders'
ideas, but a meeting between the chairmen of the RCGP's
Council and the GMSC was required to soothe relations between the two bodies.

The government also wanted to increase to 60% the proportion of a doctor's pay that was related to the number of
patients on his list, which currently stood at 45%. Ironically,
one of the key changes in the 1966 contract had been a reduction in the proportion of income paid by capitation fee
because its previous higher level was thought to have encouraged doctors to acquire large lists, and therefore a greater
income, with little incentive to improve quality. The discussion
document turned that argument on its head by claiming that
the level of 45% did not provide an "adequate incentive to
doctors to practise in ways that will encourage patients to join
their lists."[16] This philosophy ran counter to the post-1966 policy that by reducing the size of doctors' lists, and these had
fallen steadily, patients would have more consultation time
and standards would rise. It was a philosophy that ignored the
potential planning value of the fee for service, namely that it
provided a powerful lever for influencing which services
should be developed. Ironically, other parts of the new contract, such as the payments for reaching immunisation targets,
seemed to recognise this potential. The intellectual parentage
of the government's white paper looked mixed to say the least.

Other proposals included the greater availability of information about practices for the public; a simpler procedure for
patients to change doctors so that they could more readily

exercise a choice; better feedback from patients about the quality of practices; a more consumer sensitive complaints system; improved undergraduate teaching of primary care; a strengthening of the controls on manpower; a compulsory retirement age (initially 70) for doctors; assessment of doctors' hospital referral rates; greater involvement in community child health services; better preventive services; and encouragement to introduce computers into practices. Family practitioner committees were also to be given greater powers to monitor and influence the quality of services provided by practitioners.

SWEEPING CHANGES FOR PRIMARY CARE

These represented sweeping changes for primary medical care but the other contractor professions were also faced with substantial changes. Prevention was a strong suit in the document so dentists were to be encouraged to do more preventive treatment and action was to be taken to reduce unnecessary treatment. Similar retirement provisions were proposed as for doctors and the government called for a relaxation of advertising restrictions to improve patient choice. Unlike doctors, dentists did not have a continuing responsibility for their patients and the discussion document suggested a change to the dentists' contract to ensure that the full range of treatment was available to those who needed it. Dentists would be paid a capitation fee for patients under 18 who registered with them and for adults who registered with an NHS dentist a small capitation fee would be paid in addition to the fees paid for dental work, including examination.

Pharmacists had already been in prolonged negotiations about a new contract that was eventually introduced in June 1988.[17] The contract changes lessened the retrospective adjustments that needed to be made in their cost plus contracts—reimbursement of costs plus an addition for profit. There was to be a simplified remuneration system designed to encourage cost-effective pharmacies, while essential small pharmacies were to be supported and others 'bought out'. It also gave the government greater control over the opening of pharmacies which had been expanding with little regard to local needs. "The free market," said the discussion document, "does not and cannot operate 'for community pharmaceutical services' with full effectiveness because there is no price competition." It was an occasion when the government's ideological engine, 'market forces', was deemed not to be a suitable solution. The main proposal for pharmacists arose from the 'Nuffield Foundation Inquiry',[18] which had advocated an extended role for pharmacy in primary care by, for example, advising patients on minor symptoms, greater participation in domiciliary services and health education, and introducing individual patient drugs records—ideas that were later developed.

In the section on general ophthalmic services the government claimed that the expected benefits (better services and less cost to taxpayers) from the more competitive market introduced in 1985, when the opticians' monopoly had been ended, had already begun and would continue in the future. It also proposed a voucher system for those people entitled to free glasses or reduced charges. Vouchers for health care and education, with which consumers could purchase their choice of services, had long been advocated by radical proponents of the free market but ophthalmic services was the only sector in which such a scheme was introduced in the 1980s. Even so, these changes fuelled the fears of those who supported the traditional NHS that the government's 'Agenda for discussion'[15] was a step on the way to privatising the NHS, a charge vigorously denied by ministers. Nevertheless, paragraph 24 in the document declared that the government "hopes that primary care services will develop in ways that provide both an alternative source of care and also a means of comparing NHS services with those provided under quite different arrangements." In paragraph 26 the document floated the idea of health care 'shops', at which members of all the primary care professions would offer their services (such a development would require a change in the regulations that prevented anyone other than a doctor or dentist from running a dental business for profit). Although the professions did not oppose common practice premises this commercially oriented idea set the alarm bells ringing among the NHS traditionalists and the proposal did not survive into the white paper that followed the discussion document.

On the subject of cash limits for primary care, an objective that had helped to generate the review, the Department of

Health admitted that because of the demand led nature of the services "the normal discipline of annual cash limits is not . . . practicable either for the family practitioner services along or jointly with the hospital and community health services." Nevertheless, they explored ways of limiting expenditure, including possible curbs on staff and premises reimbursement schemes, ways of economising on drug prescribing, the collection of more accurate information on doctors' workload for the doctors' and dentists' pay review body and better government forecasting of family practitioner services' expenditure.

COMMUNITY NURSING

The success of the 1966 charter had led to medical practices making increasing use of nursing and other support staff and building up skilled practice teams. This development highlighted the confusion in the primary care services over who was responsible for what. Some practices employed their own nurses, who were paid for under the partial direct reimbursement scheme, and the doctors were then responsible for the work of the practice team. Other practices used the services of nurses employed by health authorities and these nurses could work in more than one practice. Practices operating from local health authority owned health centres had nurses provided by the authority. Difficulties sometimes occurred when what a practice wanted a nurse to do conflicted with the views of the authority on what duties its nurses should be undertaking. Skilled staff resources might be wasted as a result. Concerned that community nursing services might not be meeting people's needs effectively the government initiated reviews in England, Wales, Scotland and Northern Ireland. The English review team's report, 'Neighbourhood nursing—a focus for care',[19] was published simultaneously with the discussion document. The team was chaired by Mrs (now Baroness) Julia Cumberlege and ministers wanted the review to be part of wide consultations planned for in 'Primary health care: an agenda for discussion'.[15] The review supported neighbourhood based, rather than practice based, nursing services; a better use of nursing skills; an improvement in the effectiveness of the primary health care team; changes in the training of nurses; and greater public involvement in how the services were run.

The review suggested that each neighbourhood would cover a population of between 10,000 and 25,000, with the work of health visitors and district and school nurses being integrated under a nursing manager in association with community psychiatric and mental health nurses and midwives. It was argued that this would ensure a more flexible use of nursing services. The review team also commended the introduction of the 'nurse practitioner' into primary health care, a proposal that was bound to stir territorial disputes among health professionals and one that was in step with moves for greater professional independence for nurses in hospitals. While endorsing some of the review's ideas the government did not give the impression of wholehearted support, whether because of the costs that would follow or because of the opposition the proposals would provoke among, for example, doctors, was unclear.

So instead of endorsing the neighbourhood nursing concept the Department of Health simply suggested that local health services should decide on the system that suited them best. It also declined to alter the reimbursement systems for practice staff, to consider a salaried service for doctors, or to amalgamate the newly independent family practice committees with district health authorities, all ideas put forward in the review. The call for amalgamation was to be heard again at the end of the decade.

For their part the GPs argued that practice based nurses should be the preferred option because they could offer a more responsive and flexible service to patients, linked directly to the clinical care provided by GPs. They saw neighbourhood nursing as undermining the cohesion of the primary health care team. The doctors were also wary of the 'nurse practitioner', claiming that in many respects it was another name for the practice nurse.

INNER CITIES

'Primary health care: an agenda for discussion'[15] devoted a chapter to one of the NHS's intractable problems—health care in the inner cities. The uneven and often poor quality of pri-

mary care in the inner cities, particularly London, pre-dated
the NHS when patients commonly used their local teaching
hospitals in place of general practitioners. The NHS had improved the position but serious problems remained. Some
patients had difficulty registering with a GP and when they
did the premises could well be shoddy, the doctors' availability erratic, and standards below average. Many doctors
worked singlehandedly and often beyond normal retirement
age. They faced great pressures because of the social and environmental problems of inner city life, such as poor housing,
a large number of elderly people living alone, disrupted communities, ethnic minorities, a high turnover of population,
high morbidity, many homeless people, a shortage of staff and
the high cost of property. These pressures called for properly
resourced primary care services provided by skilled and enthusiastic staff working from good premises.

Although the incentives in the 1966 charter provided some
help for doctors practising in inner cities it was insufficient to
attract well motivated young doctors into these areas, and
other staff were just as difficult to recruit. Several studies had
been made of inner city medicine but little action followed and
in 1979 the Royal Commission on the NHS described the NHS
as "failing dismally to provide an adequate primary care service to its patients in these areas," warning that "no single
solution would suffice to deal with the complex and disparate
problems."[1]

Arguing that improving the quality of care in inner cities
was the most urgent problem that NHS services in the
community must tackle the commission called for the establishment of health centres, financial incentives to attract staff,
greater co-operation between GPs and hospitals, and a more
sensitive handling of ethnic minorities. Little action resulted
and in 1980 the London Health Planning Consortium initiated
a study, led by Professor Donald Acheson (before he was appointed Chief Medical Officer), on primary health care in inner
London. The report was published in May 1981 and its diagnosis, though more detailed, was the same as the Royal
Commission's.[20] Among 115 recommendations the Acheson
report called for financial incentives for group practices, closer
co-operation between GPs and other professions, improvements in premises, retirement of older doctors, better

information about services, easier registration with GPs, more positive action from medical schools to improve standards in general practice, and a range of financial measures to improve the attractiveness of practices in London. The diagnosis and proposed treatment were just as applicable to other deprived areas in the United Kingdom.

Sadly, the government took two and a half years to make a token response in the shape of £9 million for higher improvement grants over three years, which was spread throughout the inner cities and not just in London. Then in 1986 Rhodes *et al.*,[21] in a commentary analysing the effect of the Acheson report, observed that "what emerged was not a coherent plan . . . but rather a series of measures that could be introduced relatively easily and which did not have major implications for public expenditure." The response, the authors concluded, was inadequate and this despite ministerial promises of rapid and effective action in the early 1980s. Not that all was gloom. Several London teaching hospitals, including St Thomas's, Guy's, King's College, St Mary's and the Middlesex had set up academic departments of general practice that initiated research and raised standards of practice and young, committed doctors were coming to practise in the capital. But those who pinned their hopes on the green paper providing a bold impetus for change were in for a disappointment.

While expressing determination to provide high standards of primary health care in inner cities the government explained the difficulties involved and gave only a gentle push towards a solution—suggesting financial incentives to attract practitioners and promising to explore different contractual arrangements. The problems would not disappear, however, and the debate restarted with vigour in October 1992 when the Tomlinson report on health care in the capital proposed the expansion of community medical services and the closure or amalgamation of several prestigious London hospitals.[22] At about the same time Jarman and Bosanquet concluded that although primary care had improved in London that simply reflected countrywide improvements, "none of the recommendations of the Acheson report specifically oriented to London have been implemented."[23] They also reported an increasing proportion of singlehanded practices looking after more than 2,500 patients. The government's broad acceptance of Tomlinson's report, with its proposals for investing in primary care, brings some hope of improving general medical services in the capital. Judgement must be suspended, however, until it can be seen that ministers are prepared to inject sufficient funds not only to remedy existing weaknesses but also to meet the extra demands that primary care will face when hospitals are shut. At the time of writing the omens were not promising since it seemed that the £170 million 'earmarked' for London's primary care services for 1993–8 would, according to a report on a GMSC meeting in the BMJ of 24th April 1993, come from existing NHS budgets.[24]

GOVERNMENT'S OBJECTIVES WELCOMED

The government's plans for the future of the full spectrum of primary care may have been a long time gestating but their arrival provoked brisk reactions from politicians, the health professions, the public and the media. While the objectives were generally welcomed reservations abounded on the methods chosen for achieving them and some Tory activists were disappointed that private practice had not been given a more significant role. The subject was dismissed in three paragraphs. As might be expected the organisations representing doctors and dentists criticised many of the proposed changes in contracts. Indeed, over the succeeding four years of discussions and negotiations it became clear that the views of the two professions' leaders were generally more moderate than those of their constituents.

To do the government justice it did listen to the views culled during an innovative series of countrywide open meetings held over eight months by ministers and officials from professional bodies and consumer interests. So far as doctors were concerned these views were bleak. In its report to a special national conference of general practitioners in November 1986 the GMSC's Chairman, Dr Michael Wilson, described the government's 'Agenda for discussion' as showing signs of its "faltering commitment to the NHS. It contains proposals which, if implemented, could undermine the [NHS's] basic principles. . . ."[25]

The special conference opposed several of the government's key proposals, including the good practice allowance, compulsory retirement, changes in the complaints procedures, an increase in the proportion of capitation fees, and the wider distribution of practice information booklets. Not all was negative however: measures to improve education, extend preventive services and introduce informal audit were supported. As for community nursing, on which ministers had been equivocal, the thrust of the Cumberlege report did not appeal to the doctors. They wanted community nurses to be practice based and included in the existing reimbursement scheme. The general reaction of GPs to the government's discussion document was critical. So the stage was set for a confrontation on the future of primary care between the doctors and the government.

The professional opposition did not deflect the government. In the white paper, 'Promoting better health: the government's programme for improving primary care',[16] published in November 1987 as the next stage in its reform of primary care the government claimed wide support for the objectives in the discussion paper. Several themes had come through strongly:

(a) concern about preventive medicine;

(b) the value consumers placed on accessible, effective and sympathetic family practitioner and community health services;

(c) consumers' need for better information on available primary care services;

(d) the need to meet the requirements of the increasing number of elderly people;

(e) a growing interest in the promotion of good health; and

(f) the need to improve services in deprived areas, particularly inner cities and isolated rural areas.

To achieve all this the white paper promised extra resources, although without putting a figure on how much these might be. Calling on practitioners to increase the range and quality of their services the government proposed fairer and more open competition between those providing services. It wanted consumers to have greater access to information on services and for the remuneration of practitioners to be more directly linked than under existing contracts to the level of performance. Mr Fowler and his ministerial colleagues were clearly determined that competition, accountability and performance related pay should be paramount in the drive for quality.

PROFESSIONS' RESERVATIONS

Whereas the professions' general support for the objectives remained there were reservations, most vociferously expressed by doctors, about some of the methods proposed for reaching them. Ministers had, as mentioned earlier, backed down on one contentious issue, the introduction of a good practice allowance for family doctors. It was, however, kept for dentists who seemed to like the idea. The government remained firm on the need to increase the proportion of the capitation fee in doctors' pay, although they eventually agreed a lower target than the 60% it originally called for. The rest of the proposals were developments of those put forward in the consultation document. Incentives were suggested for boosting immunisation rates, health prevention services, and improving the care of the elderly and young children. The criteria for the basic practice allowance were to be tightened as a means of improving patients' access to care. Ministers also planned to introduce a new allowance based on the Jarman index of deprivation[26] for doctors working in areas of deprivation as a way to improve care in inner cities. The government's proposals on general medical and dental services were controversial but the objections by doctors attracted the greatest publicity and generated the most debate. The dentists' representatives were critical of some of the changes proposed in their contracts but were less vociferous than the doctors. Pharmacists and opticians were already working under changed contracts, the former after some protest, but the white paper contained proposals to enhance the role of pharmacists and to introduce allowances to recognise this.

Nevertheless, the message was to be the same for all the contractor professions: more competition, improved quality, greater accountability, stricter monitoring, easier accessibility, more information for patients, improved preventive measures and incentive payments. To see that this philosophy was implemented and monitored the family practitioner committees, which in England and Wales had been given independent status in 1985, were to have their responsibilities extended, their management role and structure strengthened, and their accountability (in England and Wales) switched from the Department of Health to RHAs. The loose and friendly rein by which old style FPCs guided their contractors was to be replaced by a much stronger harness and a more determined driver. Ministers promised funds to fulfil this extended role and promised initiatives and experiments on different ways of providing services. In addition, the Secretaries of State for Health were to have stronger powers to supervise the work of the national medical practices committees, which exercised overall control of the number of GPs entering the NHS.

For the government to translate its white paper into action required legislation, as well as negotiations with the medical and dental professions, to change the contracts controlling their terms and conditions of service. Enjoying a 100 seat majority in their third term of office the Tories were unlikely to have much difficulty in pushing through the necessary legislation and a Health and Medicines Bill[27] was published simultaneously with the white paper. Negotiating the new contracts was harder although, as the general practitioners were to be reminded when negotiations foundered in 1989, the Secretary of State for Health was only legally obliged to *consult* with the profession's representatives on contract changes. He had the power to make the final decision. As it turned out he did just that.

GPs' CONTRACT NEGOTIATIONS

In preparation for negotiations on the general practitioners' contract the Department of Health sent detailed proposals based on the white paper to the professions' representatives. The start of these negotiations was surrounded by uncertainty because in January 1988 the Prime Minister had announced her internal review of the NHS. The Department of Health assured the general practitioners' leaders that the principal emphasis of the review would be on the hospital service but warned that if the outcome impinged on general medical services the discussions on the contract would have to take account of this. This left an unresolved conflict over the relationship between the contract negotiations and the NHS review, which was exacerbated when the results of the review were published a year

later. The public, politicians and many in the profession saw
the two exercises as parts of the same reforming policy. GPs,
however, wanted their contract negotiations kept quite separate, fearing that their arguments might get lost in a wider row
about the NHS's future, a fear that was to prove justified.

Negotiations eventually began on 14th March 1988 and
these were to cover almost every aspect of the contract. The
meetings with officials went badly: in July the GMSC's Chairman criticised those negotiating for the department as lacking
"a knowledge and understanding of general practice."[28] He
promised to seek a meeting with ministers which duly took
place in September. Some common ground was found and a
joint statement from the new Secretary of State for Health, Mr
Clarke, and the profession's negotiators emerged, which expressed agreement on the key objective of improving services
but gave no details of the progress of negotiations.

The secrecy about the negotiations created difficulties for the
general practitioners' leaders in dealing with their constituents, who were suspicious that an agreement might be
reached that the general practitioners did not want. Meanwhile, the Health and Medicines Bill was going through
Parliament, which when it became law in November 1988
would privatise the General Practice Finance Corporation—
this provided capital to develop practice premises—introduce
compulsory retirement for elderly general practitioners, and
abolish 24 hour retirement (under which doctors aged 65 or
over could retire, draw their pension, and return to work a day
later without abatement of pay or pension). The legislation
would also enable cash limits to be imposed on the family
practitioner committees' reimbursement of general practitioners' expenditure on premises and staff. So cash limits had
at last come to the primary care services and it was a change
that general practitioners did not like,[29] rightly as it turned out.
Nor were they too happy about the privatisation of their
finance corporation, which many viewed as a further dismantling of the cherished 1966 charter.

The early part of 1988 saw yet more proposals for change
that would affect primary care, though these did not form part
of the contract discussions. These were in Sir Roy Griffiths'
report, 'Community care: agenda for action'.[30] His proposals
are dealt with in Chapter Eight and they included an extended

role for general practitioners in community care. Most of the report's suggested changes were incorporated into legislation but their implementation was put off until 1993, a decision that dismayed local and health authorities. Uncertainty was prolonged over services, particularly those for the elderly and mentally ill, which were of direct concern to primary care and which had not been operating effectively. However, discussions on these did not take place until the early 1990s which was after the contract had been introduced. GPs were worried about the implications of the community care reforms, fearing that extra work would fall on them and that some elderly people would have difficulty obtaining residential accommodation.

In parallel with the negotiations on the contracts for doctors and dentists the Department of Health was discussing with family practitioner committees their strengthened role in monitoring contractor services. This included the appointment of independent professional advisers to the committees, an innovation that reinforced the government's intention to reduce the influence of the profession's representatives in running the family practitioner services and so make them more sensitive to consumers' needs. Needless to say, the profession objected to this change, which increased the feeling that they were being challenged on all fronts, a sentiment fuelled by Mr Clarke's speech at a RCGP dinner in March 1989 when he accused GPs of "feeling nervously for their wallets" whenever the word reform was mentioned.[31]

All this did not make for a constructive dialogue between the Department of Health and the profession. Discussions on the contract had continued after the joint statement in the autumn of 1988 but when the Prime Minister published 'Working for patients',[32] the outcome of her NHS review, relations between the government and the general practitioners' leaders deteriorated even further. The review contained such fundamental proposals for change, including some affecting general practice, that the GMSC decided that there was no alternative to telling doctors where the hitherto confidential contract negotiations had reached.[33] This prompted Mr Clarke to send his proposed new contract to all general practitioners,[34] including an illustrative guide on what the government foresaw as the likely beneficial effects on general practitioners' incomes. The two documents showed the gulf between the parties. For example, they disagreed on more stringent criteria for the basic practice allowance, tighter part-time working rules, the abolition of the group practice and seniority allowances, capitation fees, changes in out of hours remuneration, the replacement of item of service fees with bonus payments, the abolition of the rural practice fund, and the introduction of cash limits. There had, however, been some areas of broad agreement, including child health surveillance, deprived area allowances and better patient information.

DOCTORS OPPOSE CONTRACT

The Secretary of State wanted to conclude the discussions by the beginning of March 1989 so that the GPs' new contract could start in April 1990. General practitioners throughout the country reacted angrily, however, to the government's proposals, with large meetings opposing them by overwhelming majorities. This opposition was demonstrated at a special conference of local medical committees on 27th April, when general practitioners' representatives voted against many aspects of the contract. They drew back from militant action, however, rejecting by a large majority a proposal for family doctors to resign from the NHS if the contract was imposed upon them.[35]

The profession's reaction prompted a rethink by central government, while in Scotland separate negotiations with the Scottish Office on a 'tartan' contract for Scottish GPs had already met some of the profession's objections.[36] On 4th May 1989 the Secretary of State for Health said that he was willing to make concessions on condition that the negotiators commended any resulting agreed package to the profession. In an all day negotiating session Mr Clarke accepted some significant practical modifications to the contract without conceding any major principles.[37] The compromise package, which owed something to the tartan contract, was reluctantly recommended to their constituents by the general practitioners' negotiators. Nevertheless, it was rejected, albeit narrowly, by another special conference of general practitioners on 21st June,[38] an outcome that eroded the credibility of the GPs' leaders. That conference called for a ballot of all NHS general practitioners and the result was a decisive rejection of the contract by 76% of those voting (81%).[39] Undeterred, the Secretary of State for Health decided to press ahead and impose the compromise package and refused any further negotiations, though he did promise to consult on the details of the changes. An attempt by a group of doctors to challenge the Secretary of State's action in the High Court was defeated[40] and the necessary legislation was approved by Parliament in the autumn of 1989, with 1st April 1990 set as the date for beginning the new contract. This was a major defeat for family doctors and presumably influenced the decision of the GMSC's Chairman, Michael Wilson, not to stand for re-election for the 1990–1 session.

Among the main changes in the final contract were:

(a) tougher criteria for the basic practice allowance, including greater availability of doctors;

(b) introduction of child health surveillance and minor surgery services;

(c) a reduction in the proportion of income from capitation fees and the consolidation of some allowances;

(d) health promotion obligations, including targets for triggering immunisation and cervical cytology payments;

(e) health checks on specified groups of patients;

(f) deprived area allowances;

(g) production of practice leaflets and annual reports; and

(h) monitoring by FPCs of prescriptions and referrals.

DENTISTS' NEW CONTRACT

Meanwhile, leaders of the country's 24,500 NHS dentists were also having protracted discussions with the Department of Health about new contracts for the 80% who provided general dental services in the NHS. Although attracting less publicity these talks were proving as contentious as those for the doctors. Inevitably, a critical factor was the amount of resources to be made available for general dental practice. The government wanted a reallocation of existing resources to fund the changes in the new contract with patients who were ineligible for exemptions paying more. Dentists' leaders argued that it would not work without extra money. The core of the financial

changes was a shift of under 20% of dentists' gross payments
(income and expenses) from item of service fees to capitation
fees, the latter an innovation for the dental profession. In 1990–
1 dentists carried out over 40 million courses of NHS treatment
in the UK at a cost of £1.2 billion, with patients' charges accounting for nearly 40% of this sum. The number of courses
had fallen from around 45 million in 1988, presumably as a
result of the introduction of an examination charge in 1989 and
the rising levels of existing charges. The National Association
of Health Authorities and Trusts (NAHAT) reported continuing concern among dentists about the effects on patients' well
being of the lost opportunities to screen for dental problems
and the effect on the uptake of treatment of the high level of
charges.[41] The new contract could well aggravate this trend,
although a report from a working party of the British Dental
Association (BDA) on detailed manpower requirements published in 1991 forecast a rise in the annual number of courses
to around 50 million by 1998.[42] The report also forecast a long-
term balance between the supply and demand for dentists if
the annual student intake remained at its present level of 800,
assuming that the migration of dentists from the European
Community (EC) was small. It is still too early to predict the
long-term effect on all these figures of the new contract, which
has caused the biggest shake-up in general dental services in
the NHS since 1948, but there are signs that some dentists are
giving up or restricting NHS dental services.

In its white paper, 'Promoting better health',[16] the government wanted:

(a) to introduce a capitation fee for children (under 18) and a partial capitation fee for adults who signed on with a dentist;

(b) dentists to give preventive advice and explain proposed treatment, to
provide out of hours emergency treatment and to agree to an inspection
of surgeries;

(c) to introduce a compulsory retirement age and improve the distribution of
dentists, especially women dentists;

(d) to negotiate a new remuneration system incorporating incentives for high
efficiency and high standards; and

(e) dentists to have mandatory vocational training and improved continuing
education.

It was July 1990 before the dentists' leaders and Mr Clarke finally agreed a revised contract. The intervening months had seen meetings of dentists strongly criticise the contract and a referendum of the profession reject the proposals by 62% to 38%.[43] Despite the opposition the General Dental Services Committee and the dentists' national conference accepted the deal, which some dentists viewed as being similar to proposals previously put forward by the BDA. Even so, dentists feared that the government would not fund the revised contract. While a leading dental negotiator described the proposals as "good for the patients," he also warned that the uncertainty among dentists was a result of the depressed fee levels and called for more realistic levels.[44]

The final agreement meant that an NHS patient would join a dentist's list for two years (renewable) for which a capitation fee would be paid. The fee would cover all routine care for children. For patients over 18 wanting normal treatment the dentist would be paid an item of service fee (75% by the patient) in addition to the capitation (retainer) fee, which would be equivalent to 10% of all fees. The dentists' warning over underfunding was underlined in May 1991, six months after the new contract started, when a survey showed that 86% of dentists were dissatisfied with the new arrangements and the BDA claimed that low morale was the result of "gross under-funding."[45] A subsequent survey by health authorities suggested that nationally 76% of dentists were routinely accepting all NHS patients, 22% were being selective, and 2% were not treating NHS patients. But in some parts of London only 25% of dentists were accepting all patients. This in part confirmed reports of patients facing difficulties in finding NHS dentists. Clearly, the revised contract was not proving a universal success and the BDA referred cautiously to "conflicting signals."[45] Even so, by 1992 30 million patients had registered which was well above the 24 million forecast. The Department of Health and the BDA remained locked in negotiations to try to resolve the early difficulties, which were later aggravated by the government's decision to cut dental fees by 7% because of substantial overpayments under the new contract, ironically a consequence of dentists working harder than forecast. Dentists were angry and the BDA ballotted its members in the summer of 1992, with the result that 80% of them opposed accepting new adults under the NHS scheme. Around 10% of dentists were restricting services in the autumn of 1992. The Secretary of State for Health described the 7% claw back as a "fair and reasonable way forward" but nevertheless set up an inquiry into dentists' pay. The House of Commons Health Committee also decided to examine dental services. Perhaps the most worrying comment as the outcome of the two inquiries was awaited came from dentists' leaders who reported a 70% fall over five years in applicants for university places, down to 1.8 applicants per place.[46]

MONITORING THE DOCTORS' CONTRACT

The doctors may have vigorously opposed the new contract but unlike the dentists they were unwilling—indeed, less able to, given their contracted 24 hour responsibilities for all citizens—to challenge its introduction by any collective action, deciding instead to monitor its operation.[47] The first two years resulted in extra administrative work for doctors and their staff, while many family health services authorities, particularly in 1990, were hard pressed to cope with the changes and all the extra information that had to be collected and processed. Generally, however, practitioners have got on with making the new arrangements work despite, for example, their doubts about the proven value of three yearly health checks or routine assessments of the elderly. In November 1992 the GMSC and the Department of Health agreed on improvements to the health promotion requirements, at no extra cost to the Treasury but amidst protests from GPs who lost out in the redistribution.[48]

It is too early to judge whether the government's optimistic predictions of a better service will be fulfilled, although a series in the BMJ in the spring of 1991 reviewing the first year of its operation suggested that the contract has had more positive effects than many GPs forecast. Anecdotal reports from GPs suggest that they are having to work harder and an indicator that the activity rates of general practitioners as a whole have risen are the considerable overpayments to general practitioners in 1990–91. Provisional figures show that on average each doctor received £6,000 more than the average income recommended by the review body, presumably as a result of payments for increased services provided.[49] If the money was on offer most seemed willing to provide the extra services. Another indication of increased workload, and from the community's point of view a success for the new contract, has been the large number of doctors who have reached the higher targets for immunisation and cervical cytology. Additionally, the RCGP reported that training course organisers were resigning because their partners saw their remuneration as too little to compensate for the time they spent away from the practice. Introduction of the contract led to a majority of practices introducing computers, influenced by the need to record accurately and quickly all the services for which they could claim a fee. An increasing number also appointed practice managers in response to the growing need for effective administration and accounting procedures. General practice was moving in the direction of business oriented rather than medical based partnerships, and many doctors were complaining of the increased burden of administration.

Not surprisingly, the imposition of cash limits caused problems. These limits are applied to expenditure on premises, staff and computing facilities and as each family health services authority (FHSA), successor to the family practitioner committee, has an overall cash limit for these it could, for example, provide more cash for computing at the expense of more staff or for innovations rather than improved premises. This could adversely affect practices which want to strengthen their staffing. Indeed, by 1993 it was clear that some FHSAs were refusing to allocate funds requested with the result that some practices were having to make staff redundant. This is an example of the new power of FHSAs compared with their FPC predecessors, which primarily acted as a conduit for paying contractors and as an umpire for patients' complaints.

The first anniversary of the revised contract brought trenchant criticism from the Centre for Health Economics at York University.[50] Reviewing the cost-effectiveness of the new arrangements Scott and Maynard concluded that for many of the services GPs were required to provide the verdict was 'unproven'. They even suggested that doctors were being induced to practise inefficiently. "It would have been judicious," they warned, "to develop the core services of the GPs' contract in the light of careful evaluation rather than system-wide reform of unknown efficacy." They urged a proper evaluation of the contract. The words might have come from the BMA rather than from health economists with a well known scepticism about how doctors provided medical care in the NHS.

Interestingly, after the profession's fierce opposition to the revised contract the GPs' new leaders adopted a proactive policy, inviting in the summer of 1991 all GPs to join them in reassessing future strategy and preparing an agenda for general practice.[51] The agenda asked which services GPs should be providing for patients, what patients expected, how GPs should be organised and how they should be paid. Subsequently, the committee sent all GPs a detailed questionnaire to which 70% responded. They wanted accreditation, less night work, more pay and to remain independent, although they no longer objected to doctors who wished to be salaried (a big reversal in attitude to remuneration).[52] A subsequent conference of GPs endorsed the findings, which one commentator argued pointed to a team future for general practice,[53] and asked for discussions with the government, particularly on out of hours cover. The Minister of State for Health responded by saying that he was willing to explore options for change with GPs' leaders as part of the regular review of their contract.[54] Clearly, 1992 was very different from the 1980s when an aggressive government, a defensive profession and bitter confrontation were the order of the day. Even so, anecdotal evidence suggested that morale among GPs was falling, with doctors complaining of rising workload.

NHS REVIEW

The first anniversary of the contract was the date when the provisions in the NHS review became operational. The NHS and Community Care Act 1990[55] converted the family practitioner committees into independent family health services authorities reporting to regional health authorities, and the increased management powers accorded to the FPCs as a result of the 'Promoting better health'[16] initiative were extended by the 1990 Act. FHSAs were made responsible for introducing indicative prescribing amounts for general practitioners to contain the drug budget, would supervise general practice funding and medical audit, and would monitor family practitioner services. To facilitate this new role the government cut the size of the authorities (with members appointed by the regional health authority); removed direct contractor representation; introduced independent, paid professional advisers; and streamlined the committee structure. This brought them more into line with the structure and functions of other health authorities and, significantly, greatly reduced the direct influence that the contractor professions had customarily enjoyed in the old family practitioner committees.

What were the other consequences of the NHS review on primary care? The radical innovation put forward in the document was the introduction of the provider/purchaser concept into general practice, with general practitioners invited to become fundholders. Practices with more than 11,000 patients, a number later reduced to 9,000, could apply for an annual budget with which to run their practices and purchase by contract certain hospital services. The government's intention was that general practitioners could shop around for the best value for money services, which was initially restricted to certain elective and diagnostic procedures, laboratory services, and outpatient facilities but later extended to some community services. They would not be restricted, however, in their choice of providers which could be local or distant, NHS or private (see also Chapter Five).

This concept alarmed not only many doctors but other supporters of a comprehensive and accessible NHS who foresaw a two-tier service developing, with the patients of budget-holding general practitioners getting priority attention. There was an added risk, too, that budget-holding GPs might be reluctant to take on chronic and/or potentially expensive patients in order to keep within their budgets. Budget-holding was also criticised as undermining the role of health authorities in meeting the health needs of their populations since budget-holding GPs would be operating independently and primarily in the interests of their own patients when purchasing services. The government saw budgets as a way of injecting an element of competition that would stimulate general practices and hospitals into providing better services for patients. As inducements to general practitioners it offered a £16,000 allowance to each fundholding practice for preparatory costs, an annual management allowance of £32,000 and better terms for running computers than non-fundholders received. Despite strong opposition to the idea from the BMA, several hundred general practitioners initially applied to be budget-holders and as the experience of the pioneers was assessed so the numbers increased. In 1992 over 2,000 doctors in 6,000 practices were fundholders, constituting nearly 15% of patients. How many signed up as convinced supporters of the concept and how many because they feared being in the bottom tier of a two-tier service is a matter of speculation. In 1993 the professional press still published the arguments of both supporters and critics but a report by Dr John Bain in the BMJ[56] reviewed the working of a big fundholding practice in Nottinghamshire and came to a cautiously optimistic conclusion.

FREE-WHEELING GPs

Already, as the scheme develops, the power that free-wheeling budget-holding GPs hold over hospitals and health authorities is becoming apparent. They are not beholden to their district authorities and can negotiate contracts on behalf of their patients with no regard to where their authority is placing its own purchasing contracts. They could make nonsense of any plans their authority had for providing services for its population. Will this prompt regional health authorities, which agree annual budgets with fundholding practices, and the new, more powerful FHSAs to co-ordinate the aims of health authorities and budget-holders? If not, this is a recipe for the inefficient and inequitable use of resources—not what ministers intended.

Indeed, the government acknowledged the potential difficulties and early in 1991 it asked fundholders to stick with their traditional referral patterns when agreeing their first round of contracts. The BMA and the Department of Health agreed guidelines to avoid a two-tier service for GPs' patients and established a joint monitoring committee. Despite these restraints fundholders' patients have been reported to be receiving preferential treatment from some providers, especially in districts where providers have been running out of funds before the end of the budget year. Another contentious development was that around 5% of fundholding practices ended their first year with substantial surpluses.[57] These practices wanted to use the money to improve their services, as the government had promised, but there were calls for the surpluses to be returned to cash strapped regional health authorities. Further surpluses were reported for the year 1991–92, though most practices were near their targets.

Once budget-holders had the freedom to negotiate their contracts consultants faced a threat to their traditional influence over local services. If they did not offer a service that fundholding GPs wanted then those doctors' patients would go where a suitable contract could be negotiated (an uncomfortable side-effect for some consultants could also be a fall in the number of patients referred privately to them). Taken to its logical conclusion, if a majority of GPs in a district become fundholders, as now seems probable, the authority could be undermined in attempting to negotiate provider contracts for its population. The GPs would dominate decisions on patterns of hospital care. Was this foreseen by the government? Certainly the opposition parties wanted none of this, strongly resisting the change on the grounds that it would undermine planning in the NHS and erode the equity of services it was intended to provide.

Interestingly, American observers, including Enthoven whose ideas stimulated the proposals for an internal market,[58] warned that the minimum criteria of 11,000 patients was far too low to operate such a scheme.[59] Their experience of hospital maintenance organisations (HMOs), which operated in a similar way, suggested that 100,000 patients was a minimum viable number to cope with the yearly variations that would occur in the incidence of costly medical events. Opponents of the concept also described it as a step towards privatising the NHS, a charge vigorously denied by ministers. There were also fears that GPs would not have the management abilities to run budgets effectively.

The BMA's high profile oppositon to the NHS review is reported elsewhere. The Royal College of General Practitioners, which had an overwhelming response about the proposals from its members, was also critical. It rejected the white paper because if implemented as proposed the outcome would do "serious damage to patient care and the doctor/patient relationship."[60] The college also condemned the white paper and its associated documents for failing to recognise the resource implications for the NHS and echoed the widespread criticism about the lack of consultation on the proposals.

The Royal College of Nursing was just as condemnatory, warning that it threatened the principles and effectiveness of the NHS. The college criticised, as did others, the white paper's lack of detail and, as Dr John Fry, an experienced London general practitioner, pointed out there was "no evidence of critical analysis of published or commissioned research data."[61] The soft centre to the white paper (and the subsequent NHS Act) was never more apparent than in the unforeseen consequences of the purchaser/provider concept for budget-holding GPs. Would the review have the unexpected outcome of crowning family doctors as the monarchs of the NHS's many castles? Or did the authors of the review look forward to the day when GPs, who dealt with 90% of the nation's health needs, would be the engines of competition in the NHS?

INDICATIVE DRUG BUDGETS AND EXTRACONTRACTUAL REFERRALS

As part of its continuing efforts to restrain the rising costs of drugs in the NHS the government introduced a proposal for indicative drug budgets in 'Working for patients'.[32] The aim was "to place downward pressure on expenditure of drugs . . . but without in any way preventing people getting the medicines they need." Operation of this new scheme, which was not universally welcomed by doctors concerned about restraints on prescribing, would be facilitated by the information becoming available under the recently introduced PACT (prescribing information) scheme. To achieve this Nirvana the government would set up an overall annual budget for drugs, regional health authorities would give FHSAs their budgets, and the authorities would then indicate a budget for each practice. This would be determined in discussions with general practitioners and would take account of existing prescribing costs and the average for similar practices. If a practice spent less than its target half the savings would be spent by the authority on practice improvement schemes (in consultation with the general practitioners). This, the government argued, would "encourage cost-effective and prudent prescribing" (see also Chapter Five).

One uncertain facet of the GP/hospital interface was what would happen about patients whom GPs wished to refer to hospitals with which the health authority had no contract. Such extracontractual referrals (by non-budget-holding GPs) include emergencies and referrals for elective, secondary and tertiary care. Their number and cost will affect purchasers and providers, yet with the limited information available to hospitals and authorities about where their patients live and the extent of cross-boundary referrals how will districts calculate the amount of money they will need to put aside to pay for extracontractual referrals? If such referrals were restricted for budgetary convenience where did that leave the government's policy of greater patient choice, which 'Working for patients' was claimed to have provided? In the South East Thames Regional Health Authority, for example, district figures varied from 0.8% to 2.25% of revenue budgets.[62] Preliminary studies suggest that the administrative workload entailed was disproportionate to the number of referrals (GPs have to obtain authorisation for extracontractual referrals, while hospitals and health authorities have to work out the costs and argue, perhaps, whether an emergency was genuine, whether it was dealt with properly and whether it would entail further attendances at the hospital concerned).

The threat to patient confidentiality is, as Forsythe has pointed out,[62] a disturbing feature of the process. Patients referred extracontractually may have their name, address, diagnosis and possible treatment faxed to people not directly concerned with their care and without their knowledge or consent. This does not sit comfortably with the white paper's title, 'Working for patients'. Indeed, it could be argued that patients will be worse off in the reformed NHS when it comes to choosing hospital treatment. Only a few patients will escape the preordained referral patterns negotiated by their health authorities and budget-holding GPs.

CONCLUSION

If the primary care services entered the 1980s in reasonably good shape their progress during the first three years of the 1990s have been a struggle to cope with hastily imposed reforms of as yet unproven value. More patients will continue to pay an increasing proportion of the costs of drugs and spectacles, while there is a serious possibility that many people may find dental care increasingly hard to obtain from the NHS—privatisation by default. The rough edges of the GPs' revised and imposed contract may eventually be smoothed down but the impact of fundholding remains as unpredictable as when it was first proposed. The GMSC's survey of GPs in 1992 showed a majority of them still opposed to the idea, with appreciable opposition remaining even among doctors who had taken that road. Setting accurate budgets was difficult because of a shortage of information and fears remained that patients of budget-holding GPs were receiving preferential treatment from hospital providers. Admittedly, the first year or two of fundholding is unlikely to provide a typical pattern for the future. Even so, as a leader writer in the BMJ observed, "fundholding remains an interesting experiment, which should continue as long as there is a commitment to monitor and learn from the experience."[63] Introduction of this market mechanism, however, has acquired a momentum of its own, with some doctors joining because they fear that their patients will be disadvantaged if they don't. That may be what ministers wanted but it is an unsound foundation for such a radical reform of primary care. Nevertheless, Professor Howard Glennerster, who studied fundholding for the King's Fund in 1992, argued that the scheme was having an important impact on the effectiveness and responsiveness of hospitals targeted by GP fundholders.[64] Further studies confirmed this view in early 1993, when he also claimed that the 'bottom-up' principle of fundholding hospitals was financially more responsive than block contracts.[65] He may be right but shortages of resources will continue, and as more GPs are attracted (or feel compelled) to sign up as fundholders the financial glow experienced by the pioneers may turn to financial blues as cash restraints for general medical services affect all GPs. Although there is ample scope for a more efficient use of resources, it is still an open question whether the recent market reforms and more consumer sensitive contracts will give the community a more responsive and cost-effective service. The reforms may well achieve the government's aim of restraining the ever rising costs of primary care, but as a recent commentator in the BMJ pointed out "general practice is still on the defensive" and the "way forward ... looks long and difficult."[66] Indeed, in October 1993 Dr Ian Bogle, the GMSC's Chairman, was warning the government of a crisis in morale among GPs.[67] Furthermore, the number of young doctors in GP vocational training schemes fell from around 2,200 a year in the late 1980s to just over 2,000 in 1992, with anecdotal reports of a sharp drop in the number of applicants for courses (BMA, personal communication). Certainly, GPs are working harder, partly due to extra administration, and the government regularly claims success for its reforms. The jury, however, in the shape of the public is still 'out'.

REFERENCES

1. *Report of the Royal Commission on the National Health Service* (1979). Cmnd 7615. London: HMSO.
2. British Medical Association (1965). *A charter for the family doctor service*. London: BMA.
3. *Report of the Royal Commission on Medical Education 1965–68* (1968). Cmd 3569. London: HMSO.
4. General Medical Services Committee (1979). *Report of the new charter working group*. London: BMA.
5. Anon (1983). NHS budget and family practitioners. *BMJ* 286: 1519.
6. Anon (1982). Announcement of Binder Hamlyn inquiry. *BMJ* 285: 1220.
7. Coopers and Lybrand Associates (1983). *Cost effectiveness of general practice*. London: General Medical Services Committee, BMA.
8. Klein R (1983). *The politics of the National Health Service*. London: Longmore.
9. General Medical Services Committee (1983). *General practice: a British success*. London: BMA.
10. Griffiths report (1983). *National Health Service management inquiry*. London: HMSO.
11. Department of Health and Social Security (1984). *Health service development: general practitioner deputising services*. HC (FP) 84.
12. Anon (1985). Secretary of State limits range of prescribable NHS drugs. *BMJ* 289: 1388.
13. *Report of the Department of Health and Social Security working group on effective prescribing* (1983). London: DHSS. (Greenfield report).
14. Anon (1984). RCGP council rejects proposals to limit NHS drugs. *BMJ* 289: 1640.
15. Secretary of State for Social Services (1986). *Primary health care: an agenda for discussion*. Cmnd 9771. London: HMSO.

16. Secretary of State for Social Services (1987). *Promoting better health: the government's programme for improving primary care*. Cmnd 249. London: HMSO.

17. Anon (1987). News items on new contract. *Pharmaceutical Journal* 238: 358–363.

18. The report of a committee of inquiry appointed by the Nuffield Foundation (1986). *Pharmacy*. London: Nuffield Foundation.

19. Department of Health and Social Security (1986). *Neighbourhood nursing— a focus for care*. London: HMSO. (Cumberlege report).

20. London Health Planning Consortium (1981). *Primary health care in inner London*. London: Department of Health and Social Security. (Acheson report).

21. Rhodes G et al. (1986). *Primary health care in the inner cities: after Acheson*. London: Policy Studies Institute.

22. Tomlinson B (1992). *Report of the inquiry into London's health service, medical education and research*. London: HMSO.

23. Jarman B, Bosanquet N (1992). Primary health care in London—changes since the Acheson report. *BMJ* 305: 1130–6.

24. Anon (1993). No new money for Tomlinson. *BMJ* 306: 1133.

25. Anon (1986). From the LMC conference. *BMJ* 293: 1384.

26. Jarman B (1983). Identification of underprivileged areas. *BMJ* 286: 11705–8.

27. *Health and Medicines Bill 1988* (1988). London: HMSO.

28. Anon (1988). LMC conference: Department of Health and Social Security's lack of knowledge hampers negotiations, warns chairman. *BMJ* 297: 74.

29. Anon (1988). LMC conference: anger at threatened introduction of cash limits. *BMJ* 297: 138.

30. Griffiths R (1988). *Community care: agenda for action. A report to the Secretary of State for Social Services*. London: HMSO.

31. Scrutator (1989). Slow down, Mr Clarke, and button your lip. *BMJ* 298: 704.

32. Secretaries of State for Health, Wales, Northern Ireland and Scotland (1989). *Working for patients*. Cmnd 555. London: HMSO.

33. Anon (1989). From the GMSC. GPs criticise government's plans for NHS. *BMJ* 298: 528.

34. Department of Health and Welsh Office (1989). *General practice in the National Health Service: a new contract*. London: HMSO.

35. Anon (1989). GPs committed to improving patient care. *BMJ* 298: 1259.

36. Anon (1989). New contract for GPs in Scotland. *BMJ* 298: 1105.

37. Ellis N (1989). Outline of proposed package of changes to GPs' contracts. *BMJ* 298: 1387–89.

38. Beecham L (1989). Contract rejected; ballot called; more talks wanted. *BMJ* 299: 57–60.

39. Delamothe T (1989). GPs vote three to one against new contract. *BMJ* 299: 285.

40. Dyer C (1990). GPs' challenge falls at first hurdle. *BMJ* 300: 768.

41. National Association of Health Authorities and Trusts (1991). *NHS handbook. Seventh edition*. Birmingham: NAHAT.

42. British Dental Association (1991). *Dental manpower requirements forty years forward*. London: BDA.

43. Anon (1990). GDSC accepts new contract. *BDJ* 168 (2): 33.

44. British Dental Association (1990). *New Dental Contract in October*. London: BDA. (Press release).

45. British Dental Association (1991). *Press release*. London: BDA.

46. Warden J (1992). Dentistry or decay? *BMJ* 305: 1316.

47. Beecham L (1990). From the GMSC. *BMJ* 300: 818.

48. Williams DM (1993). Health promotion in general practice. *BMJ* 306: 148.

49. Housden E, Ford J (1991). General practitioners' pay. *BMJ* 303: 1086.

50. Scott T, Maynard A (1991). *Will the new GP contract lead to cost effective medical practice?* Discussion paper 82. York: Centre for Health Economics, York University.

51. General Medical Services Committee (1991). *Building your own future: an agenda for general practice*. London: BMA.

52. Beechman L (1992). GPs' survey supports accreditation. *BMJ* 304: 731–2.

53. Beechman L (1992). From the LMC conference. *BMJ* 305: 57.

54. Beechman L (1992). GPs want to improve out of hours care. *BMJ* 305: 12.

55. *National Health Service and Community Care Act* (1990). London: HMSO.

56. Bain J (1993). Budget holding: here to stay? *BMJ* 306: 1185–1188.

57. Anon (1992). Should fundholders return savings? *General Practitioner* December 4, 29.

58. Enthoven A (1985). *Reflections on the management of the NHS*. London: Nuffield Provincial Hospitals Trust.

59. Smith R (1989). NHS review. Words from the source: an interview with Alain Enthoven. *BMJ* 298: 1166.

60. Royal College of General Practitioners (1989). *Summary statement on Working for patients: prepared by council at its meeting on 15th April 1989*. London: Royal College of General Practitioners.

61. Fry J (1980). *General practice and primary health care 1940–1980s*. London: Nuffield Provincial Hospitals Trust.

62. Forsythe J (1991). Extracontractual referrals: the story so far. *BMJ* 303: 479–8.

63. Coulter A (1992). Fundholding general practices. *BMJ* 302: 397.

64. Glennerster H et al. (1992). *A foothold for fundholding*. London: King's Fund Institute.

65. Glennerster H (1993). Getting better all the time. *Guardian* 17 February.

66. Iliffe S (1993). 1966 revisited: bright new contract or brave old world? *BMJ* 306: 946–7.

67. Bogle I (1993). *BMA press statement on speech to GMSC*. 20th October 1993.

5

THE INTERNAL MARKET—'WORKING FOR PATIENTS'

◆

INTRODUCTION

All governments' long-term strategy for the NHS has been based on a number of deeply felt and continuing convictions:

(a) the NHS is a political football 'with the big match' played every five years. The NHS has always been one of the top three or four major issues at every general election for the past 20 years and is a factor of the greatest political significance. For a time it was at the top of the agenda in April 1992 with squabbles over the Labour party election broadcast featuring the case of 'Jennifer' and her grommets;

(b) it is also a continuing irritant, a running sore. No party can get it off the political agenda and for the Conservatives, whatever their stated commitment or the level of additional resources pumped in over the years, it has been an uphill struggle to make the public believe that the NHS 'is safe in our hands';

(c) the 1948 principles of equity and access to comprehensive health care must remain inviolate as to break with them would be political suicide;

(d) the NHS must remain funded almost solely from general taxation. However attractive alternative systems involving social insurance schemes might appear successive reviews in the 1970s and 1980s came to nothing. A significant role for private insurance schemes would lead to the two evils of increased bureaucracy and rising costs that the government is determined to control;

(e) it is a monolithic bureaucracy which generates its own momentum, or lack of it. It is one in which demand and supply, and the style and systems of operation, are largely determined by the work-force, primarily the medical profession, and are often manipulated by the strongest of trade unions—the BMA;

(f) traditionally the wishes of the people who use the service have either not been sought or ignored—the take it or leave it syndrome. Patients have generally been treated with patronising concern, like naughty children who are too ignorant to know what is in their best interests; and

(g) the NHS is a bottomless pit where however many additional resources are put in it is difficult to demonstrate any positive improvement in services let alone in the health of the nation. The Black report[1] drew

attention to continuing inequalities in health in 1978 and there is no
reason to believe, or evidence to suggest, that the situation has improved
since then.

So what should be done? Since 1979 governments had held
long-term objectives based on greater devolution, better value
for money and stronger accountability. Much had been
achieved. Lines of communication from top to bottom had
been shortened. More decisions affecting operational services
were being taken locally—at district but not yet at unit level.
Through competitive tendering, and other central initiatives,
'protectionist' policies were challenged leading to improvements in the costs and efficiency of non-clinical support
services. Stronger and more clearly defined roles, relationships
and accountability had been established for managers but little
had been done for the key professional groups, who generally
determined the content, style and costs of services to patients.

After 40 years the NHS offered a comprehensive range of
health services to the whole population irrespective of income,
based on a history of strong primary health care provided
through general practitioners. It appeared to be more cost-effective than other health care systems, with an equitable
method of allocating resources and with firm control of expenditure through the cash limit mechanism, probably the best of
any government department and the envy of the Americans.
Amongst the serious weaknesses were the following:

(a) inadequate or perverse incentives to be more efficient in the use of re-
    sources to improve the quantity and quality of care. The more work a
    hospital did the sooner it risked breaking its fixed cash limit and the
    greater the need to reduce capacity, often by closing beds in the last
    quarter of the financial year during a period of peak demand;

(b) huge variations in performance, both between and within hospitals and
    primary health care providers, as determined, for example, by waiting
    lists, referral and admission rates, lengths of stay, proportion of day case
    surgery, unit costs and drug prescribing rates;

(c) poor data to help local professionals and managers to improve their de-
    cision making, affecting levels of clinical service in terms of treatment and
    costs; and

(d) limited opportunities for patients to exercise choice over the doctor they
    would like or the alternative services available to them for their hospital
    care. The doctors were slow to review critically their own clinical out-
    comes let alone allow patients information on good and bad performance.

Resources invested in health care continued to rise relent-
lessly but public concern about inadequacies also continued to
increase, stimulated by more intense media attention. What
was needed, the government concluded, was the political will
to tackle not just the structure and management but the very
dynamics of the system. Roy Griffiths had introduced the concept of business management. Why not go further and make
the whole NHS more susceptible to business disciplines and
market forces? Why not retain the founding principles of the
NHS but change its culture and ethos, in a word 'destabilise'
the bureaucracy. This would be a mammoth task fraught with
political difficulty, for after all the NHS employed one million
people, more than any other organisation in the world bar
two—the Soviet military and the Indian Railways. But there
was also cause for hope. Mikhail Gorbachev had managed to
impose on the Soviet military establishment a series of reforms, reductions and negotiations with which they were
unhappy. All that was needed was the political courage.

ENTHOVEN

In 1985 Professor Alain Enthoven wrote an essay for the
Nuffield Provincial Hospitals Trust.[2] This was intended as "a
sympathetic review of some problems of organisation and
management with particular focus on incentives for efficiency
and innovation." He was searching for opportunities for constructive change which "should be nurtured not politicised or
otherwise abused," and which were aimed at breaking the
'gridlock' that had resisted NHS development.

He observed with satisfaction the high level of dedication of
NHS staff, a vital asset which should be capitalised upon, but
he was concerned about the 'perverse incentives' which frustrated and inhibited experimentation and innovation. He was
supportive of Griffiths' concept of general management but
critical of the method of its introduction by central prescription. "A decree requiring all authorities to implement general
management is an unlikely way to implement change," because "national uniformity should not be a requirement in
such organisational matters." He strongly recommended loos-
ening the bureaucracy through a "greater use of
demonstration projects," which the American experience sug-

gested would bring major benefits. On medical leadership and the involvement of doctors in management he was concerned about the poor management background of senior clinicians in general but of specialists in community medicine (regional and district medical officers) in particular. He suggested more effective management training for selected clinicians who would progressively influence their colleagues locally.

Enthoven also believed that it was vital for the NHS to develop 'cost finding systems'. He was concerned that "the NHS doesn't know its own costs and so isn't able to recognise a good deal when it sees one." With better costing systems "the NHS could become more of a discerning purchaser of services from competing private suppliers and thereby realise some of the benefits of efficiency and innovation that competition in the private sector offers."

On the allocation of resources he was against the concept of self-sufficiency and recommended "dropping the implicit assumption that people must get all their services in their own district, equalising the need-adjusted per capita spending on the people in each district by appropriating the funds to the district health authority and letting districts buy services from other districts as needed." One of the advantages he envisaged was that "this might let the London teaching hospitals compete for referrals from other districts rather than face being ground down by the relentless application of the Resource Allocation Working Party (RAWP) formula" (anything which might reduce the 'London problem', with major political implications, would be particularly attractive to the government).

In such a situation Enthoven saw that "each district would receive a RAWP based per capita revenue and capital allocation. It would continue to be responsible for providing and paying for comprehensive care for its own resident population but not for the care of other people without current compensation at negotiated prices. Each district would resemble a nationalised company. It would buy and sell services to and from other districts and trade with the private sector." This line of thinking could lead to an 'internal market module' based on 'market socialism', rather than 'privatisation'.

Enthoven had also extolled the virtues of the health maintenance organisations (HMOs), whose enrolled membership had increased to 17 million in the United States at the time of writing. He saw this system as one which harnessed the motiv-ation and dedication of clinicians, made them more cost conscious and raised quality standards. An HMO accepted responsibility for providing comprehensive health care ser-vices for a "fixed periodic capitation payment set in advance." Enthoven claimed that they had "cut costs roughly 25% com-pared to fee for service," which itself had "insured patients with a cost-unconscious free choice of doctor" and by doing so had increased spending on health in America in recent years to a "crisis proportion." The NHS could gain useful insights "from the HMO experience which would help to optimise the high level of dedication of all NHS staff . . . Economic interest can even motivate doctors to expel poor performers from their group. In competition doctors impose on themselves controls they would never dream of accepting if the government tried to impose them. Thus clinical freedom is giving way to effec-tive control of quality and cost-effectiveness," an issue at the very heart of the government's aims. The lessons which could be learnt from the American experience were not all so encour-aging. Was it not true that although in the early years HMOs had produced major cost savings (mainly through lower rates of hospital admissions) by 1989 private sector insurers were hitting back? They offered the low risk section of the popu-lation (the young and the professional middle-class) lower rates and so enticed customers away from the HMOs. The HMOs in turn had to increase the cost of their standard pre-payment policy for comprehensive care as the proportion of their high risk members (the poor, the elderly and the blacks) increased.

Enthoven had pointed the way towards an internal market. It was reported that his essay had made an impact on the Prime Minister, and perhaps equally importantly on the future Secretary of State for Health, Mr Clarke, whose commitment to the NHS and whose in-depth knowledge gained as Mr Fowler's Minister of State was unrivalled. It was to be he who would 'dot the I's' and 'cross the T's' in the final draft of the white paper.

MARKET MODELS

Throughout 1988, whilst it was being drafted behind closed doors, rumours abounded about the contents of the white paper. It was suggested that those districts which treated a lot of patients from other districts should be given a fair deal for their cross-boundary flows. There was talk of 'shopping around' for treatment to cut waiting times, with the GPs acting as gatekeepers. Concern was expressed, however, that this had little to do with patients' choice as in this situation choice might be made not by GPs but by managers. There was also concern that the causes of the crisis over funding, which had forced the Prime Minister to set up the review, were unlikely to be addressed.

In the run-up to publication there was discussion amongst clinicians, managers and academics about what was meant by an internal market. A paper by the National Association of Health Authorities (NAHA) highlighted the options under consideration.[3] Two distinct models stood out. In model one the health authority received funding for its population, defined its health needs and purchased services to meet that need through contracts with:

(a) its own hospitals (the district managed units (DMUs));

(b) other authorities' hospitals;

(c) self-governing hospitals; and

(d) the private sector.

The district health authority (DHA) might not necessarily manage any hospital units directly. In model two the health authority received funding for its population but allowed patients to seek treatment anywhere they chose and guaranteed to reimburse the chosen provider at cost or through a negotiated fee.

Model one implies that the majority of residents, if not all, had to be treated within contracts that the DHA had arranged with approved providers, thus clearly limiting both patient and GP choice. NAHA suggested that the health authority would be operating "much like the health maintenance organisation in America," in which case the patient and GP would have little choice of the place where treatment is obtained because the health authority would have made its own assessment of value for money services from units in the public and private sector. In model two if the reimbursement was retrospective the arrangements would be similar to the insurance based systems, which offered no real incentive for cost-effectiveness to the providers since the providers knew that they would be paid whatever the price. The danger here was that costs would rise rapidly as they had done in the USA. On the other hand, prospective payment systems have the advantage that health care suppliers are paid for the amount of work they do and they are encouraged to be aware of the cost per case.

Model one has the disadvantage of providing limited freedom of choice for both patients and general practitioners as referrals are very much determined by contract. It does, however, have the significant advantage of enabling the health authority to determine priorities of need and to ensure that these priorities are addressed through a pre-determined contract. It also has the major advantage of comparatively strict expenditure control. In model two patients and GPs have greater freedom but the health authority is disadvantaged in trying to ensure that its resources are used effectively to meet its assessment of need and there are difficulties in maintaining financial control. In considering these two extreme ends of the internal market the government had to decide how to balance the objective of extending patient choice with the Treasury's reluctance to agree to anything which would weaken the cash limit system.

There were already elements of model one and model two operating within the NHS. In the case of model one DHAs had often entered into agency agreements with NHS and private hospitals to provide a particular service for a specific patient population, such as hip replacements. From model two cross-boundary flow adjustments were already incorporated into the RAWP formula to ensure that there was a fair distribution of resources for patients who travelled across administrative boundaries. Whichever way the government went it could claim a natural progression from existing developments.

Whilst these discussions were continuing the opposition made their position clear. Mr Robin Cook, shadow spokesman for health, in a Fabian tract wrote:

"An internal market would not widen choice for the patients. Choice would be exercised by management who would decide which hospital offered the best buy. To that extent the scope for the patient, in consultation with the GP, to express a preference for a particular hospital would be reduced. Indeed, implicit in the model of the internal market is the right of management to instruct the patients that they will not be treated at the local district general hospital because they have been placed in a bulk order at a better rate, in another hospital."[4]

So much for patients' choice and clinical freedom! Political battle lines were drawn even before the reforms were implemented.

THE WHITE PAPER: DEVELOPMENT PROCESS FROM CONCEPT TO IMPLEMENTATION PLAN

The white paper was written over a period of one year by a small policy group working directly to the Prime Minister (a free-floating 'think tank' which only leaked intentionally), whose members were distinguished by both their political affiliation and by their ignorance of the day-to-day workings of the NHS. Their work was undertaken in isolation and was surrounded by secrecy. They developed numerous new concepts based on political imperatives and they struggled over time, and with some success, to integrate them into a coherent framework for a new-style NHS. The level of nervousness over secrecy was such that neither senior clinicians nor senior managers from the service were directly involved at any time. In fact, Whitehall itself proved to be the great divide between the existing strategic managers of the service in the Department of Health and the new policy makers in Number 10. Only occasional missives were sent across the road to Richmond House demanding urgent comment on the latest bright idea. It is believed that the Chief Medical Officer, who was the adviser to the whole of government and not just the Department of Health, was only consulted intermittently and then on highly specific and isolated issues, and that he did not know how the proposals were developing until just before its publication. The Department of Health waited expectantly. The NHS waited anxiously and with increasing concern. The white paper was to be released at the end of January. During that month drafts were finally flashed before one or two NHS confidants and then regional chairmen and general managers were given prior warning: they were called in on the day before publication and asked to read copies and then leave them behind!

'Working for patients'[5] was published on 31st January, almost one year after the NHS review had been announced abruptly by the Prime Minister on the BBC Panorama programme. In the foreword Mrs Thatcher reiterated the government's long-term objectives, "we aim to extend patients' choice, to delegate responsibility to where the services are provided and to secure the best value for money . . . the patients' needs will always be paramount." This time they really meant 'patients first'!

The white paper detailed the government's strategic aims with seven specific objectives in mind, which included the new self-governing status for hospitals, practice budgets for GPs and the principle of money following the patient. Although the document did not specifically advocate a purchaser/provider split, the cornerstone of what came to be called the reforms, it was implied through the definition of the new roles of RHAs and DHAs (the purchasers) and the hospitals (the providers). RHAs and DHAs would "concentrate on ensuring that the health needs of the population for which they are responsible are met, that there are effective services for the prevention and control of diseases and the promotion of health, that their population has access to a comprehensive range of high quality, value for money services." More specifically, "each DHA's duty will be to buy the best services it can from its own hospitals, from other authorities' hospitals, from self-governing hospitals and from the private sector."

The Department of Health was confronted with a new and radical policy document to which it had contributed little. It had the task of developing the new concepts (such as self-governing hospitals, GP budgets, the new revenue allocation system, capital charges and asset registers) and seeking to integrate them into an implementation plan. They also had the urgent task of drafting primary legislation to give the proposals legality. The civil service approach to tackling a complex task is always, quite logically, to break it down into its constituent elements. As a result no fewer than 32 project groups (later increased) were established. Each project group beavered away discreetly and produced draft reports in isolation. It was disappointing that more than 12 months passed before a limited number of critical projects were identified, upon which the successful implementation of the proposals depended, and the project leaders had begun meeting each other on a regular basis as a critical results project managers group (CRPMG).

These 32 groups did not work unsupervised. Attempts were made to co-ordinate their output at or near 'the top of the office' through a somewhat Byzantine system. Both the First Permanent Secretary, in charge of the Policy Group and the drafting of legislation, and the Second Permanent Secretary, in charge of NHS management, had an interest in translating the white paper concepts into practical proposals for change. Both had small and separate units to undertake this work. Both chaired co-ordinating committees to which progress reports were channelled. A white paper steering committee was chaired by the First Permanent Secretary, whose membership included the Second Permanent Secretary, the Chief Medical Officer and the Chief Nursing Officer. A white paper working group chaired by the Second Permanent Secretary sought to influence and co-ordinate project development from the management perspective and sent its minutes to the steering committee. It was also disappointing that when these two separate bodies received the same progress report, one a week or two before the other, it looked like wasteful duplication in time and paper, yet when the two groups received significantly different reports it was even more worrying. Months passed before the anomaly was sorted out and the two committees became one under the Second Permanent Secretary. Yet more months passed before it was decided that its work was complete and the further development of the white paper proposals was left to the CRPMG, which would report to the Management Executive.

PUBLIC INFORMATION AND PR

Mr Clarke presented the white paper to the House of Commons on 31st January 1989. It claimed that "the proposals in the white paper put the interests and wishes of the patient first. They offer a new, exciting and potentially rewarding challenge to all who work in the NHS. They add up to the most significant review of the NHS in its 40 year history. And they amount to a formidable programme of reform which will require energy and commitment to carry it through."[5]

The Secretary of State for Health immediately embarked on

a major communications exercise to transmit the strategy, the concepts and the main messages to the management of the service through the medium of tele-conferencing. All chairmen, general managers and selected clinicians, a total of over 800, were invited to television studios in Birmingham, Bristol, Leeds, London, Manchester, Newcastle and Nottingham. Mr Clarke and other ministers presented the government's proposals with the aid of a video and then entered into a discussion on the major issues through a nationwide TV link-up. The occasion was particularly notable for the Secretary of State's personal role, as he not only conveyed his strong commitment to the service but also revealed his in-depth knowledge of its workings and needs. It was a remarkable personal triumph which did much to increase the confidence of the management of the service in its political leadership. Critics argued that the whole affair was unnecessarily expensive and that it was a public relations showbiz exercise with flashing lights, dramatic music and general razzamatazz. The majority of managers applauded the fact that for the first time ministers had sought to explain major policy to the NHS face to face and their general reaction was to give the Secretary of State for Health good marks for his initiative and congratulations on his personal success.

One of a manager's first responsibilities must be to share the aims of policy with his staff. It was vital that the one million people working in the NHS should learn about 'Working for patients'[5] and its programme of radical change from local managers as soon as practicable. General managers were immediately exalted to 'cascade' the white paper proposals to the entire work force within the following week.

To help them in this mammoth task they were given an information pack which included:

(a) a 20 minute video (which was clear in its message, if rather long, and contained a preface by the Prime Minister that, unfortunately, had the effect of upsetting some of the entrenched political sensitivities of NHS staff);

(b) a detailed briefing pack with speaking notes and overhead transparencies; and

(c) a question and answer brief covering major issues and likely concerns.

This material was extremely helpful in assisting managers to give clear, concise and consistent messages to their staff. In retrospect this support was an essential means of communication. The white paper had been written in secret and, although leaks and rumours had been rife, most managers heard of the proposals for the first time at the tele-conference yet were expected to grasp the individual concepts and their relationships, understand the new thinking behind them and then convey what it all meant to their staff within a week. The pack was of high quality in its clarity of message and form of presentation and most managers responded positively to the challenge. Although the success of the cascade was highly variable across the service and was determined in part by the political complexion of the locality, the majority of managers were won over by the opportunities which the proposals offered through greater devolution and local decision making, abandonment of the RAWP allocation process distrusted by both the 'haves' and 'have nots', and the clearer definition of the core functions of health authorities resulting from the separation of the purchasing and providing roles.

Communications round one, the need to inform and persuade the management of the service, was generally successful. It was crucial because ministers expected the new cadre of general managers to deliver their objectives and implement the change process. Round two, convincing the work force (the doctors, nurses, physiotherapists, porters, cooks, cleaners, the British Medical Association (BMA), the Royal College of Nursing (RCN), the National Union of Public Employees (NUPE) and the Confederation of Health Service Employers (COHSE) and round three, persuading the general public, were to prove far more difficult in the remaining years of the Tory administration.

The white paper launch began well but by the autumn of 1989 the Secretary of State for Health became increasingly concerned that his message about the opportunities presented by the reforms was not being conveyed effectively to staff at the operational level. On his tours of hospitals he constantly met nurses, paramedical staff and others (who spent their time treating and talking face to face with patients on a daily basis) who had not even seen his video, let alone taken part in local discussions about what the white paper really meant for them and their services at unit level. He was particularly concerned because he believed that an NHS that was run better would be an NHS that could care better. He also stressed that the programme of action was aimed at two key objectives: to give patients wherever they live better health care and greater choice of the services available, and to produce greater satisfaction and rewards for NHS staff who successfully respond to local needs and preferences. He expected that as the staff were so highly committed to the NHS and to the quality of services provided for patients they would respond positively. He also hoped that in turn they would influence the attitudes of the general public.

In the primary care sector the Secretary of State had also become increasingly concerned that the proposed changes were being misunderstood. The objectives here were to integrate primary and secondary care more effectively and to redress the balance of influence within the medical profession by giving general practitioners a stronger role. He was offering the GPs a package which included their own budgets to purchase hospital care, the right to retain any savings to improve their own practices, the opportunity of developing surgical and diagnostic services nearer to their patients, the opportunity of persuading the consultants to come out of their distant hospitals and to work with them in the community, and enhanced pay for an expanded role in health promotion. The package had become confused with the new contract, which included the provision for GPs to be rewarded by raising the proportion of their pay derived from the number of patients on their lists from 46% to 60%.

This new contract, however, was being forced on GPs after a long and bitter battle. Personal relationships between the representatives of the profession and ministers were at rock bottom. Although the contract and the white paper were separate issues they became inter-related and detrimentally influenced the GPs' attitude to the changes over the next two years. The Royal College of General Practitioners was moved to criticise "the lack of proper evaluation prior to such major changes" and the tight timetable allowed for consultation.[6] Dr CH Zuckerman, Secretary of the Birmingham Local Medical Committee, described the proposed contract as "a surrender document" which would lead to confrontation. He believed that if the package was accepted general practitioners would lose their independent status and would tear up the 1966 charter. He claimed that "patient care would suffer. Bitter and disillusioned doctors would provide a bitter and disillusioned service. Let Mr Clarke impose a contract . . . because if he did the government would carry the profession round its neck like an albatross until the next election."[7] The national publicity given to these wrangles confused and bored the general public, some of whom found that they were being got at whenever they visited their doctors' surgeries.

During the autumn of 1989, therefore, the Secretary of State became increasingly concerned that the white paper proposals, politically a very high risk strategy, were not understood by the one million staff who worked in the NHS nor by the public and, therefore, were not being given a fair hearing. Concern was heightened when the results of Mori polls commissioned by the Trent RHA, which were internally distributed but were not published, demonstrated the level of public ignorance and anxiety. Most people believed that the proposals were aimed at cost-cutting and reductions in standards rather than improvements in the quality of care. Worst of all, cynicism and mistrust of the proposals was greatest in those sections of the public that had direct interface with the NHS through relatives working in the service!

The political concerns came together with increasing management concerns about the service's ability to deliver the huge management changes in the very tight timescale of 24 months. The Policy Board, successor to the old Supervisory Board, considered and approved a major management/staff communications programme undertaken with the help of a consortium of management consultants. This programme had two objectives:

(a) in the short-term to help managers explain the NHS reforms to their staff, to improve local understanding of the issues, which would facilitate implementation, reduce frustration born of ignorance and, hopefully, gain an increasing level of commitment; and

(b) in the long-term to raise the overall standard of management by improving the quality of communications within units (for it was at unit level that most patients were treated and most staff worked) and between units and the rest of the NHS.

Eighty-seven per cent of all general managers and two thirds of all units were directly involved and 250,000 staff took part in attitudes surveys. Over a period of 18 months evidence was collected which indicated that:

(a) local managers' understanding of their communications responsibilities had been enhanced (something that was at the heart of good management);

(b) understanding and relationships between managers and staff had improved; and

(c) the new concepts in the reforms had been translated into local and practical proposals and staff more readily understood how their daily working lives might be affected.

During the period between the publication of the white papers in 1989[5,8] and the NHS and Community Care 1990 Bill[9] becoming law in July 1990 numerous attempts by ministers to publicise their proposals were attacked by opposition parties for using public funds for party political purposes. Amid fierce political charges of wasting public money on propaganda, 'The NHS reforms and you', an information leaflet in English and nine ethnic languages, was prepared and delivered to every family in the country. It was seen by the political parties as either a final and necessary exercise in public information to help to implement the new act or the last straw in public relations to gain the acceptance of an unpopular policy.

By this time communications round one had won over most general managers throughout the service. Even though the shadow Secretary of State for Health might have warned that if a Labour government was returned at the general election many general managers might lose their jobs most of them recognised that now the changes had the force of law behind them everything should be done to take advantage of the opportunities offered to improve patient care. A top priority even for the much maligned bureaucrats!

Round two was able to demonstrate some limited achievements: staff attitudes in general, particularly amongst consultants, were to make the best of the situation. In many cases it was felt that at least if they gained trust status they might gain local freedom and increase their share of resources from the Department of Health whatever the long-term future might hold.

Communications round three, intended to win the support of the general public, was not a success. Despite the fact that it is generally agreed that most national newspapers support the Conservatives the government still failed to win over the majority of the population. In part this may have been due to the high profile campaign organised by the BMA to oppose the changes. Ministers were increasingly concerned that time was running out since a general election had to take place by the early summer of 1992. This left little time to demonstrate any major successes from the reforms or any potential benefits. The public was still confused by the jargon of the purchaser and provider split and many felt that April 1991 might be the beginning of the end of the NHS through 'creeping privatisation'.

The government's nervousness was demonstrated when the Prime Minister announced that she had appointed a well known chairman of a major public relations firm to help Mr Clarke get his message across, which was subsequently denied by the Secretary of State for Health in the House of Commons. When William Waldegrave subsequently became Secretary of State for Health another well known chairman of a very large public relations firm, whose brother was a cabinet minister, was appointed to help him as a member of his policy board!

The white paper had been prepared in a somewhat haphazard fashion and, therefore, it was not surprising that some commentators and critics thought that they perceived major weaknesses and intellectual inconsistencies in its various proposals for creating an internal market system.

THE 1948 PRINCIPLES AND MARKET FORCES

Mr Clarke repeatedly assured the House of Commons that the principles upon which the NHS had been founded (comprehensive services, universal access, and financed out of taxation) were safe and would continue to be so well into the next century. The health economist, Allan Williams, commented in the spring of 1989 that "the NHS review offers us the curious prospect of a militantly libertarian government apparently seeking to strengthen a popular egalitarian institution. This ideological dissonance makes one wonder whether one can rely on assurances that the principles which have guided the NHS for the last 40 years will continue to guide it. It seems that although legalistically this may be true, the intention is that the NHS will play a diminishing role in the overall health care system of the UK, with the ability-to-pay sector growing at the expense of the according-to-need sector. Where the two overlap we shall have a two-tier system."[10] He feared that the NHS would be thrown into chaos.

An extreme reaction perhaps, but just how far was it possible to reconcile the principles of comprehensive care with an internal market if a market meant winners and losers, with hospitals or their individual services each succeeding or failing by their ability to attract custom and generate cash to cover their costs? What would happen if a specialist service fundamental to the health care of the local community became unprofitable and was discontinued to balance the books? The government thought it had the answer. It had listed certain 'core' services that had to be guaranteed by all hospitals, such as accident and emergency and obstetrics services. From the start, however, they accepted that for other types of care patients might have to travel out of their locality to the nearest NHS (or private) hospital providing that particular service.

Again, critics questioned whether the range of highly specialist and expensive multi-district and regional specialties would be maintained if their future existence and viability were at the whim of the market? What would happen if one of the new self-governing hospitals decided that it could not afford to provide an established but costly centre, weekend on-call cover or ENT services? To what lengths might patients have to go for emergency specialist treatment? Alternatively, if certain regional specialties looked particularly attractive from a financial point of view what would prevent the market developing a plethora of mini-regional centres, each with minimal facilities and minimal consultant specialist cover to keep the costs low and each bidding for an equal share of the market? Could the public rely on the new trusts to implement professional and safety standards recommended by the royal colleges or the Department of Health? Who would monitor the level and quality of these services? Might their customers and previous patient referrals be placed at increasing risk?

What would happen if some parts of a clinically important service proved to be more profitable than others? With plastic surgery, for example, breast reconstruction should generate cash, but the hospital might decide that it cannot afford to repair harelips on business and not clinical grounds. How far might an anxious mother be driven (literally) with her disfigured baby to find the appropriate treatment?

What would happen if all NHS secondary care providers eventually became trusts? Would the purchasers view their negotiations and relationships with trusts and private hospitals the same?

Would the total provision (at least acute hospital care) in reality be separate from the NHS? Would it have 'opted out'? This possibility was viewed by some to be privatisation or at least commercialisation of the hospital service. A government dream or a nightmare: enough to make Mr Bevan turn in his grave.

What about the future of the priority cinderella services in the internal market? New legislation and the growth of private nursing homes had shown that fortunes could be made from the care of some sections of the elderly, but would market forces take care of the mentally ill and mentally handicapped, the most vulnerable members of our society?

When it came to budgets for general practitioners some critics asked how we might avoid the dangers experienced in the United States. They predicted that with larger group practices having their own budgets clients who are expected to become relatively costly patients, either through a high frequency of use or a low frequency of expensive use, will become financially less attractive and may be 'deselected'. This is still a danger even if capitation makes allowances for the risk categories of patients. These will be prepayments based on existing patient characteristics so they will still place GPs in a conflict between purely medical and financial incentives, with the latter still encouraging 'deselection of the worst risks'. Who will look after the worst risks?

Did all this mean the beginning of the end of comprehensive health care and an eventual break with the 1948 principles? As the UK approached the 21st century might the rump of the NHS be left to cope with 'the great unglamourous burden of chronic disease'?

In the eyes of the opposition parties and some leaders of the caring professions the market will certainly lead to the end of a politically planned NHS. If the pattern of provision were genuinely to be determined by the arbitrary interplay of mar-

ket forces it would put at serious risk the fundamental principles of equity, access and the availability of comprehensive
services to all whether in Cornwall, Coventry or Caithness.

CLINICAL FREEDOM

Traditional medical ethics demand that a doctor does his/her
best for each and every patient under care to alleviate suffering
and to preserve life. Doctors must not only care for patients
today, but also for patients tomorrow and, therefore, they
must engage in research and the teaching of the doctors of the
future. But no doctor can escape from the responsibility of
using whatever resources are available in the most effective
way for each patient who presents himself or herself.

So what exactly is meant by clinical freedom and how far can
it legitimately be prescribed? The President of the Royal College of Physicians wrote in 1987 that "there is no such thing as
clinical freedom, nor has there ever been."[11] It is quite proper
that personal, moral, ethical and even legal constraints should
be observed. To these must now be added the constraint of
limited resources. But how much of a constraint? Had clinical
freedom always been 'a cloak of ignorance and at worst an
excuse for quackery'? Was it a breach of clinical freedom, the
thin end of the wedge to require hospital clinicians to be 'accountable' to managers for any aspects of their clinical work?
Would the new contracts place unacceptable impositions on
referring GPs?

If the DHA was the purchaser and the hospital the provider
and the DHA spent its budget on contracts for a certain number of patients, types and levels of care, to what extent were
GPs able to exercise their cherished clinical freedom? It was
understood that the proposals allowed for the district to consult and involve GPs about establishing patterns of referral
and future preferences before it entered into contracts, but
thereafter, except for 'emergencies', was a GP obliged to refer
patients to the DHA approved contractor? If so, would the
number of 'emergencies' significantly increase in the interests
of maintaining clinical freedom? GPs who held their own budgets, however, were in a privileged position to send patients
anywhere, but for the rest, still in 1993 the majority, was their

clinical freedom being unacceptably prescribed? Did these GPs have to refer patients not to where he or she believed the best treatment might be obtained, or where the patient chose, but to where local managers had decided and, therefore, in effect had pre-empted the decision? Did this mean a two-tier service? To what extent did it negate a founding principle?

ACCOUNTABILITY TO PARLIAMENT AND THE SELF-GOVERNING HOSPITALS

Since 1948 the Secretary of State for Health has been personally accountable to Parliament for the provision of all health services. Self-governing hospitals (SGHs) were to be given new and special freedoms and would therefore stand apart from the region/district line of accountability, but because they would still be 'within the NHS' they would remain ultimately accountable to ministers. So far so good. In turn, the Chief Executive of the NHS was held accountable by ministers for total service performance. He was the accounting officer for the NHS responsible for the expenditure of some £35 billion. To what extent would he be able to control and account for the new trusts?

The proposals suggested that each SGH would be given a fixed budget following the public expenditure review each year and they would not be allowed to make a consistent loss. But their new status allowed them the freedom to borrow, admittedly within limits, to change the conditions and rates of pay for all staff outside national agreements (including clinicians), and to change the mix and patterns of services according to the requirements of their business plan. How would the accounting officer ensure that these very large sums of public money were spent effectively when SGHs were expected to conduct their business in comparative secrecy (like any other business) and only had a minimum requirement of reporting to the Management Executive?

Since 1974 RHAs had progressively gained a stronger control over their regions by setting objectives, allocating or withholding resources and monitoring performance against a strategic plan. For this they were held directly accountable by ministers. The new SGHs were to be independent of 'regional bureaucracy', would report directly to Whitehall and would be called upon to ensure compliance with national objectives, quality standards, safety regulations (such as radiation hazards), financial propriety and keeping within fixed cash limits. The Treasury wanted to be reassured that the department could monitor SGH performance and fulfil this onerous task effectively. While the number of SGHs was small the Management Executive could give a reasonably firm assurance, but as they increased in number might the tail begin to wag the dog? Would the Treasury discover that its own bark was worse than its declining ability to bite? The extension of devolution and delegation down to a local level had been matched by accountability upwards but with SGHs was there a risk that the balance would be tipped too far?

It was these early uncertainties, apparent inconsistencies and concerns which suggested to many that the NHS was in for another period of turbulence and change, which, despite the Secretary of State's assurances, would mean not just a change of pace but very much a change in direction. The individual white paper concepts were understood and yet the ultimate objective was not clear. The NHS was embarking upon an ocean of cultural change without there being any kind of vision of the destination.

PURCHASER/PROVIDER SPLIT

Since 1948 the NHS has grown to be a monolithic organisation searching for better integration of primary and secondary services with the objective of providing continuity of care. It has always been vertically structured and over the course of 40 years has developed stronger lines of accountability to the centre, whereby health policy decisions taken in Parliament have been implemented more effectively. Almost all resources come from the centre and, despite government concerns about the rise in public service expenditure and within it the increasing slice devoted to the NHS, in volume terms allocations to health have risen substantially. The government can claim that progressively it has known not only where the money has been spent but how it has been spent. Through the work of the House of Commons Public Accounts Committee and its Social Services Select Committee the taxpayer now knows what services his money is buying. Generally, the taxpayer has believed that he has got a pretty good deal and year after year opinion polls have suggested a satisfaction level of 85% or more.

The NHS began life as a predominantly hospital service but since 1974 has been evolving into a genuine comprehensive health service with increasing attention being given to identifying health improvements and objectives, and channelling resources to meet these objectives. It has always been, however, an organisation in which the decision on which services were needed and the provision of these services was the responsibility of one agent. Since 1982 the DHA has decided both what you needed and what you got, which was usually simply a little more of what you had received the previous year.

The white paper proposals were aimed at both cultural and structural change. The intention was to create a market environment in which there were clearly identified separate roles for purchasers and providers. In structural terms the objective was to destabilise the unified vertical bureaucracy by focusing activity on the horizontal relationships and the interplay between two authorities, which had a mutual interest in serving and developing a healthy and happy local population. This would be achieved through local health objectives identified jointly by the purchaser and its community (what they needed and what they wanted) being met by the provider, who would seek to meet those needs and wishes with increasingly good quality and user friendly services.

NEW ROLES AND GREATER DELEGATION

Emphasis on local and horizontal relationships was fundamental to the market environment and could be achieved by 'new core' functions for the centre and health authorities and greater delegation to the local level (provider level). This has been a driving principle of government policy since 1979 but one which has proved to be an illusory objective.

The market demanded a new and clearer role for the centre. In May 1989 Duncan Nichol, Chief Executive of the NHS (but, equally importantly, an ex-regional general manager), sent an executive letter to all NHS general managers and Family Practitioner Committee (FPC) administrators entitled, 'Greater sharpness in central management'.[12] In the future he intended both to widen the gap between management and ministerial roles in Whitehall and to bridge the gap of understanding between the centre and the NHS.

The new Policy Board (successor to the Supervisory Board) would distance itself from the new Management Executive (successor to the Management Board). A new relationship would be created between NHS management and those in the centre by improving effective communications. His directors would visit regions to talk to local managers and a former Regional General Manager (RGM) joined the Management Executive as communications adviser to establish a clearer corporate role for the Management Executive and to form a closer bond with the service to enhance mutual trust. This executive letter forecast that the benefits of these new arrangements would include:

(a) "a clearer role for management;

(b) stronger leadership from the centre;

(c) greater freedom for managers to determine their local priorities; and

(d) greater willingness to listen to managers close to the action."[12]

The Chief Executive of the NHS would in future listen carefully to what managers in the service had to say and his door would always remain open. It did. It became a revolving door and RGM after RGM went in and out to develop a system of genuine joint working on major policy areas affecting the internal market, with an RGM and Management Executive director sharing responsibilities. For a long time it had become clear that despite ministerial doubts about the regional role the centre could not exercise effective and direct management of 190 districts and 90 FPCs (the span of control was too wide even for Whitehall). This meant the centre had to work through regions, which effectively meant working through RGMs collectively and individually. A new role and new 'core' functions had to be spelt out for regions as agents in the main chain of accountability. Over the following two years they would become the indispensible implementors required to create the new environment and ensure that the internal market operated effectively.

A further executive letter, 'Delegating responsibilities in regions and districts', pointed the way.[13] The RHAs' core tasks in future would be to:

(a) "monitor and promote the health of their population;

(b) determine with districts and FPCs the health needs of their resident populations;

(c) plan and ensure ready access to appropriate services;

(d) allocate financial (including capital) resources and manage the capital programme;

(e) set district performance targets and objectives and monitor performance, including quality of service;

(f) plan for the regions' manpower needs and monitor performance against them; and

(g) manage change and the implementation of government policies."

In order to undertake these tasks regions were instructed to carry out an urgent review of regionally managed services with the objective of relieving themselves of operational responsibility. This could be done by establishing alternative organisational arrangements, such as delegating to DHAs, contracting to the private sector and putting services on an agency 'trading' basis at arms length from the health authority and where the level of provision was determined by their DHAs' needs. This review covered a wide range of regional services that had either developed for reasons of economy of scale or had just 'grown' like topsy over the previous 40 years. At one end of the scale services which consumed substantial resources provided direct patient care, like blood transfusion, the ambulance service and highly intensive regional clinical services. At the other end of the scale there were support functions, like estates works and supplies, management services and computers, press and public relations. The intention was to off-load the direct management of operational responsibility, a distraction from their strategic role, to lose staff and save resources, which would be reinvested in the new services that were required to fulfil the new core tasks necessary for the reforms. Implementing the reforms would be expensive because of the need to provide the necessary information technology and improved financial and billing services, and these extra costs might be minimised if RHAs were slimmed down.

DHAs also had to slim down and delegate more. Their core functions were to ensure that the health needs of their population were met, that there were effective services for the prevention and control of diseases and the promotion of health, that their population had access to a comprehensive range of high quality value for money services, and that targets were set and performance monitored in those units for which they continued to have responsibility. They also had special responsibility for the management of their consultants' contracts and ensuring an effective system of medical audit. They were required to equip themselves for their new role by delegating key management functions (such as personnel, accounting and information) to units. The intention was to reduce the headquarter's staff by delegating to the operational level so that they could focus on new specialist support needed for their commissioning role of identifying need, supervising contracts and measuring outcomes.

In an exercise similar to the break-up of area managed services in 1982, when districts had sought to grab their share of area services and when 'district self-sufficiency' had been the aim, units now wanted their share to enable them to act as semi-independent providers with 'operational self-sufficiency' as the key objective. There were, however, too few staff to go round and a tug of war resulted between the old districts and the aspiring units, who were flexing their muscles. Many district general managers (DGMs) felt intensely insecure in the process, seeing their power base and 'little empires' crumble at a time of great uncertainty about their future role, if any, in the new market.

These reviews of the headquarter's functions and regional and district based services had to be completed urgently so that resources could be released early for the new market functions. The section entitled 'Form of submissions and timetable' in the executive letter[13] instructed RHAs to submit to the Management Board, through their regional principals, proposals for streamlined structures showing:

(a) "organisation as at 31/3/88, including costs and staffing (WTES by grade) for each function broadly grouped into core functions, regionally man-

aged patient or clinical services, and regionally managed suppoil services;

(b) proposals for reorganisation in accordance with the requirements of this
letter, showing clearly changes in costs and staffing (including grades)
and management arrangements, the action taken to consult the DHAs
and the outcome of such consultations. Where proposals are made for any
service function to be carried out away from RHA HQ the benefits expected should be quantified, and similarly retention of any or part of a
centrally managed clinical or support service should be fully justified in
comparison with other options;

(c) similarly, changes in costs, staffing and management arrangements for
assuming the additional functions referred to in paragraph three of this
circular; and

(d) levels of authority at which districts are required to seek regional approval in various areas."

It goes on to say that "initial proposals not fully worked up
in detail but indicative of the main features of the region's
approach should reach the department by the 5th May" (six
weeks from the issue of the letter). Fully detailed proposals,
agreed by the authority, had to be received by 30th September
1989, by which time the DHAs were required to report the
results of their own slimdown reviews. After that RHAs had to
submit quarterly reports to the Department of Health. It needs
to be remembered that this executive letter was on the subject
of greater delegation. The centre still wanted to second guess
the health authorities' staffing and costs, at a time when general managers in the service hoped and believed that the new
culture would be one of stronger local management, exercising
wider discretion and operating in the business of risk taking to
improve patient care, with hopefully less interference from the
centre.

NHS management, as always, loyally followed orders. The
outcome of the reviews, however, was not all that was expected. The expectation of a significant reduction in RHA
headquarter's numbers and costs was not achieved. In fact,
they both increased because of the costs of the transition and
the new staff and services required by the market. Some regional services were privatised but many were hived off on an
agency basis. This meant that they were managed at arms
length from the RHA/RGM, whereas accountability, the setting of objectives, the review of performance and the costs of

the services still remained the responsibility of the authority. One of the main difficulties had been that the market required extra specialist staff, such as qualified finance staff to cost contracts and create billing systems, personnel staff to exercise local freedoms in negotiating pay and conditions, epidemiological staff to help develop a better understanding of population health needs essential for the existence of an effective purchasing role, and information technology staff to create the new systems which would enable the performance of both purchasers and providers to be monitored and assessed for both cost and quality.

These specialist staff had always been in chronically short supply, for example DHAs with budgets of over £30 million had been forced to operate with only one or, at times, no qualified accountants. This was due to poor recruitment and comparatively low rates of pay determined by the Whitley Councils working under close government supervision—a scandal which had persisted for decades. This problem might be solved in parts of the service by trust freedoms but it is one which will continue in the rest of the NHS for years to come.

In March, as Chairman of the Management Board, the Chief Executive of the NHS had written to the service, in MB59, about delegating responsibilities.[13] In May he wrote[12] as the Chairman of the new Management Executive. The development of the executive letter as a means of communication followed an earlier review of written communications from the centre to health authorities (health circulars (HCs)), which began in the early 1980s prior to the establishment of general management. The review was aimed first at reducing the number of health circulars, which had increased exponentially over the years, and second at trying to focus that reduced number onto major issues, like resource allocation and waiting list control. To a certain extent these initiatives were a success, although it generated a great deal of extra work in the department, which caused one senior civil servant to remark that he was exhausted and felt as though he had been 'kicked in the circulars'. It did, after all, reduce the number of health circulars, which in part was due to a ruse of incorporating in every circular a self-destruct date at which time the circular ceased to be effective. It was true that the service no longer received gratuitous advice on how to cope with the trivial, such as how

to cook your Christmas turkey, which was an old time favour-
ite. That was the good news. The bad news, however, was that
as the number of HCs declined new forms of communications
increased, such as executive letters, dear administrator letters,
dear doctor letters and dear manager letters. These multiplied
in an uncontrolled way until by 1989 these forms of written
communications had increased the total by a third, and meant
that health authorities and general managers were receiving
more than one formal written instruction a day for every day
of the year!

As the use of executive letters spread, from the Chief Executive to all management executive directors and beyond,
anomalies began to appear. The final straw came in 1990 when
an executive letter signed by a management executive director
was sent to two pages of addresses, including RGMs, regional
directors of public health and the royal colleges, regarding a
new policy on the use of babies' feeding bottles and teats!
Within a matter of months a new system was introduced
whereby all draft circulars, executive letters and other communications to the NHS from all parts of the department were
vetted by the central management executive communications
unit. This enabled drafts to be stopped for being unnecessary
or trivial, to be co-ordinated with other communications so as
to reduce the risks of duplication, and to ensure that they were
being written in user friendly language. The format was also
improved by placing an executive summary at the beginning
of the circular to ensure that the recipient was able to differentiate between what was advice and what was mandatory.

In the case of the latter concern was expressed by ministers
about the extent to which communications from Whitehall
might place constraints on the freedoms of the new trusts,
which were to operate within the NHS. As a result trusts
would usually receive copies of circulars addressed to health
authorities and were expected to take notice of what they
thought was relevant to them. A somewhat take it or leave it
policy.

SELF-GOVERNING TRUSTS

The providers operating in the internal market were to be of
various kinds—SGHs, other NHS hospitals (DMUs), private

hospitals and GPs. Initially, all NHS hospitals and, later, other 'units', such as community units and ambulance services, were invited to apply for trust status. This was done not by a formal resolution of the health authority but via a simple 'procedure', which meant that "a variety of groups would be able to start the ball rolling, such as the hospital management team or a group of staff, with the Secretary of State taking the final decision."[14] The procedure declared that before the Secretary of State could make a decision the groundwork had to be covered by the RHA or by regional management through stimulating hospitals to show an interest, helping to vet their financial viability and management commitment, undertaking appropriate consultation, and making a formal recommendation to the Secretary of State for Health. This procedure was criticised by opposition parties and unions as unconstitutional and undemocratic. A group of doctors or managers could bypass their own health authority. A ballot of staff opinions was called for—a call to which ministers were implacably opposed.

Hospital trusts were set up with separate legal status as semi-autonomous agents of central government, acting with a degree of independence but remaining in public ownership. Each would have freedoms not given to other provider units in the NHS. Each would be free of district and regional control and from interference in their operations, being accountable direct to the Department of Health. Each would be free to determine the pay and conditions of their staff and to write consultant contracts and job descriptions. Each would be free to borrow money with certain constraints. Each had obligations to generate income to cover costs by selling services by contract to earn a 6% target return on capital assets and to remain within fixed annual cash limits, with the threat of withdrawal of trust status if it repeatedly failed. This independence was intended to provide fair competition in the market place and, by doing so, to improve performance and introduce entrepreneuralism. Enthusiasts, who sought to become trusts in 1991, hoped for extra revenue support to aid the development of the new services that were required to operate effectively in the market place, to bring forward schemes of high priority in the regions' capital programme and a bailing-out facility should their books not balance at the end of the first year. One of the additional incentives for these hospitals was their expec-

tation that the government could not afford politically for any
of them to fail in the run-up to the general election scheduled
for the spring of 1992 at the latest.

Would the trusts, however, be in fair competition with
DMUs? As the DHA would still be accountable for its own
provider units it was important that their purchaser function
be seen to be separate from their continuing accountability for
their own provider performance in DMUs. It was necessary to
create 'chinese walls' to minimise, if not avoid, internal
conflicts of interest. A DHA would still be responsible for the
financial viability of its own hospitals and in some circumstances that could act as a constraint on its placing of contracts
with other providers. The theory and reality of working an
NHS market would only become apparent when the majority
of public sector hospitals had been transferred to trusts, as the
separation of roles in those circumstances would then become
both an organisational and managerial reality.

GP PRACTICE BUDGETS

Two of the key objectives of the reforms were to enable patients to exercise choice and for money to follow these choices
to prevent successful providers from running up against a
fixed cash limit. Since GPs were traditionally both the gatekeepers to secondary care and the patients' means of
expressing choice the logic was for GPs to be entrusted with
the patients' health money. Large practices (initially proposed
at 11,000 patients on the list and later 9,000) were invited to
apply for their own budgets with which to obtain a defined
range of services from hospitals: outpatients, restricted inpatient treatments, day patients and diagnostic tests (see also
Chapter Four).

Savings from the budget could be ploughed back into improving the practice at the end of the year. The intention was
for GPs to support their referral decisions directly with cash
and thus make hospitals more responsive to them and their
assessment of their patients' needs.

GPs would also receive from the region indicative prescribing budgets that were arrived at by costing historical patterns
of treatment. The government's intention was to use these
budgets as a long-term means of bringing 'downward pres-

sure' to bear on drug expenditure, which in 1990 was running at a rate of almost £3 billion a year. Prescribing analysis and costs (PACT) were proving useful in analysing expenditure and the apparent over-expenditure on drugs, but GPs would need in future to consider developing improved local information systems to enable them to justify future patterns of prescribing and the consequent budget. These budgets were only indicative but any persistent violation of them would lead to visitations from the FPC adviser and, if no satisfactory explanation could be found, it would be possible for the FPC or its successor, the FHSA, to withhold payment.

This approach to drug effectiveness went hand in hand with the need to develop improved arrangements for medical audit. All GPs found that whether they sought to hold their own budgets or not the pressure was on them to improve their information and monitoring systems with or without computers and to take part in medical audit. The costs of these developments in cash and the prescribers' own time would be considerable. This put an extra administrative burden on a large and busy practice and enhanced the need for competent practice managers to ensure that the business was run properly and could take advantage of the market.

GPs had barely recovered from the exhausting and protracted arguments with ministers about their new contract. They now found that the white paper reforms would put further pressure on them. The two things came together in the fact that it was now easier for patients to change their GPs through the new arrangements operated by the FHSAs, which were the invigorated and managerially more aggressive successors to the FPCs. Also, the proportion of GPs' earnings accounted for by capitation fees increased from 46% to 60%. This pincer movement was intended to provide a strong incentive for a better performance.

TESTING THE MARKET—THE RUBBER WINDMILL

1989 was a year of explanation—explaining the cultural and organisational aspects of the white paper and taking the first steps to plan implementation in two years time. NHS managers were given a change agenda and the department bombarded them with detailed working papers on the main proposals to test out the implications. The 32 project groups worked furiously to tease out the implications and prioritise the key changes, which were not only dear to the hearts of ministers but would partly determine whether the market would succeed or fail. The centre believed that only the most vigorous and aggressive action by general managers would break the mould. They had to stand up and be counted: their performance pay was at stake. There was a fear that unless they did the still professionally controlled NHS would go through the motions without significantly changing behaviour or environment. The BMA's continuing public campaign against the reforms showed the strength of opposition among many doctors to the government's plans.

1990 was a year of clearer understanding about what the market would really mean, a year of moving from writing about new and interesting ideas to 'owning' the changes. A year of increasing commitment and a sense of urgency about implementing the reforms. At '42 weeks and counting' opposition from within the service reached its peak and it staged a last ditch attack with the Secretary of State for Health being challenged in the courts by an eminent professor from Guy's Hospital (always earmarked for trust stardom). After a few tense weeks the battle and the war was won. The Secretary of State for Health relaxed and implementation proved comparatively easy from then on.

In July the Bill was passed, the reforms were put on the statute book, the time for argument was over and now it was time to get on with the job. The protagonists felt more confident and the sceptics felt resigned to the inevitable. The former were determined to make it work effectively to improve the lot of patients, while the latter took the view that if it was going to happen, come what may, then why not make it work to their own advantage. Many hospital doctors who had opposed the formation of trusts became reluctant supporters and felt that short-term gains might outweigh long-term doubts.

From the start there had been much discussion about the need for experimentation. The BMA called for pilot projects which the Secretary of State for Health consistently opposed, believing them to be unnecessary and used as delaying tactics. The policy, therefore, was to be learn as you go. The department saw the wisdom not in pilot but in 'demonstration' projects—a subtle difference but an opportunity to provide extra cash to produce early results.

Initiatives and innovation were introduced into the NHS itself, of which the Rubber Windmill[15] attracted most attention, management interest and ministerial misgivings. NHS management insisted on seeing through the mist of ministerial rhetoric and assessing the practical implications of the reforms on their future behaviour. The objective was to test the dynamics of the new contracting environment and to understand and predict market behaviour. Waiting to see what happens and then muddling through, however, was not an acceptable strategy.

In the spring of 1990 the East Anglia Regional Health Authority and the Office of Public Management held a workshop for managers, clinicians and policy makers, aimed at simulating the proposed contracting arrangements over a period of three years. The intention was to test the market to the point of failure, and so, hopefully, to learn how to make it successful. This exercise suggested unforeseen weaknesses and concerns before the system collapsed in year three. DHAs felt 'bounced' in the first year by the providers and they responded by forming consortia to exert greater pressure. Non-budget holding GPs complained of second class treatment. Providers sought to negotiate directly with GPs and bypass the local purchasing authority. Purchasers, when under pressure, would reduce quality to maintain price and volume.

Although it was only a workshop simulation the results were revealing:

(a) purchasers (DHAs, budget-holding GPs and local authorities) were likely to pursue competing purchasing strategies, thus undermining the DHA's own responsibility for meeting the health objectives of their population. Lesson one: it was crucial for DHAs to get alongside GPs and develop a coherent framework of quality objectives. Would mergers of DHAs and FHSAs be the answer?;

(b) financial stability would be essential to the success of the internal market. Lesson two: if you want it to work in the early years then fill it with money;

(c) there was a need for someone to hold purchasers to account for delivering national and local health objectives to avoid the tendency to put quality at risk, and in the case of budget-holding GPs there was a need for them to be accountable to someone for securing value for money in terms of health outcomes. Lesson three: perhaps a new role for the new FHSAs to be carried out by manipulating the GPs' contracts; and

(d) the experience of the simulation was that the situation constantly fell outside the existing rules and required time consuming intervention from both the region and the department. Lesson four: perhaps the only way to prevent the system from blowing up in the early years, with disastrous consequences, was to regulate the market. Might this be a new role for the regions and, if so, what levers could they use to contain market forces and retain balance and control?

MANAGING THE MARKET

From the summer of 1990 the concept of managing the market attracted considerable attention and increasing respectability but also raised many questions. What was meant by managing, who would manage and just how much management would be involved? How do you differentiate between problems and failures created by management incompetence and those resulting from legitimate market signals, and, very importantly, how do you handle the politics of failure in the market place. The problems in London would be particularly significant. If purchasers' natural desires to optimise the power of their budgets meant reversing historical flows of patients into the capital, which had previously offered lower waiting lists and quicker and better treatment than local hospitals, what might happen? Could any of the much loved teaching hospitals, which had stood their ground against previous attacks, be allowed to close for good market reasons: high costs and over-provision.

Who would be responsible for encouraging research and development in the market environment? Who would regulate a symbiosis of professional standards and market dynamics? Who would deal with contract failure conciliation, arbitration and adjudication? After all, a contract had a certain legal status. How would GP fundholders behave and could they be guided towards objectives set by the DHAs' health gain agenda? All GPs were free to refer patients to consultants of their choice. DHAs were expected to match contracts to GPs' referral patterns and to retain funds to cover expected levels of extracontractual referrals (ECRs). When a GP made an ECR did it mean that in all cases the DHA would meet the cost? Ministers made it clear that they would normally expect DHAs to fund the referrals as quickly as resources allowed, while recognising that this could involve relatively long waits. Who would hold the ring and see fair play?

If regions were called upon to press levers, manage or regulate the market what would their relationship be with free standing trusts? RHAs felt that if they were to develop coherent and comprehensive purchasing strategies, for the health gain of their population, they needed to exercise some authority over trusts. But there were suggestions that trusts would not be accountable to regions but to the Secretary of State. This implied that regions would work through the purchasing line to ensure that the contracts placed with trusts would achieve national health care priorities and reflect local needs. Did this mean that regions would manage half the market yet ensure the provision of comprehensive health care? Questions of this kind made the market place look a hostile and dangerous environment, both to NHS staff who looked back to the 1948 principles and to politicians who looked forward towards the general election.

What was meant by managing the market remained a bit of a conundrum through 1990 and 1991. RGMs undertaking joint policy work with Management Executive directors tried to tease out some of the complexities and develop simple rules. One RGM, Brian Edwards, compiled a list of suggested market rules for regions: 25 affecting providers, 16 for purchasers and eight others, making a total of 49 rules to help them regulate the free market.

RHETORIC AND REALITY

It is in the nature of politics for there to be an inexorable gap between high sounding statements of policy and intention and eventual delivery. In January 1989 the white paper had envisaged a new style for the NHS, or at least for the mainly acute services, operating in an open market environment. Ministers made bullish speeches about the cut and thrust of market forces introducing entrepreneuralism into a tired bureaucracy. The professions would be more accountable and better managed. More accurate costing and billing systems were needed to identify the costs of care. Money would travel with the patients, a GP's freedom of choice would be enlarged and he would have a budget so that he could put his 'money where his mouth is'. Providers of all kinds would go into the public relations business and shiny brochures would keep their customers better informed about the goods on offer. Patients would look for the best buy, in terms of both the GP they wanted and the hospital care they were told they needed. Purchasers would drive up quality by tight contract specifications and providers would either improve services to meet local needs, and thus retain or increase their share of the market, or they would fail. There would be market winners and losers but the patient would be the ultimate winner.

Planning and implementing these proposals, however, proved to be far from easy. Over the next two years, as the magnitude and complexity of the move towards the market became clearer, attitudes and language changed and softened, as did the Secretary of State for Health. Attempts were made to convince the public that the NHS would not become a huge supermarket. The free-for-all interplay of market forces became the managed market. The freedoms of self-governing trusts were progressively constrained. Purchasers became commissioners for a time, but as this was too soft and as no one understood what it meant exactly they returned to being purchasers. GPs with practice budgets became fundholders, a subtle nuance. Patients' choice was accepted as GPs' or managers' choice and winners and losers became only winners as losers had to be bailed out of their financial difficulties, at least in the run-up to the general election. Contracts sounded legalistic, service agreements much less so, but contracts persisted. The London problem, which would have been the greatest test of the market with the closure of one or more famous hospitals, was postponed—kicked into touch out of the level playing field at least until after the general election—to be subsequently reviewed by an eminent Professor and experienced Regional Chairman, Sir Bernard Tomlinson, from Newcastle.

As D-Day approached everyone was in the business of 'smooth take-off' while crash landings were not on the agenda.

The interplay of market forces would operate in a 'steady state' environment. The much heralded reforms would come in on 1st April 1991 not with a bang but with a whimper.

REFERENCES

1. Black D, Morris JN, Smith C, Townsend P (1982). *Inequalities in health: the Black report*. Harmondsworth, Middlesex: Penguin.

2. Enthoven A (1985). *Reflections on the management of the National Health Service*. London: Nuffield Provincial Hospitals Trust.

3. National Association of Health Authorities (1988). *Funding the National Health Service: which way forward?* Birmingham: National Association of Health Authorities.

4. Cook R (1988). *Life begins at forty: in defence of the National Health Service*. London: Fabian Society.

5. Secretaries of State for Health, Wales, Northern Ireland and Scotland (1989). *Working for patients*. Cmnd 555. London: HMSO.

6. Sims J (1989). GPs force college to reject 'damaging' white paper. *Health Service J* 99: 468.

7. Anon (1989). Contract rejected; ballot called; more talks wanted. *BMJ* 299: 57–60.

8. Secretaries of State for Health, Social Security, Wales and Scotland (1989). *Caring for people: community in the next decade and beyond*. CM 849. London: HMSO.

9. *National Health Service and Community Care Act* (1990). London: HMSO.

10. Williams A (1989). *Creating a health care market: ideology, efficiency, ethics and clinical freedom*. Occasional Paper 5. York: University of York Centre for Health Economics.

11. Hoffenberg R (1987). *The Rock Carling Fellowship 1986: Clinical freedom*. London: Nuffield Provincial Hospitals Trust.

12. Department of Health (1989). *Greater sharpness in central management*. EL (89) MB 102.

13. Department of Health (1989). *Working for patients: delegating responsibilities in regions and districts*. EL (89) MB 59.

14. Department of Health (1989). *Working for patients: Self-Governing Hospitals*. EL (89) MB 58.

15. East Anglia Regional Health Authority (1990). *The rubber windmill: managing better health*. Cambridge: East Anglia Regional Health Authority.

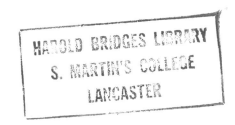

6

CLINICIANS IN MANAGEMENT

———————— ◆ ————————

INTRODUCTION

The government, Sir Roy Griffiths, managers and doctors all agreed: clinicians must be involved in management. Since the mid-1970s there has been wide recognition, even among doctors, that for the NHS to be successfully and efficiently managed and for it to provide a quality service clinicians and managers have to work together. A key to this co-operation was the introduction of medically qualified managers. This objective has proved difficult to achieve, although, of course, community physicians, later metamorphosed into public health doctors, had traditionally been involved in management. Perhaps the not always successful recruitment of nurses into the management structure in the 1970s had made clinicians wary. There were, however, more convincing reasons for the reluctance of clinicians to take up full-time management in the NHS. First, folk memories lingered of the association of administration with the less than popular, old style public health doctors—the medical superintendents. Second, the 1974 reorganisation of the health service, with the introduction of consensus management, had still left clinicians with a powerful influence on the hospital and community health services: no doubt they expected that influence to survive further reorganisations. Third, they were dubious about trying to combine the roles of clinicians and managers, fearing that their clinical skills would suffer. Fourth, few were keen to leave clinical practice altogether and become full-time managers in case the changes did not work out and they were left stranded in mid-career.

Over the decade a handful of clinicians did enter full-time management with varying success and a British Association of Medical Managers was launched in 1989. Most of the clinicians who were interested in or persuaded into management, however, did so in a combined role, for example as clinical directors, and in this role have played an increasingly important part in the management of provider units while their

124

public health colleagues have developed their management role for purchasing authorities. Both had particular contributions to make to improve management. Most importantly, they could develop the supply of accurate clinical information and encourage all clinicians to develop effective medical audit. Nobody, least of all the medical profession, which had traditionally treated patients on the basis of their individual needs, had much idea of what doctors' clinical activities cost. Nor was information readily available about the outcome of those clinical activities and quality of outcome was to become a critical measure in the purchaser/provider, consumer sensitive NHS of the 1990s. Purchasers and providers would need to know whether the way a doctor treated a patient was the best way, whether the patient got better and, if so, how much better. Despite the efforts of a handful of innovators in the profession, and despite its widespread use in North America, medical audit was notable by its absence from most clinical departments and general practices in the NHS.

During the 1980s, however, medical audit came to be accepted in principle (implementation was another matter) as an essential part of the management revolution, which will be discussed later in the Chapter. But first is a commentary on the launch of resource management in the health service at six experimental sites in 1986. This was an initiative that superseded a less than successful trial of management budgeting started in 1984 that was intended to pioneer a move away from traditional functional budgeting to budget-holding by individual clinicians. The saga illustrates the problems of leading a profession accustomed to treating patients solely on the basis of clinical need towards managing clinical activities within a defined budget.

IMPROVING THE INFORMATION

For much of the NHS's existence doctors and nurses have had little idea of the cost of their decisions and activities. Decisions on treatment and care have been taken on the basis of what was judged to be in the patient's interest. Such a laissez-faire approach could not survive as the demands for and the costs of medical care steadily rose. The NHS reforms are making health professionals aware of these costs and engaging them in management decisions that take account of clinical costs.

In order to take valid decisions doctors, nurses and managers need valid information. The NHS has always collected information but its accuracy, relevance and the use to which it could be and was put was commonly criticised. Furthermore, the information obtained in clinical practice and from epidemiology was rarely, if ever, used to improve the use of resources, though it must be said that doctors too often inadequately recorded clinical information in patients' notes. Annual statistical returns were made to the Ministry of Health from 1948 onwards and central demands for more information was a regular feature of the service. The Hospital Organisation and Methods Service (1954), the Hospital Inpatient Enquiry (1957) and Hospital Activity Analysis (1969) were examples of developments in information provision for health services planning. Studies of the potential of clinical budgeting, the first attempt to do so in the NHS, were carried out by Iden Wickings and his colleagues in the 1970s.[1]

Despite these developments, the Royal Commission on the NHS in 1979[2] criticised inadequacies in the collection of statistics and called for a forum to examine the question of information in the health service. Much of what was available was of little use to staff running the NHS on a day-to-day basis. Clearly, if the efficiency and cost effectiveness of the service were to be improved information systems had first to be overhauled.

The incoming Conservative government in 1979 soon set up the Steering Group on Health Services Information, chaired by Mrs Edith Körner. Various working groups covered specific areas of information and their overall aim was that management information should be a by product of operational systems, not a separate exercise, and that it should be accurate, up to date and relevant. Six reports were published between 1982 and 1985, with others following later, and in 1984 health circular HC (84)10 gave a timetable for implementation.[3] During the 1980s all the central groups dealing with information were collected together under the Information Management Group, which now advises the NHS Management Executive. Improvements were also being made to the collection and use of data in the family health services. So the foundations of an information base were being built, an essential prerequisite for the development of more effective management.

Soon after the Körner Inquiry was launched the DHSS started to develop performance indicators and in 1983 it published a set of over 140,[4] with others being provided by health authorities. These identified areas of low and high achievement and though the indicators had weaknesses they at least raised questions about varying standards of services. The indicators were refined in the light of recommendations from the Körner groups and renamed health service indicators, which have been further refined in the light of the reforms introduced as a result of the NHS review.

These efforts to improve the relevance, accuracy and use of information in the service were largely concerned with facts and figures of particular use to management but some were relevant to clinical practice. In the wake of the Griffiths report on management[5] clinicians, nurses and other health professionals were to find themselves taking greater interest in such information. Griffiths had argued that senior clinicians were the "natural managers" of the NHS because they had the most influence on the workload and use of resources. Clinicians had long been doubtful about the value and use of NHS statistics and for them to become committed to the management of resources they had to be confident of the reliability of the information on which decisions were based. The reforms in information strategy would, if successful, help to build that confidence.

MANAGEMENT BUDGETING FOR CLINICIANS

As a result of the Griffiths report the Department of Health introduced pilot management budgeting schemes in October 1983 and for those to be effective clinicians had to participate. In an experiment aimed at, among other things, drawing in clinicians four district health authorities were selected to explore the feasibility and benefits of clinicians becoming budget-holders. The number of sites were later increased to 14. Budgets were based on the total costs of individual specialities or on the caseloads of individual doctors. These clinical budgets were supported by ward budgets administered by nurses and efforts were made to improve the costing of workloads

and budgetary control for departmental managers.[6] Despite
initial optimism among some participating consultants and
extra funding from the DHSS to overcome information system
problems the experiment failed. In part this was because most
doctors did not want to become budget-holders—the experiment had adopted a top-down approach with plans imposed
on those providing the services—and in part because of
difficulties over the collection and validity of information. The
manual procedures for collecting the activity data necessary
for preparing budgets were too slow and inaccurate, and accounting staff were unable, because of their commitments, to
introduce new computer systems and to prepare data in the
way clinicians wanted. Nor had they the time to provide the
necessary financial expertise to help the clinicians. This outcome confirmed fears expressed by the BMA at the start of the
experiment that information systems were too unreliable for it
to be successful. The NHS was clearly way behind the corporate sector in information technology and this was seriously
handicapping attempts to bring its management structures
and processes up to date. The experiment also suffered the all
too recurring handicap of change in the NHS: an over optimistic timetable decreed by the DHSS.

RESOURCE MANAGEMENT PILOTS

This attempt at clinical budgeting was abandoned and the
department tried again, launching the resource management
initiative (RMI).[7] Six districts were given funds to pioneer a
less hasty conversion from traditional functional budgeting—
centred on the district level head of each professional and
management function—to clinical budgeting. This time the
NHS Management Board made a determined effort to take
clinicians along with the exercise. The six sites chosen were the
Freeman Hospital in Newcastle-upon-Tyne, the Royal
Infirmary in Huddersfield, the Royal Hampshire County Hospital in Winchester, Guy's Hospital in London, the Arrowe
Park Hospital in Birkenhead and the Pilgrim Hospital in
Boston. The three most important components of RMI were:

(a) the development and maintenance of a credible clinical database, which
    required accurate diagnostic and operational coding;

(b) the establishment of a case-mix management system for recording the resources used in treating patients and their costs; and

(c) implementing effective methods of nurse management.

In launching this initiative the DHSS and Management Board agreed with the Joint Consultants Committee, which represented the royal colleges, faculties and the BMA, to sponsor jointly the six test sites. As well as acknowledging the need to win the hearts and minds of doctors and nurses, the board unequivocally accepted that the sites were experimental. They would be monitored by a group containing professional and board representatives, "culminating in a final evaluation against pre-determined criteria." The agreement also contained a firm commitment that "the new sites will be objectively evaluated before any final decisions are taken about what is right or appropriate for the NHS as a whole."[7] A welcome promise that, sadly, was not fulfilled. In addition to the agreed joint evaluation the department (with no great enthusiasm) agreed to commission an evaluation by the Health Economics Research Group from Brunel University. This group produced an interim report in June 1989 and a final report in April 1991, both mainly based on a detailed analysis of two specialties at two sites, the Royal Hampshire County and Freeman Hospitals.[8]

Resource management was intended to bring together cost-effective performance, the provision of information, and managerial participation and process. In launching the initiative the DHSS said that the aim was "to enable the NHS to give a better service to patients by helping clinicians and other managers to make better informed judgements about how the resources they control can be used to maximum effect."[7] Despite the failure of the department's previous attempt at management budgeting that exercise had provided insights into the management and costing of clinical activity, a complex process that the diverse North American health care system had for long been trying to master. A warning signal from the American experience was the cost, especially of manpower, with the computing and information costs of clinical inpatient care amounting to 20% of total costs. Although the management budgeting experiments launched in 1983 had been deemed failures—the Brunel group[9] later described them as exercises in accountancy which failed to link financial information to how patients were looked after—in two community sites the scheme had met with some success in identifying activity on the basis of individual patient contacts, and it was planned to extend management budgeting to all community units by 1991. Certainly the lessons learned were of help in setting up the RMI in the six acute units.

What the DHSS wanted from resource management included:

(a) medical and nursing ownership of the system covering both the management process and its supporting information systems;

(b) patient case-mix planning and costing by identifying the costs of defined groups of patients so that the actual and expected use of resources in their treatment could be compared; and

(c) improvements in the accuracy of basic patient activity data so that it commanded medical confidence.

The department forecast that successful resource management should eventually release 1% of annual expenditure for redirection to services for patients.[6] It expected this to be achieved by strengthening existing specialty costing and planning systems, experimenting with the use of diagnostic related groups and other approaches to case-mix planning, developing advanced nursing dependency and management systems, and linking financial and activity systems. This was a formidable task yet the DHSS wanted sufficient progress by 1988 for a judgement to be made on the success or otherwise of the initiative. The plan was to implement resource management in other acute units between 1988 and 1992.

OBJECTIVES FOR CLINICIANS

For clinicians the RMI was expected to provide information that enabled them to:

(a) identify areas of waste and inefficiency;

(b) benefit from clinical group discussion and review;

(c) highlight areas that could most benefit from more resources;

(d) identify and expose the health care consequences of given financial policies and constraints; and

(e) understand the comparative costs of future health care options and hold
     informed debates about such options.

The pilot sites were allowed to develop RMI in different
ways, which was one important initial feature of the scheme.
The Royal Infirmary, Huddersfield, was the least radical, making little change to its traditional management structure. At
Guy's, the Royal Hampshire County and Arrowe Park Hospitals, on the other hand, clinical directorates were created, with
each directorate being responsible for managing all aspects of
its affairs. This system was eventually adopted by all the sites.
These clinical directorates were a significant innovation for
NHS hospitals, the clinical structure of which since 1948 had
largely been based on consultant-led 'clinical firms', which
were later integrated into the less than successful cog-wheel
system that linked clinicians with managers. The directorates,
along with the introduction of computerised information systems, were the key to bringing clinicians fully into
management and establishing clinical budgeting as a potentially workable process.
    Clinical directorates were a radical decentralised manage-
ment structure pioneered in 1985 by Guy's Hospital, London,
which based its scheme on that of John Hopkins Hospital in
Baltimore, USA. The aim was to combine the clinical responsibilities of doctors with managerial responsibility for resources.
It was a lead subsequently followed by hospitals throughout
the UK, with local variations to the central theme. To take the
example of Guy's, the Hospital was organised into 14 clinical
directorates, each headed by a clinical director who was supported by a manager and a nurse. Above the directorates sat a
management board comprising a chairman, 14 clinical directors, a chief executive, directors of nursing and midwifery
services and officers from the finance and personnel departments. Each of the main medical and surgical departments
were responsible and accountable for consultants and other
medical staff in his or her directorate. The director also had
responsibility for the nursing, administrative/clerical, technical and support staff. The business manager's responsibility
was to ensure achievement of the directorate's objectives, set
out in its business plan. The directorate managed a wide range
of activities, including inpatients and outpatients, quality as-

surance, customer relations, medical and nursing resources, and back-up services, such as medical records and technical activities. An evaluation of RMI in 1989 by the BMA[8] recorded Guy's Hospital's belief that its decentralised structure would achieve:

(a) greater efficiency with resources freed for patient care;

(b) more responsive management close to clinical services;

(c) day-to-day management delegated to clinical teams; and

(d) improved operational performance and environment for inpatients and outpatients.

Guy's was the front-runner and rates of progress varied at the different sites but by April 1989, when Brunel's interim report appeared, none of them had been able to implement a full resource management system. "All sites," said Brunel, "have suffered significant delays at some stage in their project timetables," and the interim report referred to over optimism about the speed at which RMI could be implemented.[9] The delays and cost overrun were not surprising. The cost of the exercise greatly exceeded the government's original estimates—the biggest expense being the information hardware. A major problem was the general scarcity of computing and information staff and the necessary use of agency staff added greatly to the costs. Of more immediate significance than timetables and costs, however, was the publication in January 1989 of the white paper, 'Working for patients',[10] (see Chapter Five) in which the government announced that resource management was to be introduced in acute hospitals throughout the NHS. This decision was made three months before the interim evaluation by the Brunel group appeared, which meant the government had reneged on its promise not to introduce resource management until the test sites had been properly evaluated. Mr Clarke, the Secretary of State for Health, faced a dilemma. He wanted to get the radical proposal for an internal market in the NHS up and running before the forthcoming election so that it would be hard for a succeeding government to unpick the reforms. The internal market, with its contracts between purchasers and providers, would be unworkable without operational management budgeting that involved clinicians so he decided to go ahead. He later told the

House of Commons Select Committee on Health, when answering questions about piloting schemes for the reforms, that there was no need for formal monitoring and evaluation, arguing that calling on the advice of academics in this way was a sign of weakness.[11]

RESOURCE MANAGEMENT FOR ALL

In March 1989 the details of implementing resource management were published in an information package for acute hospitals. This included a mid-term report from Mr Ian Mills, the Director of Resource Management on the NHS Management Board. He claimed that RMI would "put doctors and nurses back in the driving seat in managing the resources they used," allowing them "to make rational decisions based on hard information about changes in the pattern of treatment that should provide better and more effective care." Mills promised managers "vastly superior data with which to plan and monitor their hospital's work. They would acquire information with which to challenge the use of resources by clinicians, by nurses and by all other health care professionals."[12] As if to pacify the health professionals for that potentially confrontational promise to managers he said that RMI would also provide a clinical database to help consultants in carrying out medical audit, allow nurses to be better deployed with appropriate skill mixes, and enable feeder systems to be developed for service departments, such as pathology, so that they could improve the use of resources. These promises were based, according to Mills, on sufficiently encouraging results from the (unpublished) interim evaluation by the Brunel group. He admitted, however, that the evaluation was an unfinished product with important issues still to be resolved. These included such fundamentals as ensuring the accuracy and compatibility of data, the best management structure for hospitals and the cost of the system. This was not a promising launch pad for such major changes.

Under the government's 1989 proposals between 40 and 50 major acute hospitals were to be prepared for RMI, with 20 starting to implement the full system during 1989. The government wanted RMI in place in 260 acute units by 1993. After these proposals had been announced the publication of

Brunel's interim report on RMI,[9] six months later than originally intended, might have seemed irrelevant. Yet it contained information that managers and health professionals, grappling with the new world of the internal market, would find relevant. The report's conclusions were cautious and the results from the six sites provided insufficient evidence to have convinced managers or clinicians that the systems tested were ripe for immediate expansion. "The current state of RMI," reported the Brunel group, "typically involves some service providers, some functional departments, some information systems and some managerial processes. As a consequence it is still too early to say how far the ultimate aim will be achieved of enabling hospital doctors, nurses and managers in the six sites to adopt better care practices and take more informed strategic and operational decisions . . . Neither is it possible to evaluate costs and benefits of RMI in terms of its various outcomes. . . ."[9]

With that cautious verdict it was no surprise that later in the year the BMA's Central Consultants and Specialists Committee should express reservations as a result of its own evaluation of RMI.[8] The joint evaluation with the board had not materialised. The consultant's committee was predictably dismayed that the government had breached its commitment to allow full evaluation of the sites before a decision was made on extending resource management. "Firstly, it undermined the trust and co-operation . . . between the profession and the Management Board over the development of RMI, and, secondly, it meant that the new sites would not be in a position to learn from the experiences of the six initial sites. . . ."[8] The report also argued that the introduction of self-governing hospitals would jeopardise progress on resource management. It claimed that the proper development of resource management would have helped to achieve the white paper's objectives without introducing an internal market—namely, the greater involvement of clinicians in management, better information systems and the ability to match resources more closely with clinical activity.

Despite its anger over the white paper's call for RMI to be implemented throughout the NHS, the consultant's committee was encouraged by the experience of the pilot sites. Certainly, the tone of its 19 recommendations was generally positive, if cautious. Most importantly, it saw clinical directorates, for which Guy's Hospital had provided a flagship model, "as a positive way forward for consultants" and wanted medical audit "to play a large part in determining information requirements." The report warned, however, about the cost and the time needed to establish information systems and the need for adequate supporting staff.

This caution was understandable since resource management meant a substantial cultural change for the NHS. Furthermore, doubts about the capabilities of the information systems, the time taken to install them, concern about whether sufficient capital and revenue funds would be forthcoming, and the task of persuading sceptical clinicians to take part in clinical budgeting all suggested that a gradualist approach might in the long run be more effective than the big bang introduction proposed by the government. Anyway, ministers were determined to press on without waiting for Brunel's final evaluation and the information package for acute hospitals laid down the ground rules.

Phase one of the Department of Health's plan would see the introduction at up to 50 sites of outline clinical management and pricing systems. Phase two would involve 20 more hospitals with others to follow. It aimed at consolidating the participation of doctors and nurses in local management, setting up computerised clinical databases accessible to clinical interrogation, providing diagnosis related group information for doctors, implementing nurse management systems with ward terminals, and generating hospital wide reports to help plan and monitor activities. Phase three was planned as a parallel development of hospital information systems. These phases would use information drawn from the experiences of the six pilot sites, but as an experimental exercise the initiative had been absorbed into the accelerated resource management programme for the whole NHS. The final report from the Brunel Group, which did not come out until April 1991 when the NHS reforms were being implemented, contained some useful information for clinicians and managers.[13] It identified the key elements of RMI as follows:

(a) service providers collaborate in setting objectives, priorities and plans;

(b) resources are allocated to service providers to achieve agreed priorities;

(c) service providers exercise responsibility for managing the resources they
    commit;

(d) services provision and resource use are regularly monitored; and

(e) the value of the service provided is reviewed.

The report admitted that clear evidence of benefits was
sparse, in particular commenting that "RMI may or may not
produce benefits to patient care." That was not an encouraging
comment for the many staff already engaged in setting up the
system in units throughout the service. The Brunel Group did,
however, describe the doctors and nurses participating in the
pilots as being "broadly positive" about RMI. About 50% of the
former and 76% of the latter believed that it would improve
patient care, while key managers believed that it had
significantly helped units to manage change. However, the
timescale was insufficient to assess the information systems
and the verdict on the "relatively expensive infrastructure of
computer systems" remained open. Costs were, in fact, more
than double the top of the range expected by the Department
of Health at the start of the exercise. They ranged from
£354,000 at Arrowe Park (where the computer systems were
delayed) to over £2.6 million at Guy's Hospital.

The Brunel team calculated that the total investment costs
represented an extra cost per inpatient episode of between
£7.80 and £27.30, increases of between 1.4% and 3.3%. But
these costs did not include reallocated staff time, which would
add substantially to the bill. So it would be difficult to assess
whether the government's estimate of an overall saving of 1%
for redirection to patient services was realistic or not.

To describe the resource management initiative as an abort-
ive exercise would be unjust. It was incomplete and it was
frustrating that a proper evaluation had not been done before
launching the NHS down the path of RMI. Apart from the
political arguments about this, RMI introduced many clinicians to management, it made the health professions' leaders
think about clinical budgeting, and in the shape of clinical
directorates, particularly as pioneered at Guy's Hospital, it
offered a practical framework for health professionals to take
part in management. RMI also confirmed the complexities of
introducing computerised information systems into such a
variegated institution as the NHS and their crucial importance

to effective clinical and management budgeting. It showed the high cost of these systems and the need for adequate numbers of trained supporting staff. Not surprisingly, given the chequered international history of measuring clinical outcomes, RMI failed to offer well defined measures of outcome of patient care. Medical audit suffers from the same weakness and until audit is working effectively it is probably unfair to expect RMI to resolve this critical gap in the clinical and financial management of health care. So it was not surprising that effective medical audit throughout the NHS was a prime objective of the government's 1989 reforms.

MEDICAL AUDIT
BACKGROUND

The 1980s saw a drive for cost-effectiveness, improved quality and consumer sensitive services in the NHS. In 1980 the House of Commons Social Services Committee,[14] reporting on the government's spending plans, strongly criticised the lack of information for assessing the effects of public expenditure on the scope and quality of health services. As a result the Department of Health and Social Security developed a set of performance indicators designed to compare the activities of district health authorities. These indicators, despite modifications, were far from perfect, being based on hospital data systems set up for administrative purposes and reflecting activities in the NHS rather than outcomes. Nevertheless, it was a start—albeit a belated one compared with health care systems in North America and Australia—in the quest for improved quality in the NHS. This was given a boost in 1983 by the Griffiths inquiry into NHS management,[5] after which NHS authorities were expected to make quality a priority for all services to patients: quality assurance became a buzz word. They have responded by trying to ensure that services are more sensitive to consumers' needs.

Successful quality assurance may be summarised as the definition of standards, the measurement of their achievement and the mechanisms to improve performance.[15] It depends on three constituents: external audit, accreditation and medical audit. External audit is the province of statutory inspectorates, such as the Audit Commission and the Health Advisory Service; national bodies responsible for training, such as the royal colleges, and consumer interests, like community health councils. Accreditation is a process in which standards are set and monitored nationally, in agreement with professional and consumer interests, and which relate to the organisation of services within a health care setting, for example acute hospital or long-term care, and to the systems and activities necessary for an effective and economic service to consumers. With the help of the quality improvement programme set up by the King's Fund Centre, accreditation is being piloted in about 50 hospitals and plans are in hand for a council of consumer and professional representatives to advise on the development of organisational audit activities. This development will be important for the effective implementation of the internal market introduced by the NHS and Community Care Act 1990.[16]

The service agreements between commissioners and providers of health care have to include clear specifications for the quality of services provided. The accreditation system does not guarantee quality of patient care, but it should show that the necessary systems and processes are in place to support a clinical service of appropriate quality. Quality depends on several constituents: fairness and accessibility, acceptability to the patient and provider, and efficiency and effectiveness. Effective medical audit makes an essential contribution to improving and maintaining quality and making the service more cost-effective.

The development of a comprehensive system of medical audit throughout the NHS was proposed in 'Working for patients'.[10] Doctors welcomed it in principle despite reservations about its practical application, especially over the measurements of outcomes of health care, which was the least developed and most controversial part of audit. NHS doctors had been dilatory in developing medical audit despite its use in several western health systems. In the United Kingdom it had remained the province of enthusiasts and most doctors did not practise medical audit despite repeated evidence that standards of practice varied unacceptably among hospitals and within general practice. For example, the analysis of potentially avoidable deaths has shown large variations between health authorities.[17,18,19] But the tide of events was running against the profession's traditional reservations and the general use of medical audit could no longer be left to an osmotic spread among doctors. It required legislative and financial backing. The government had already in 1979 joined with the King's Fund in setting up a research programme into clinical accountability, service planning, and evaluation (CASPE). CASPE research has worked closely with senior clinicians in a series of projects to develop measures and information systems for quality assurance. The aim has been to produce indicators of quality, tested by clinicians and other professionals using self-audit. The work is providing a lead on the practical conduct of audit.[20]

This initiative and the successes of the triennial 'Confidential inquiry into maternal deaths' (started in 1952), the 'National external quality control scheme for pathology laboratories' (started in 1969), the more recent 'Confidential inquiry into perioperative deaths' (extended nationally in 1989), and the 'Lothian audit of surgical practice' made it surprising that the government had not acted earlier to introduce audit. But the white paper set a target of April 1991 for the arrangements for medical audit to be in place in hospitals and general practice.[14] That was a daunting timetable considering the NHS's inadequate information systems, the time and resources needed for audit, the radical changes taking place in the NHS and the need to educate most doctors in its use.

WHAT IS MEDICAL AUDIT?

Medical audit was described in 'Working paper 6',[21] which explicated 'Working for patients',[10] as "the systematic, critical analysis of the quality of medical care, including the procedures used for diagnosis and treatment, the use of resources, and the resulting outcome and quality of life for the patient."[11] The Standing Medical Advisory Committee in its 1990 report, 'The quality of medical care',[22] defined the essential nature of medical audit as "a frank discussion between doctors, on a regular basis and without fear of criticism, of the quality of care provided as judged against agreed standards but in a context which allows evolutionary change in such standards." The Standing Committee compared the principles of medical care with those of feedback loop control: "the expected standard of care is defined . . . reality is compared with the defined standard and practice is changed in the light of this comparison." This audit cycle incorporates three segments of medical care: structure, process and outcome. Structure is concerned with the amount and type of resources, such as buildings, beds and staff, which are readily measured but may not be a good guide to quality. Process concerns the type and extent of activity in treating patients, it is more relevant in measuring quality than structure, provided that sufficient resources are available, and is relatively easy to measure. The best indicator is outcome but this is the hardest to measure, particularly as it may not be evident for some time after treatment, and has caused the greatest controversy. This includes mortality, morbidity, residual disability, relief of symptoms, including pain, and, an aspect too often disregarded by a profession reared on the physiological measurement of illness, patients' satisfaction (or otherwise) with their treatment. Health economists have introduced the concept of QALYS—quality adjusted life years—to measure the quality of life as well as the extra number of life years that results from medical intervention. The Standing Medical Advisory Committee saw the development of outcome indicators as urgent but a major difficulty has been the collection of relevant national data.

Although the Körner recommendations on health services information are being implemented these are largely concerned with management rather than with clinical information. Even so some of these data should help in developing some outcome indicators. Until these indicators are more widely agreed and routinely available the full value of medical audit cannot be achieved. The improvement of medical records and databases will make an essential contribution to this.

'Working paper 6' argued that because a patient's primary concern was for a correct diagnosis and effective treatment medical audit "must be central to any programme to enhance the overall quality of care" for NHS patients. It went on: "An effective programme of audit will help to provide the necessary reassurance to doctors, patients, and managers that the best possible quality of service is *being achieved within the resources available.*"[21] The italics are ours and this phrase is highlighted because it epitomised the fears of some doctors that medical audit was, or would soon become, another name for cutting costs despite the white paper stating that it "is essentially a professional matter . . . a means of ensuring, through peer review of medical practice, that the quality of medical work meets acceptable standards."[14] Among the profession's reasons for being slow to introduce medical audit had been its anxiety that doctors' clinical independence might be constrained not just by their peers but by NHS managers acting in the interests of administrative convenience or economy rather than in the interests of patients. Indeed, some health authorities have already started producing clinical protocols.

That tension between quality and resources that existed was apparent in 'Working for patients'[10] (paragraph (5.8)), which stated: "The government's approach is based firmly on the principle that the quality of medical work should be reviewed by a doctor's peers, whilst recognising also that management itself is responsible for ensuring that resources are used in the most effective way." But even the profession was recognising reality. In its response to 'Working for patients' the BMA council commented: "Medical audit should be used as a means of assessing and maintaining standards and the overall aim must be to ensure that patients receive the best care possible from the resources available."[23] The Royal College of Physicians of London commented: "Ideally, review should include both clinical outcome and cost; unnecessarily extravagant practices used for some patients deprive others of their appropriate share."[24]

The Royal College of General Practitioners has been a staunch advocate of audit, insisting that practices training general practitioners should undergo audit and launching its own quality initiative in 1985.[25] The other royal colleges and faculties now check whether clinical departments are practising audit before approving junior posts for training purposes. They have also prepared guidelines and are conducting audit studies in their specialties. So both the profession's leaders and the government supported the principle of audit. Whether practising doctors in the NHS followed suit would depend on the sensitivity, pace, mechanics and resourcing of change. As the Standing Committee on Postgraduate Medical Education observed in December 1989: "Though audit has been widely welcomed by the profession it is still at an experimental stage. The operational and managerial strengths need to be explored

and researched."[26] A coded message, perhaps, to the government to slow down its pace of change. Certainly, successful
audit would depend on accurate, up to date and relevant information, and given the poverty of such information in the NHS
it could be some time, possibly years, before effective medical
audit is part of routine clinical practice in the NHS.

FRAMEWORK FOR AUDIT

In the event, the Department of Health allocated funding for
audit and, according to NAHAT, the NHS managed to get the
framework into place by April 1991.[30] That framework encom-
passed regions, districts, trusts, and postgraduate and
continuing medical education facilities.[27] Regional health authorities had to ensure that district authorities were making
arrangements for developing medical audit in which every
doctor took part. The Department of Health acknowledged
that patterns would need to match local circumstances. It envisaged that doctors might conduct audit within a single
specialty or in conjunction with other specialties and disciplines, and that they might want to take part in regional or
national audits. The department defined the committees' responsibilities as ensuring:

(a) regular, systematic medical audit covering the work of each medical firm
or team with every doctor participating;

(b) adequate links between medical audit and local postgraduate and continuing medical education programmes;

(c) that the results of medical audit in respect of individual patients and
doctors remained confidential at all times;

(d) appropriate action where audit revealed serious problems in medical
practice; and

(e) that managers had regular, anonymised reports that should identify areas
where management action could realistically be expected to improve the
quality of care.

  The Department of Health said that in preparing forward
programmes, and agreeing these and the necessary resources
with local management, local audit committees, which would
be chaired by a senior clinician, should take account of college
guidelines as well as local circumstances. Regular reports
would be given to doctors and management on the general

results of audits, along with an indication of action taken or recommended. Medical audit was to be based on provider units (in Scotland a working party examined how management could use the results of audit in negotiating contracts). Health authorities were asked to ensure that similar arrangements were in place in trusts with whom they placed contracts: the market philosophy was presumably no audit, no contract.

The Standing Medical Advisory Committee has emphasised that consultants in public health medicine have a particular duty to advise on the health status of the population and to report annually.[22] Their specialist training in epidemiology and statistics, the committee said, provided "a valuable resource for clinical colleagues undertaking medical audit." It saw them as having "a natural liaison role with management" and helping districts and regions to develop medical audit.

On the educational value of audit, the Standing Committee on Postgraduate Medical Education observed that "effective links between audit structures and existing educational structures are essential if the wider educational opportunities offered by systematic audit are to be seized and the newly identified educational and training needs are to be met."[22] Recognising this, the department advised that "the results of audit may highlight the need for specific educational programmes aimed at altering clinical practice," which would require close links between those co-ordinating audit and those involved in postgraduate and continuing education. This is crucial since there is little value in identifying good or bad practice unless action is taken to spread the former and eliminate the latter.

GENERAL PRACTICE

Some general practices have been in the forefront of audit while for others it has been an intrusion into how they like to run their practices, but the pressures of the new contract and the requirements of the 1990 NHS Act mean that all will have to participate.[16] Medical audit for family doctors is complicated by their contractual requirements, such as the recording of procedures for the purpose of claiming payment. The dividing line between this financially oriented management audit and the quality and educationally oriented medical audit is

blurred, but this can be turned into an advantage since re
sources and skills can be shared between the two activities. As
in the hospital service there will be advisory machinery to
supervise audit, in this case the Medical Audit Advisory
Group (MAAG). The group comprises up to 12 doctors appointed by the family health services authority.[28] Most will be
practice principals but the group will also contain doctors experienced in audit, a local consultant and a public health
doctor.

This group will be responsible to the FHSA for ensuring that
all doctors take part in regular and systematic audit, for establishing adequate procedures to protect confidentiality, for
establishing methods to resolve problems identified by audit,
and for reporting on the general results of the audit programme. The government expected all general practitioners to
be involved in regular and systematic audit by April 1992.
Although progress has been made in establishing the framework, audit is not yet universal. Different FHSAs are setting up
different procedures with many considering audit networks
based on devolution to local units. Clearly, one medical audit
advisory group cannot conduct audit in a FHSA that covers
several hundred general practitioners. A solution may be to
appoint local audit co-ordinators, as suggested by the Standing Medical Advisory Committee.[22] Whichever way the
groups decide to operate they offer the means to improve
medical care. But as Richards has warned, "initial benefits in
the hands of enthusiasts may be tempered by the subsequent
onset of side-effects when the activity is more widely applied."[29] The RCGP has given a determined lead in audit and
there are many practical examples of how it can be made to
work but application is still patchy.

RESOURCES FOR AUDIT

Effective audit consumes resources. The department acknowledged in its working paper that audit required "a commitment
in terms of clinicians' time, good and accessible medical
records, adequate information and secretarial staff." Without
promising how much extra money would be provided the
government went so far as to say that any costs of developing
medical audit would "have to be assessed and considered in

future public expenditure surveys."[21] As a statement of intent it was ambiguous enough to make managers and clinicians nervous about whether sufficient resources would be made available to do the job properly.

The National Association of Health Authorities and Trusts (NAHAT) has also identified clinical time as a key issue, breaking this down into "the provision or reimbursement of clinical time for collecting data, preparing data, preparing audits, meetings and co-ordination and follow-up."[30] Estimates of the time clinicians need for audit vary. Some consultants have suggested one hour a week. However, a survey in one district (in 1990) showed that 90% of consultants estimated a session a week, while half of the managers in the survey believed that audit could be done within existing timetables.[31]

Junior doctors should also take part in audit, which has to be fitted into a working week that the NHS is already under instructions to reduce. This has implications for staffing levels and therefore resources. Those consultants organising or co-ordinating audit must spend more time on it than other clinicians and so some districts are appointing public health doctors or retired consultants to do this work or allocating audit sessions to a particular consultant. Supporting staff and improved data are also necessary. To fund these extra requirements the Department of Health allocated £48.8m to audit activities in 1991–2. Of this £10.3m was earmarked for central development, including funds for the royal colleges. The remaining £26.9m 'non-recurring' revenue and £11.7m capital was allocated according to the number of consultants in a region.[32] The release of some of the money depended on a satisfactory account of how the 1990–1 funds were spent and on approved spending plans for 1991–2.

The use of the phrase 'non-recurring revenue' was a reminder that earmarked funding for audit would stop after 1992–3: after that it will be included within general overheads. This seems too short a time for audit to become an established part of the NHS. Medical audit's potential to improve standards and cost-effectiveness may take several years to materialise. To do so it needs adequate investment 'up front', especially in skilled staff and information technology. One outcome of audit may not be palatable to the government for, as Jost points out, quality assurance and medical audit can save money, but they can also "illuminate the need for extra re-sources." He argues that the government's reluctance to support hospital accreditation (mentioned earlier) as a part of quality assurance may in part result from a reluctance to pay to bring facilities up to accreditation standards.[32] The increase in accurate information on NHS activities that will flow from the reforms is quite likely to show up deficiencies in the service that have up to now been hidden by a fog of ignorance.

Potential deficiencies in clinical services worried doctors, and when the reforms were announced in 1989 they soon voiced their anxieties that the market style NHS might imperil standards if managers made cost effectiveness their prime ob-jective. The medical royal colleges were particularly concerned, and in an effort to head off public opposition to his plans from the colleges, Kenneth Clarke gave one of his rare concessions to the professions. He included in the 1990 NHS Act powers to set up the Clinical Standards Advisory Group (CSAG)[16]. The group, comprising members nominated by various profes-sional bodies, would assess and monitor clinical standards of care in NHS hospitals and units and in independent hospitals treating NHS patients.

Its work would be complementary to the Standing Medical Advisory Committee and parallel health advisory committees. William Waldegrave told Parliament that CSAG would "play a crucial role" in maintaining and improving standards. If doctors saw CSAG as a protection against managers deciding clinical standards the government probably saw it as a way to raise standards nationally and iron out some of the wide vari-ations in the quality of clinical care in the NHS. So from the point of view of those responsible for local medical audit CSAG could prove a valuable national marker, although any attempt by the Management Executive or managers to impose clinical protocols on doctors would be resisted by the pro-fession. CSAG's initial studies were to encompass topical subjects such as neonatal intensive care, bed sores, cystic fibrosis, childhood leukaemia and coronary bypass grafting, with the group visiting local hospitals and units. If provided with adequate resources—the initial annual budget was al-most £1 million—and if politicians and management give CSAG sufficient elbow room the group could prove a valuable innovation in the NHS.

The administrative and clinical complexities of introducing audit are such that it may be some time before an accurate analysis can be made of the national picture. Doctors and managers have been busy setting up the audit processes but the outcome of audit—its effect on standards of care—are not yet available. So far, doctors' fears about confidentiality and loss of clinical autonomy do not seem to have been justified, at least not if judged by the lack of complaints in the professional press. Perhaps they are too busy trying to make the system work to complain. Anecdotal information, however, suggests that there may have been a sea change in doctors' attitudes to audit. They may be realising its potential for improving the care of patients and for producing hard evidence about how and where the NHS is failing to deliver. What is reasonably clear is that medical audit, the responsibility of doctors, is one step on the road to audit involving all members of the clinical team—nurses and therapists as well as doctors. In that respect it may also help to convince doctors of the importance of clinicians participating in management. It is also clear that the opinions of patients themselves will become an essential part of audit. After all, they are the ones whom audit is intended to help.

REFERENCES

1. Coles J, Davison A, Wickings I (1976). Allocating budget to wards: an experiment. *The Hospital and Health Services Review*: 309–12.

2. *Report of the Royal Commission on the National Health Service* (1979). Cmnd 7615. London: HMSO.

3. Department of Health (1984). *Report of steering group on health service information: implementation of programme*. HC(84)10.

4. NHS Management Executive (1991). *Health service indicators*. London: Department of Health Information Systems Directorate.

5. Griffiths report (1983). *NHS management inquiry*. London: Department of Health and Social Security.

6. Department of Health and Social Security (1985). *Management budgeting*. HN (85) 3.

7. Department of Health and Social Security (1986). *Health services management resource management (management budgeting) in health authorities*. HN (86) 34.

8. *Resource management initiative: an evaluation of the six experimental sites by the CCSC* (1989). London: BMA.

9. Buxton M, Packwood T, Keen J (1989). *Resource management: process and progress*. Uxbridge: Brunel University.

10. Secretaries of State for Health, Wales, Northern Ireland and Scotland (1989). *Working for patients*. Cmnd 555. London: HMSO.

11. *Government's plans for the future of the NHS* (1990). House of Commons paper 148 (i). London: HMSO.

12. Mills I (1989). *Resource management initiative: past progress and future plans*. London: NHS Management Executive.

13. Health Economics Research Group (1991). *Final report of the Brunel University evaluation of resource management*. Uxbridge: Brunel University.

14. House of Commons Social Services Committee (1980). *The government's white papers on public expenditure: the social services*. Vol. 1: report. House of Commons.

15. Shaw C (1989). *Medical audit*. London: King's Fund Centre.

16. *National Health Service and Community Care Act (1990)*. London: HMSO.

17. Charlton JRH, Hartley RM, Silver R, Holland WW (1983). Geographical variation in mortality from conditions amenable to medical intervention in England and Wales. *Lancet* i: 691–6.

18. Charlton JRH, Lakhani A, Aristidou M (1986). How have 'avoidable' death indices for England and Wales changed? 1974–78 compared with 1973–83. *Community Medicine* 8: 304.

19. Charlton JRH, Holland WW, Lakhani A, Paul EA (1987). Variations in 'avoidable' mortality and variations in health care. *Lancet* i: 858. (Letter).

20. CASPE (1992). *Research report 1991–92*. London: CASPE.

21. Secretary of State for Social Services (1989). *Working for patients: medical audit*. Working paper 6. London: HMSO.

22. Standing Medical Advisory Committee (1990). *The quality of medical care*. London: HMSO.

23. British Medical Association (1989). *Special report on the government's white paper: working for patients*. London: BMA.

24. Royal College of Physicians (1989). *Medical audit: a first report. What, why and how?* London: Royal College of Physicians.

25. Royal College of General Practitioners (1985). *What sort of doctor?* London: RCGP.

26. Standing Committee on Postgraduate Medical Education (1989). *Medical audit: the educational implications*. London: SCOPME.

27. Department of Health (1991). *Medical audit in the hospital and community health services*. HC(91)2.

28. Department of Health (1990). *Medical audit in the family practitioner services*. HC(FP) (90) 8.

29. Richards C (1991). Impact of medical audit advisory groups. *BMJ* 302: 153–155.

30. National Association of Health Authorities and Trusts (1991). *NHS handbook. 7th edition.* Birmingham: NAHAT.

31. Smith HE (1992). Medical audit: the differing perspectives of managers and clinicians. *JR Coll Physicians* London 26: 177–180.

32. Jost TS (1990). *Assessing the quality of medical practice.* London: King's Fund.

7

THE INDEPENDENT SECTOR

◆

INTRODUCTION

When the dust has settled on the Thatcher decade its main achievements may well be judged to have been the emascula-tion of the unions and the privatisation of many of the bloated public sector services, with those that escaped this fate being severely slimmed down. The NHS, the largest public sector service, was one of the escapees despite the fears of its many supporters that privatisation would be inevitable under Mrs Thatcher's premiership. Even her widely publicised electoral promise that the "NHS is safe in our hands"[1] was viewed with scepticism. It was regarded, perhaps, as a politically necessary statement but one made with her fingers discreetly crossed to reassure the free market activists in her party who argued that privatisation or part-privatisation of the NHS was the key to relieving taxpayers of an ever growing financial burden and making health care more consumer sensitive. In the event they were to be disappointed: for all her free market proselytising Mrs Thatcher was a political realist.

The prospect at the end of the 1970s of a rapidly expanding independent sector even enticed some American health providers to enter the British market. They were to withdraw disappointed by the middle of the decade. By the end of it 11% of the population was covered by private insurance, a long way from an optimistic ministerial forecast of 25% made in 1980. Then in 1989 Mr Clarke's cleverly designed reforms for the NHS introduced the market concept without jettisoning the principle of a (more or less) comprehensive service (mainly) free at the time of use.[2] Yet not everyone was reas-sured that the NHS was safe. Some of its supporters saw the novelty of independent health trusts and GP fundholders as Trojan horses for future privatisation. That does not now seem an immediate danger given the Major government's many other political and economic preoccupations. Nevertheless, the budgetary constraints on the NHS and its freedom to buy services from the independent sector could well result in a continuation of the steady, if by NHS standards modest, expansion in independent care that occurred in the 1980s. Such an expansion could conceivably lead to 'creeping privatisation'. Proponents of Mr Clarke's internal market, however, might argue that it will so improve the NHS that demand for private care will wither away. An alternative scenario might be for the NHS itself to offer such competitive 'private' services that the independent sector will struggle to survive. Realistically, however, some patients will always want independent care outside the public sector and one way or another the market will provide these, probably through the many provident and commercial insurance schemes now available.

HOW BIG IS THE INDEPENDENT SECTOR?

By its very nature the competitive independent sector does not make for the easy collection of statistics, but Laing's 1992 review of the sector estimated that in 1990 acute independent hospital care (excluding NHS pay beds and other NHS 'private' income) was worth more than £1.4 billion, while non-acute nursing home care was valued at over £1.6 billion.[3] Together this represented over 16% of all UK institution based treatment, nearly double the proportion in the mid-1980s, with much of it concentrated in London and the south of England. For comparison, the net-revenue and capital costs of the UK's NHS hospitals in 1990 was nearly £16 billion. The independent sector in England, where most non-NHS medicine is done, employed the equivalent of 78,500 full-time qualified and auxiliary nurses, around 20% of the 400,000 working in NHS hospitals in England. So the independent sector in the UK contributes significantly and increasingly to hospital based health care—more and more using day care facilities—but only in certain activities. It does not, for example, provide accident and emergency services and its psychiatric inpatient facilities are small (mainly directed at substance abuse), as are those for obstetrics. This chapter does not discuss the many other independent medical activities, such as medicolegal work, insurance medical services, physiotherapy, opticians' services or complementary medicine.

The funding for the acute independent sector comes mainly (70%) through private medical insurance taken out by individ-

uals or companies on behalf of their employees. The rest comes
from direct fees paid by UK or overseas patients, the latter a
declining source of work for the independent sector. Payments
for fertility regulation, which includes termination of pregnancy, are mostly paid for by individuals though charities do
provide help. Paradoxically, much of the funding for the
biggest growth area in the independent sector, long-term care
of the elderly, has come from the state via the social security
budget, even though since April 1993 the system has changed.

Although the title independent sector is widely used it is to
some extent misleading. The viability and nature of this sector
has been and still is, surprisingly, dependent on the NHS and,
as the care of the elderly shows, other government departments. The extent to which the independent sector provides a
particular service is commonly dependent on the availability
and/or quality of that service in the NHS—fertility regulation,
elective surgery and care of the elderly are examples. Where
NHS provision is good, as in general practice, or expensive, as
in intensive therapy units, the independent sector has not usually attempted to compete. The dependence on the NHS is,
however, more fundamental than that. Since 1948, in the tradition of British compromise, the NHS and non-NHS medical
care have enjoyed a symbiosis, the genesis of which was due to
the political founder of the NHS, Mr Bevan. This symbiosis is
discussed later but its existence may to some extent explain
why the independent sector has neither replaced the state
scheme nor, with the notable exceptions of elective surgery in
London and long-term care outside the capital, evolved into a
robust and comprehensive competitor to it.

That said, the most significant reason for the NHS's survival
is, of course, political. The service has been such a reassuring
part of postwar society in Britain that any party threatening its
existence risks electoral suicide. This strong attachment to the
NHS owes much to the success of general practice. GPs provide 90% of the population's health care and they have
generally offered an effective front line service, as well as acting as a long stop for patients when hospital services have been
curtailed by industrial action or financial difficulties. Consequently, there has been no demand for private facilities in
primary care. This lack of a bridgehead in general practice has
probably held back the expansion of the independent sector as

a whole. There is no broad support in the community for the culture of private care, not even after a decade of politics in which the 'free market' has been the dominant political philosophy in Britain.

Then there is the question of resources: whether health care is provided by the state or is individually 'purchased' by consumers the community's ability to pay is finite. Increased private purchase, whether via insurance, controlled local markets, such as hospital maintenance organisations, or as items of service is unlikely to conjure up substantial extra resources, especially from communities battered by recession and long accustomed to state provision. For them buying health care is not the same as buying telephone services or steel, however ferociously some health economists may argue otherwise. Interestingly, the health economist, Professor Alan Maynard, in his 1982 essay on private health care in Britain concluded that "privatisation solves none of the basic health care problems, it merely sets them in new institutions which will be regulated in new ways in order to achieve efficiency and equity in the health markets."[4] Nothing that has happened in health care in Britain during the ensuing decade suggests that this judgment needs revising.

Certainly, the serious difficulties facing health care provision in other western countries, whether provided by the state, privately on a fee or insurance basis, or by public/private mixes, suggests that turning to the independent sector would be no easy, let alone quick, fix for Britain's problems in providing cost-effective, good quality medical care. Indeed, most western European countries are, according to a recent report from the Organisation for Economic Co-operation and Development, converging towards managed markets in health care, with Britain and the Netherlands in the lead.[5] Free market insurance systems, like those in the United States of America, have not been a favoured solution. That is not to say, however, that the independent sector has nothing further to offer in the UK or that the injection of commercial experience, though not necessarily commercial values, cannot improve the effectiveness of health care. Indeed, in a free society people have a right to purchase individual medical care if they so wish, and in the cases of dentistry, where the NHS is faltering badly, and optical services more people are having to do so. The government has shown, too, that the introduction of entrepreneurial practices into the state service has improved efficiency and made those running the NHS more aware of its costs.

THE FIRST 30 YEARS

The survival of private practice alongside the NHS was helped by the compromise Mr Bevan, the Minister for Health, agreed with the doctors in 1947 when the then Labour government was launching the new service. Despite his party's ideological dislike of private medicine, with its implications of privilege and unfairness, he allowed it to cohabit with the NHS to overcome the medical profession's opposition to the government's terms for working in the NHS. Pay beds were provided in the hospitals and consultants were offered the opportunity of part-time NHS contracts so that they could also conduct some private work. Thus, Mr Bevan defused consultants' fears of a whole-time salaried service, which had fuelled much of their opposition to his plans for the state scheme. Inevitably, private practice dropped off markedly after the NHS was launched but at least its existence was legally recognised by the government and the pay beds, along with the 230 or so (largely religious and charitable based) private hospitals, provided the necessary inpatient facilities to allow it to function. With some adjustments to the pay bed system in the mid-1960s private medicine flourished modestly in the shadow of the NHS for over 25 years until the Labour government's initiative in the mid-1970s to remove pay beds from the NHS.[6] That initiative was to prove a watershed for the independent sector, which subsequently entered a period of steady growth.

In the mid-1960s the NHS had around 6,000 pay beds with a similar number of acute beds provided outside the health service by a mix of non-profit hospitals (mainly Nuffield Hospitals), those run by religious foundations and a handful of profit making hospitals. In 1966 the underuse of pay beds prompted the Labour government to cut their number to around 4,600, through which around 120,000 patients a year passed, and at the same time removed the fee ceiling on what consultants could charge for treating pay bed patients. Otherwise, the compromise remained intact and these arrangements broadly met the public's demands for private care. They also enabled the part-time consultants to treat private and NHS patients on the same site (the 'geographical whole-time' concept), gave some consultants (predominantly surgeons, obstetricians and anaesthetists in the Thames regions) the opportunity for extra income, and provided the NHS with some revenue and the Exchequer with a modest source of foreign exchange from overseas patients. The main players in the acute private sector—the three provident associations, providing the bulk of the medical insurance cover, which funded about 70% of acute private treatment, the various private hospitals and the profession—were content to accept the status quo.

There was no aggressive marketing of private insurance or by private hospitals, and many of the part-time consultants, whose main responsibilities were still to the NHS and who in 1965 comprised around 57% of all NHS consultants,[7] had sufficient private practice and so had little incentive to campaign for more.

Two pressures broke the mould, one political the other financial. First, the 1974 Labour government, urged on by the militant NHS unions, wanted to abolish pay beds and remove all private practice from the NHS, seeing the existing arrangements as parasitic rather than symbiotic. Opponents of private practice criticised patients in pay beds for jumping the NHS waiting list and they accused consultants of abusing their flexible contracts to the detriment of the NHS. Critics also claimed that the NHS equipment and facilities used for private treatment were not adequately paid for and that NHS equipment was improperly borrowed for use in private hospitals. Furthermore, some NHS staff, including junior doctors, objected to providing services for private patients without receiving extra pay. Not surprisingly consultants contested these charges. In the face of this strong professional opposition, despite industrial action for the removal of pay beds by some NHS unions, the government modified its policy. The outcome was that in 1976 a phased reduction of pay beds started, supervised by an independent health board which also controlled the supply of private beds outside the NHS.[6]

Second, the rising demand for NHS services and the inability of successive governments to provide resources to meet these demands, aggravated in the late 1970s by disruptive industrial action in the NHS, meant lengthening waiting times for patients needing hospital admission, especially for elective surgery. That pushed those who could afford it to consider private treatment, which gave people the specialist of their choice and treatment at a time of their choosing in more congenial surroundings than most NHS outpatient departments or wards could offer. Despite having already 'paid' for the NHS via their tax and national insurance contributions more people were willing to seek treatment outside the health service, paying for it mainly by insuring with the provident associations. Increasing numbers of employers were also providing private medical insurance as a 'perk', mainly for managerial staff, in part to offset the adverse effects on employees of government incomes policies. The cost of this could be offset against a company's tax liabilities. The independent sector also benefited from a steady flow of patients from overseas, especially from the Middle East. The independent sector was also expanding in another direction, namely the provision of beds for long-term care, mainly of the elderly. In 1970 out of a total in the UK of almost 268,000 the private and voluntary sectors had nearly 85,000 residential and nursing home places, which by 1980 had risen to 107,000,[3] and will be discussed in greater detail later in this Chapter.

The NHS's difficulties in meeting the community's needs and people's increasing use of the private sector brought on to the public agenda the arguments of some health economists and politicians that the private sector might offer solutions to resolve the pressures on the NHS. Thus, as the new Conservative government took office in 1979 the stage was set for changes not only in the public sector of health care but also in the independent sector and its relations with the NHS.

Before moving on to the 1980s it is worth emphasising again that the private sector had made virtually no headway in general practice since the NHS had been launched. Only a handful of general practitioners (mainly in London) practised whole-time in the private sector and not many NHS GPs had any private patients. Despite one provident association offering a private insurance scheme for general practice few people signed on. An attempt by the BMA to launch an insurance scheme during the crisis in general practice in the mid-1960s failed[8] and, interestingly, a similar local initiative in north London 20 years later, when privatisation of the NHS was being mooted by some economists and politicians, also failed. Clearly, the NHS's family doctor service and the availability of medicines, notwithstanding rising prescription charges, met the public's need. There were no 'waiting lists' to see the family doctor.

THE 1980s

As has been made clear change had already started in the independent sector during the 1970s, albeit not what the then Labour government had intended. Its legislative assault on NHS pay beds had stimulated a rise in the number of private hospitals providing acute surgery from 105 in 1975 to 153 in 1980,[4] with American health companies entering the British market for the first time. The Conservative government soon reversed public policy on pay beds with the 1980 Health Services Act,[9] which abolished the statutory Health Board and delegated control of new private development for more than 120 beds to the health authorities. One result was the reversal of the falling trend in the number of NHS pay beds, which soon rose towards 3,000. Significantly, the government also allowed all NHS consultants to conduct private practice, though with a financial ceiling imposed for full-time consultants of 10% of their NHS salary. This relaxation, coupled with the easing of controls on building private hospitals, signalled the government's encouragement to private practice, with one minister forecasting that by 1990 25% of the population would have private insurance.[10] He was over optimistic, but between 1980 and 1990 the number of subscribers did more than double, from over 1.6 million to 3.25 million, many of whom were in employers' schemes. Thus, at the decade's end 6.66 million people had insurance cover, representing 11.7% of the UK population, and in 1990 total spending on private acute inpatient and outpatient care (including NHS contracts, insurance paid care, directly paid fees and doctors' fees) was nearly £1.5 billion, a rise of 17% on 1989. Independent acute hospitals and clinics accounted for £847 million of this sum, fees to doctors for £480 million.[3]

With the exception of terminations, most treatment in the independent acute sector has been confined to elective surgery and gynaecology, procedures such as hip replacements, vari-

cose vein stripping, hernia repairs, renal transplants, cholecys-
tectomies, hysterectomies and an increasing amount of heart
surgery. Neither maternity care nor termination of pregnancy
have normally been covered by insurance, and privately provided obstetric services are not widespread. Nevertheless,
terminations, sterilisations and the treatment of fertility problems, all of which come under the umbrella title of fertility
regulation, were increasingly carried out in the independent
sector, either in charitable institutions or with patients paying
the fees directly. In 1989 the combined independent market for
fertility control was around £25 million. Termination is now
the most common procedure in the independent sector and
nearly 50% of all terminations on UK residents are being done
privately.[3] Sometimes these are paid for by health authorities,
which have 'contracted out' such operations to the independent sector. Many women have also come from overseas,
particularly Eire, for terminations. A few authorities also contracted out some elective surgery to the independent sector,
using funds provided for under the government's initiative to
cut NHS waiting lists for surgery. The extent of this contracting out was, however, less than might have been expected or
what the government may have hoped for, given
the length of waiting lists and the independent sector's spare
capacity.

EARLY SURGE IN ACUTE SECTOR GROWTH
DECELERATES

The acute long-stay sectors expanded rapidly in the 1980s and
the sharp growth in (mainly surgical) beds in the acute sector,
over 100% in real terms between 1978 and 1984 and a less
striking 60% or so up to 1990, was largely in for profit hospitals, was dominated by American companies and occurred
primarily in London and the south east of England. Scotland,
Wales and Northern Ireland had few private hospitals, a
consequence of tradition and the fact that per capita funding of
the health services in these parts of the UK was much higher
than in England. The expansion in England outpaced demand:
that and a higher throughput of patients per bed contributed to
falling bed occupancy. After 1984, however, when private bed
occupancy was sometimes barely an unprofitable 50% expan-

sion decelerated markedly. Even so, from over 7,000 acute beds in 1979 the number rose to over 11,300 in 1992[11] and during the first half of the decade the number of elective inpatient surgical procedures carried out on English and Welsh residents in the independent sector rose by over 75%, while the comparable figure for NHS pay beds showed a fall of nearly 40%.[3] But the overcapacity in the independent sector raised unit costs, which were already much higher than for NHS pay beds. Some critics claimed that this was an unfair comparison because the NHS calculated its charges on marginal costs that did not reflect true overheads or capital charges. Anyway, worried insurance companies put pressure on hospitals to contain costs—there were accusations about overcharging—and on doctors to restrain their fees. Indeed, in 1992 the Monopolies and Mergers Commission started an inquiry into professional fees for private medical care on the grounds that BMA recommended fees constituted a restraint of trade. The BMA contested the accusation but submitted evidence.

In 1986 25% of elective surgery in the four Thames regions was carried out in the independent sector, and in England and Wales as a whole the figure was 16.7%.[12] The rise in the number of beds was accompanied by a shift in the pattern of ownership. Charitable ownership declined and for profit groups boosted their share of the market from 28% in 1979 to 56% in 1989. By then American owners (partly for domestic reasons and partly because of spare capacity in independent hospitals) had largely sold out to British and European health groups. Hospitals became concentrated in the hands of fewer operators, so much so that BUPA hospitals, which had the largest market share, attracted the attention of the Monopolies and Mergers Commission.[10]

The changing ownership of hospitals had its counterpart in the expanding medical insurance sector, where the previously comfortable division of business between the three main non-profit provident associations, British United Provident Association, Private Patients Plan and Western Provident Association, was rudely disturbed by the entry of large commercial insurance interests, such as the Norwich Union. The insurance companies scented an expanding market and wanted some of the action.

Despite the overcapacity, profitability for the independent

hospitals tended to rise during the second half of the 1980s and in 1989/90 they showed an average pre-tax profit of 7.7% on revenues compared to 5.5% in the previous year. Revenue per available bed in 1989/90 ranged from £160,000 for a top for profit hospital in central London down to £60,000 for the Nuffield Nursing Homes Trust, with some for profit enterprises producing pre-tax profits nearly twice as large as the surplus generated by Nuffield.[3] At that stage investors in the independent sector seemed to be doing reasonably well. But the effects of the recession and the long period of high interest rates had yet to work through, nor had the determination of insurers to get providers to curtail their costs achieved its full impact. Still, by the decade's end there was hope that the market-style NHS would provide some opportunities for the independent sector to exploit, as is discussed later.

TASTING THE FREE MARKET

Early in the decade the government began to open the NHS up to competition, introducing in 1983 compulsory tendering for the three 'hotel' services: catering, domestic and laundry.[13] This did not necessarily result in them being privatised but it gave the health service its first real taste of the free market. In 1983 the government had also urged health authorities to consider putting other support services out to tender. Some contracted with the independent sector for laboratory and x-ray services, and medical and surgical equipment, but such developments were not widespread. Greater opportunities for the NHS to generate income—and to compete with the independent sector—were granted by the Health and Medicines Act 1988.[14] This gave authorities the freedom to offer skills, clinical and laboratory services, amenity beds, catering and conference facilities, as well as ideas, to organisations outside the NHS.

In 1989 the Department of Health issued guidelines on income generation,[15] with the result that some health authorities joined with the independent sector in providing services, such as integrated day surgery units, or exchanged surplus land for private capital, which was invested in new NHS buildings and equipment. The occurrence of such schemes was, however, limited although the independent sector had feared that the

new freedom might mean health authorities "competing ag-
gressively for private patients at a time when the rate of
growth in the private sector may not be sufficient to absorb
additional capacity."[3] The sums involved in these new initiatives were small in the context of the NHS's budget but the
Department of Health told the House of Commons Health
Committee in May 1991 that its 1989–90 target of £26 million
and the 1990–91 target of £50 million had been met. Perhaps
the government's main achievement, however, lay in initiating
change in the service's public sector traditions, with entrepreneurial attitudes becoming more acceptable in the NHS.
Undoubtedly, the potential was there for greater competition,
as well as more co-operation, between the two sectors in the
provision of services, particularly in such clinical based activities as pathology, radiology, physiotherapy and fertility
treatments, which were all well established in the independent
sector. One type of care in which tacit co-operation rather than
competition was operating was long-term residential and
nursing care, where a significant shift in provision had occurred away from the NHS and local authorities towards the
independent sector.

The independent sector had done quite well out of the first
10 years of Tory rule and the announcement by the Prime
Minister in 1988 of her review of the NHS raised expectations
among supporters of the independent sector that this was the
opportunity they had been waiting for to ease the health service out of the embrace of the state. In the event, when
'Working for patients',[2] the outcome of her review, was published in January 1989 at first sight it contained only modest
encouragement for the independent sector. The NHS was not
to be handed over to commercial operators as had happened
with steel, telephones and the utilities. The government con-
tented itself with pointing to the potential use of the
independent sector by general practitioner fundholders and
NHS purchasing authorities, cautioning that any private services used should have standards of care comparable with
those in the NHS. That was a somewhat ambivalent statement
given that the origins of the review lay in public and professional anxieties about underfunding and falling standards
in the NHS. A cynical explanation for the essentially modest
support for the independent sector might be that the inquiry

members saw their proposals as a way of destabilising the NHS and thus paving the way for future privatisation. Such an incremental attack would have attracted less electoral opprobrium than outright privatisation. It was a plausible scenario and one about which the right-wing think tanks were "well aware," as the Financial Times pointed out.[16] The review had been conducted in secret and to a tight timetable, with no call for formal evidence from outsiders, though that did not deter some from submitting papers. Furthermore, the review team did not produce a report in which arguments for and against its conclusions could be judged. Motives and intellectual positions had to be guessed. One credible assumption is that the Prime Minister's team saw their proposals for an internal market as sufficiently radical to pacify the government's right-wing supporters without antagonising the public by undermining the principle of tax funded health care, free at the time of use. Furthermore, the changes would also shake up a service hidebound by tradition and entrenched interests. Although the white paper was significant as much for an absence of supporting arguments and practical details as for its innovative plans for an internal market, it carried the personal imprimatur of the Prime Minister and muted, at least temporarily, any meaningful public exchanges between the government and radical marketeers on the merits of developing the independent sector as a robust competitor for, or viable alternative to, the state scheme.

One immediate step the government proposed to encourage private medicine was to give income tax relief for medical insurance premiums to people over 60, a benefit opposed by the Treasury but supported by the Prime Minister. Given the limitations some provident and insurance companies placed on cover for the over 60s, however, this controversial change, incorporated in the 1990 NHS and Community Care Act,[17] was not the major boost to private care that it seemed at first sight, and BUPA and PPP, the two leaders in provident insurance, admitted their disappointment. In 1990 Propper[18] calculated that the Treasury could lose nearly £150 million of tax revenue every year, a loss which would presumably reduce the government's ability to allocate resources for the over 60s in other ways. This assessment proved to be over-pessimistic but the government has lost revenue, probably around £60 million in

1991–92, according to Maude, with the number of people claiming relief estimated at 330,000.[19] According to Petchey, "the scheme has done little to create new subscribers," and he argued that this state subsidy "will have made the market less efficient by lowering the price that existing subscribers are willing to pay."[20] Furthermore, those with private insurance had higher than average incomes and were, therefore, likely to be healthier, so the scheme also reduced equity of access. "It is ironic," he concluded, "that reforms intended to increase efficiency . . . should have undermined (market disciplines) in the one sector in which they already existed." It seems that the Treasury's objection to the subsidy was valid.

The white paper also called for an increase in competitive tendering over a wider range of services, not only the whole-sale 'buying in' of treatments from private sector hospitals and clinics but also the buying in by local managers of private sector services to improve services to patients. The government also advocated expanding joint ventures between the NHS and the private sector, for example, by sharing the construction of hospital facilities through the use of private developers to provide new hospitals or by purchasing from the private sector expensive technological medical services, such as lithotripsy.

The white paper did not signal a government hell bent on an immediate expansion of the independent sector. This caution was somewhat surprising given that the 1980s had been resonant with the sounds of radical right-wing politicians and think tanks advocating the conversion of the NHS into a free market service. Indeed, the Financial Times spoke of the think tanks as producing the "ideas behind the white paper."[16] If these ideas had included outright privatisation, for example a nationwide insurance based system with a safety net for the needy or local independent hospital maintenance organisations along the lines of the North American model, the radicals must have been disappointed at the outcome. Why did the result fall so far short of the privateers' hopes? Had the civil service persuaded ministers to take a more cautious route on practical grounds? Did the substitution of the 'liberal' Tory, Kenneth Clarke, for John Moore, a strong Thatcherite, during the review inject some healthy political realism into the exercise? Or perhaps the participants in the review acknowledged that for all its faults and inefficiencies the NHS was still a remarkably effective way of providing comprehensive care. Or would the cynical judgement of the review as an excercise in NHS destabilisation prove to be correct? Perhaps the participants' memoirs will provide some answers.

OPPORTUNITIES IN PURCHASER/PROVIDER SPLIT

As the implications of the white paper were digested by the health care sector it became clear that the most significant change in relations between the public and private sectors would be the proposed purchaser/provider split. From April 1991 purchasers, whether district health authorities or general practice fundholders, would be free to buy services from the independent sector as well as from NHS providers. Although the NHS had for many years contracted with the independent sector for certain specialised care (in 1986, for example, it spent £45 million on 26,000 inpatient treatments and had recently bought surgical services from the independent sector to cut the NHS's waiting lists) the internal market opened up much greater possibilities for health care providers outside the NHS. Such providers could contract with the NHS not just for supplying bed based services, day surgery and diagnosis but also for facilities such as screening for NHS patients—the private market for screening was about £32 million in 1990 with 186 clinics offering services[3]—and occupational health services for NHS staff.

Two factors have constrained the development of contracts for clinical services with independent suppliers. First, the Department of Health put a brake on negotiations over initial provider/purchaser contracts by advising purchasing health authorities to stick to existing referral patterns, a move motivated by fears that hasty changes, based on inadequate information, could have caused a serious disruption of services. This policy favoured keeping the new contracts within the NHS. Second, it was difficult to make meaningful cost comparisons between services provided by the two sectors and the publicity about overcharging by private hospitals and doctors did not help. As the National Association of Health Authorities and Trusts cautioned in its 1991 handbook: "NHS contracts with independent acute hospitals are unlikely to take off until health authorities are willing to consider contracting out lumps of service, where cost comparisons between independent and NHS provision incorporate capital investment and overheads."[21] Nevertheless, as purchasers become more confident and providers more proficient in costing their services existing patterns of care may begin to change. But the private sector will need to project a more positive and open image than it has in the past, which, given its highly competitive environment, may prove difficult.

The aim of the government's reforms is for a more efficient and cost-effective health service. If this objective is achieved within the NHS the private sector will have to look at its own efficiency in order to compete successfully. At present, the measurements of efficiency in the private sector are even less visible than in the NHS. Whether this is due to commercial secretiveness, the lack of data or the failure to agree on how to measure efficiency and quality is unclear, but such information will have to be available if NHS purchasers are to treat the private sector as a serious candidate for contracts. NHS providers will also have to cost their services fairly to ensure a level playing field in the competition for contracts. For example, a National Audit Office report in 1989 showed that the cost of treating patients under the waiting list initiative was a startling 90% more in the independent sector than in the NHS.[22] If this was a fair comparison it was a potentially damaging one for the independent sector. When considering the private sector as a supplier, NHS purchasers will also want information on such factors as the extent of emergency medical cover, access to clinical support services, and the junior and resident doctors available, all aspects of independent care that have been criticised.

'Working for patients'[2] stated that health authorities would be required to determine the needs of their populations and the services required to meet them. This requirement covers all the population, whether treatment takes place in the public or the independent domains. At present, as McKee et al. have pointed out,[23] a health authority has no way of knowing whether some of its population's needs are being met outside the NHS. The independent sector is, McKee et al. said, willing to help solve the problems but there are practical difficulties. He and his colleagues believed that these could be overcome, pointing to parts of the USA where the law requires *all* hospitals to provide standard data on their patients. This should be feasible in the UK as well.

The consumer, too, will want comprehensible information because individual private patients will also be making comparisons. Traditionally, they have chosen private care for the reasons given earlier: a consultant of their choice, treatment at a convenient time, and a congenial environment. If a much improved NHS can fulfil these needs where is the incentive to pay for private care? It may be some time before such an ideal state is achieved, if ever, and in the meantime NHS trusts and directly managed units will see the provision of private services by the NHS, whether in beds or as day treatment, as a potentially valuable source of income. Certainly, in the short-term they will find it easier to raise standards in a handful of pay beds than in a hospital or unit as a whole. Since income generation was first encouraged in the mid-1980s the NHS's receipts from private care have risen to £113 million in 1990–91, an increase of 14% on the previous year. There is scope for a much greater increase since the total revenue in 1990 of independent acute hospitals and clinics was estimated at nearly £850 million, up 17% on 1989.[3]

Many NHS trusts and directly managed units may be content to develop and run pay beds themselves. Others wanting revenue from private treatment may prefer to contract out the management of these services to an independent corporation or enter into partnership with one. A handful of contract-managed pay beds and partnerships had been set up by the start of 1991, as permitted by the Health and Medicines Act 1988.[14] In the partnership arrangements the independent sector partner invests capital in a project in return for a long lease on an NHS ward or site with the revenue going to that partner, though the NHS partner may take a share of the profits. Such mutually beneficial partnership arrangements, which the government is strongly encouraging, could prove a constructive way forward for the two sectors, especially for trusts, though it might weaken the competitive element that the government is determined to foster.

General practitioner fundholders, the wild card in the NHS pack, are proving to be an unpredictable influence on the pattern of contracts within the NHS. They also inject uncertainty into the development of the public/private mix of health care. Will many of them buy diagnostic and clinical services from the private sector if the NHS is unable to provide what they want? It is hard to predict, though preliminary indicators are that fundholders are purchasing about 5% of their services from the private sector.[24] Nevertheless, if most general practitioners become fundholders, as seems likely since a Conservative government was returned to power, NHS providers should be prepared for greater competition from the independent sector in supplying services to fundholders' patients. This competition will be enhanced if the range of services that fundholders can purchase is broadened, as has already happened in the case of community care, a prominent activity for the independent sector.

Another way in which fundholders may provide a boost for the private sector is for them to persuade patients to move into the private sector for elective treatment. Every patient in a fundholding practice who takes out private insurance (or is willing to pay private fees) is one less financial charge on that practice should the patient need diagnostic or elective surgical procedures. For fundholding practices under financial pressure, and as more GP's become fundholders budgets will be much tighter, the temptation to act as agents (informally or otherwise) for the independent sector will be great. In such circumstances the doctor may not necessarily have the influence on the standards of care that should be the case in a negotiated contract for services, whether it be with a private or NHS supplier.

STAFFING

Competition may be a path to greater efficiency but true competition between the state and private health care providers is inhibited by the availability of one essential resource: the human one. Almost all doctors working in the NHS have been trained in it, either as undergraduates or graduates or both. The private sector plays no part in providing this expensive resource yet it is almost entirely dependent on those NHS doctors for its medical services. Only 2% of doctors are wholly employed by the independent sector, while those NHS consultants doing private work earned average *gross* fees of around

£40,000 in 1991.[3] So long as the independent sector has remained a modest size governments have allowed the NHS's doctors to provide the independent sector with the skills it needs, and consultants have been the gold standard of those skills. The government's control over the total supply of doctors, however, is bound to influence the extent to which the private sector expands. Were the government to allow or encourage the transfer of more medical resources from the NHS to the independent sector it would be reasonable to expect the independent sector to contribute to the training of doctors to ensure fair competition between the two sectors.

In fact, the 1990 Act empowered health authorities to tighten their control of consultants' working practices.[2] The Labour government had been unhappy that some consultants were not fulfilling their NHS contracts: the Tories, too, were critical. Indeed, the arrival of self-governing trusts, which have more freedom than DMUs in how they employ staff, will almost certainly mean even stricter contracts for doctors. Trusts that are competing for work will not wish to see one of their most valuable assets being loaned out 'for free' to their competitors in the independent sector. The new NHS structure and the likely break-up of centralised pay settlements could also affect the private sector since trusts should be able to offer premium salaries for the best staff. Higher NHS pay could well raise the market value of successful consultants and, as previously mentioned, independent hospitals and insurers are already worried about the size of the fees charged by consultants. This could erode the competitiveness of the independent hospitals, especially in cities with centres of medical excellence where private practice tends to be concentrated.

So on the face of it the independent sector suffers from a crucial restraint on its expansion, especially as any substantial increase in the number of hospital beds would require it to address the problem of out-of-hours cover, an aspect of independent hospital care that has been criticised. How many doctors and of what experience will be required will depend on how the independent sector evolves, and by its nature market forces rather than collective decision making will map the course. But whether an expansion of day procedures; an increase in the number of small units with beds; more beds in fewer, larger units; or a mixture of these is the outcome extra doctors will be needed. They can be recruited from the NHS, from the European Community (EC) or from overseas. EC doctors have shown no great enthusiasm for working in Britain and employment of non-EC doctors is constrained by legislation. The latter could, however, be used as supporting staff and given training, which is a necessary criteria for most overseas doctors gaining entry to the UK. As already said, a competitive NHS might resent the recruitment of staff that it had expensively trained and for which a supposedly balanced career structure had been tortuously constructed but it could not stop staff moving over. Since, however, any significant expansion of the independent sector will presumably be at the expense of the state sector the NHS could well be shedding doctors as its services contract, so the recruitment of doctors by independent hospitals could be seen as a mutually beneficial outcome. An example, perhaps, of the constructive operation of market forces.

London provides a pointer to such a development. The effects of the internal market in the capital led to the Tomlinson review[25] and the planned closure of many hospitals. Doctors will be losing their jobs: some will retire early, others will move to the provinces, some might try Europe or more distant shores, but a few may choose to enter the independent sector, which may attract more patients because of the destabilisation of London's health services. This could mean former NHS consultants and even 'junior' staff entering the independent sector full-time, splitting their services, perhaps, between different hospitals. Given that the Tomlinson solution is likely to be applied to the health services in other large cities the way may be open for a new pattern of medical employment in the independent sector, making hospitals in this sector less dependent on NHS consultants working part-time for them. There is a downside in this for the independent sector, however, as more doctors means higher costs, especially if they work full-time. As mentioned earlier, it would also be costly for independent hospitals to set up training schemes for junior doctors or contribute to the NHS's training costs. Market forces would presumably determine how many extra doctors the independent sector could afford to employ, with the quality of the care they provide being a critical factor in a competitive environment.

Although nursing and paramedical staff do not customarily work simultaneously for the state and independent sectors, even though there is some moonlighting, most of the 7% of the UK's employed qualified nurses who work in the latter, over 41,000 in 1990, were trained in the NHS and there are only limited training facilities in independent hospitals. In 1985 the NHS suffered a net loss to independent hospitals and nursing homes of about 1,100 qualified nurses, roughly 0.4% of the total—a small number compared with the NHS's turnover of nurses. Even so, the nurses recruited by the independent sector were usually under 30 and had specialised skills, such as renal or theatre nursing, oncology and intensive care. A survey by the Medical Care Research Unit at the University of Sheffield, which produced these figures,[10] suggested that growth in the private sector might significantly deplete the pool of qualified theatre staff available to the NHS. That might make the service less sanguine about losing nurses to the private sector, especially those who are highly skilled.

There are also two other significant factors affecting the overall supply of nurses: the fall in the number of teenagers entering the labour market and the introduction of Project 2000, which by emphasising the academic input into nurse training and reducing the bedside training element will effectively cut the number of nurses caring for patients in the NHS. These two developments will put a strain on the health service and may make health authorities and trusts more competitive in retaining not only nurses but other skilled, paramedical staff, such as radiographers and physiotherapists. This could disadvantage the independent sector, especially if it were obliged to start training its own skilled staff with the extra costs that would entail. Some might argue that it would make for a more level playing field in the competition between the state and independent sectors: in fact it would tip the competitive balance even further in favour of the NHS's 'private services' if state hospitals continue to price these services at marginal cost.

LONG-TERM CARE

Nurses are in great demand for the long-term care of the elderly, which is now the most extensively privatised sector of

health care, with institutional care consuming the bulk of resources. The picture is somewhat confused by the overlap of
residential homes, nursing homes and residential homes with
nursing care, and the three different suppliers: the NHS, local
authorities and the independent sector. Some private institutions look after the 'fit' elderly, others provide nursing care for
the unwell and disabled elderly, while some provide both
types of care. The voluntary and private sectors are now also
significant providers of facilities for the long-term mentally ill,
mentally handicapped and the disabled because facilities for
them in the NHS institutions have been run-down as a result
of public policy decisions made in the 1960s. In 1990 the two
sectors provided around 23% of all long-term beds for the
former group of patients and 24% for the latter, figures that are
likely to increase.[21]

In the case of the elderly the shift from public to private
provision started as a result of the crisis in public sector
finances in 1976. The resultant spending cuts halted any development of local authority part III residential accommodation.
Private residential homes expanded to meet the need and
when the numbers of NHS beds for long-stay geriatric and
psychogeriatric patients were subsequently cut, in part to save
money and in part as a response to several public scandals
about poor standards, the private sector once again stepped in
to provide the facilities. Much of the funding for this expansion, which continued steadily throughout the 1980s, came
from the social security budget since individuals on limited
incomes and with under £8,000 capital were usually eligible
for help. This state support for fees made up for the absence,
until very recently, of insurance cover for residential care and
enabled voluntary and private homes to expand to meet the
increasing demand. With the number of elderly people increasing funding from this source rose nearly 200-fold, from
£10 million in 1979 to over £1.87 billion in 1991,[10] an unplanned
expansion in government funding that was a factor in prompt-
ing Mr Clarke to ask Sir Roy Griffiths to review community
care (see Chapter Eight). When the phased introduction of the
community care reforms, based on Sir Roy's report, was completed in April 1993 funding for these long-stay patients was
transferred from the social security budget to local authorities.
They are responsible for co-ordinating, purchasing and moni-

toring services in this sector. This is a formidable responsibility: in May 1991 231,000 residents of nursing and residential homes were receiving social security support, a rise of 42,000 recipients over 1990, and by 1991 the proportion of state funded patients in these homes had risen to 69%.[3]

Whereas there were Treasury restraints on the annual increase in this financial support there had been little control over the expansion in the numbers of those receiving it and hence over the demand for state support. As the proportion of elderly people in the population rose this represented an open ended government commitment from which the private sector has been benefiting. Nevertheless, the limitation on annual increases in support, the effects of the recession on institutional home-owners and the inability of the better-off elderly to sell their houses to fund their purchase of private care have checked the rate of expansion of this sector. The effects of the transfer of budgetary control to local authorities in 1993, however, could well introduce much severer restraints since the Conservative government has consistently curtailed spending by local authorities.

Although local authorities will receive 'transferred' funds for community care these are less than health and local authorities think are needed. A substantial proportion (85%) of these funds will have to be spent in the independent sector, but that would probably have happened anyway since the NHS will be in no position to provide long-term beds—indeed, quite the reverse, as provision is being steadily cut. Nor will local authorities have the capital to build residential homes—in 1991 they provided only 3% of the country's accommodation. Add these limitations to the stricter disbursement by local authorities of funds transferred from the social security budget and a crisis in the care of the elderly is probable. The NHS may be unable to discharge elderly patients from acute care because of a shortage of places to send them, thus blocking valuable NHS beds, and carers and primary care teams may struggle to cope with elderly people at home who really need residential care. Carers could also face difficulties because funding for respite care may be adversely affected by the new system.

The likely outcome of what could become a sensitive political issue is uncertain (see Chapter Eight). What may result as private homes attempt to economise is a fall in standards and the Royal College of Nursing for one has expressed serious concern about this. From being a profitable growth area for independent operators (it was the salvation of many small hotel owners) care of the elderly may prove, at least in the short-term, to be an unpredictable activity for investors and providers. In the run-up to April 1993 some nursing homes were already reporting difficulties because local authorities had been tardy in signing contracts for care. Tough spending limits on community care may 'shake out' unsatisfactory care homes and there were forecasts that up to 15% might close. On the other hand, the strict rules introduced by the government on how local authorities can spend their budgets favour the independent sector and this should benefit it in the long run if the costs of running homes are controlled by owners.

CONCLUSIONS AND SPECULATIONS

As can be seen from this chapter the independent health sector is a disparate but growing collection of undertakings owned by organisations that range from big foreign multinationals to modest religious foundations. At the start of the 1990s they provided about 11,000 acute surgical and medical beds, over 1,600 psychiatric beds and nearly 35,000 nursing and residential home places. Some independent health organisations are there to make money, others are altruistic. The NHS is also a player in the independent market, offering 3,000 or so pay beds which have survived the vagaries of party politics since they were set up under the Bevan compromise in 1948. This is not the only link between the two sectors, which have existed in symbiosis since the NHS was founded. The independent sector has always been dependent on the NHS and the health service has for a long-time contracted with the independent sector for some of its services, albeit on a small scale until the changes of the 1980s. The NHS trains most of the staff employed in the independent sector and in the case of doctors allows its consultants to work part-time in private hospitals. In London the dependence of private hospitals on NHS consultants is reflected in the fact that a considerable part of their collective income comes from private practice, although it absorbs only a relatively small proportion of their time. This dependence of the independent sector on the NHS may well, paradoxically, grow if the sector continues to expand.

Since the mid-1970s the independent sector has grown in part because of government policies and in part because inadequacies in the NHS have increased the demand from patients for private care. Most of this growth has occurred in two areas, elective surgery and care of the elderly and the disabled, although independent hospitals and clinics have also contributed substantially to fertility control services. General practice has remained resolutely in the state sector. About 70% of the revenue for independent acute care has come via private medical insurance, which despite some hiccups in the late 1980s looks set to increase steadily, a factor that has enticed commercial insurance companies into an activity once totally dominated by the three main provident organisations. In a commercial context the value of the independent sector is significant: in 1991 revenue was established at £1.4 billion for acute health care and nearly £4 billion for the care of the elderly and disabled. Against these sums the £110 million or so that NHS hospitals earn from their private services is pocket money. But set in the context of the NHS's annual budget of over £30 billion the independent sector is still a modest enterprise.

Collaborative ventures between the state and independent sectors, encouraged by legislation during the 1980s, have not grown as rapidly as the government would have wished. This should change. Certainly, competitive tendering, income generation and joint ventures have exposed the NHS to the financial disciplines, management techniques and consumer pressures that are familiar to much of the independent health sector. Fears that these changes were priming the NHS for some form of privatisation did not materialise. Even so, the National Health Service and Community Care Act 1990[17] has left some NHS supporters suspicious that the internal market is a Trojan horse that will eventually lead to a private takeover.

Proponents of the internal market, however, argue that the NHS will, given time, provide an effective, consumer sensitive service that will marginalise the independent sector, except, of course, in the care of the elderly. Such an outcome, however, would almost certainly require substantial extra resources for the health service, an unlikely prospect at present. Another possibility is that NHS providers, especially trusts, will so expand and upgrade their NHS private facilities that the independent sector will find it hard to compete. Despite successive Tory governments' low key encouragement of the independent sector the probable outcome will be a steady if unspectacular growth. As the internal market beds in and purchasers, including GP fundholders, become more innovative the independent sector could offer stiff competition for the NHS, particularly in niche activities such as elective surgery, pathology and fertility control, where the sector is strong. Occupational health services and screening also offer opportunities for the independent sector. To achieve success, however, hospitals and units in the sector will need to provide full financial information and outcome measures on which NHS purchasers can base their decisions. This has not been widely available so far.

Another avenue for expansion will be to develop further joint ventures with NHS providers: for example, private units on NHS land. There should be scope, too, for joint pathology and radiological services, especially in places like London where demand for private care is strong. The area in which the independents 'compete' very effectively with the NHS is in the care of the elderly. Despite the new community care arrangements, introduced in April 1993, which include stricter criteria for state financial support for those in long-stay accommodation, private and voluntary, care for the elderly will continue to expand helped by the severe restrictions placed on local authorities about how much of their transferred community care funds can be spent in the public sector. There may be an initial 'shake out' of unsatisfactory or inefficient private homes, but demographic change means that the market will be expanding for some years to come. Furthermore, the state sector is reducing its services for these patients.

A potential obstacle blocking the expansion of the independent sector overall is the recruitment of skilled staff, such as doctors, nurses and therapists. First, increasingly cost conscious NHS providers will be reluctant to see their skilled staff defecting to or moonlighting for their independent competitors. Second, the number of doctors being trained in the UK is controlled by the government and unless the NHS contracts in

THE INDEPENDENT SECTOR

the face of successful competition from the independents, thus releasing doctors, private hospitals will have to look elsewhere for more doctors. They could, of course, offer more attractive employment packages than the NHS but trusts now have considerable freedom to negotiate local deals with staff. European doctors have shown limited enthusiasm for migrating to Britain and non-EC doctors face strict entry criteria. One thing seems likely: the independent sector will have to think very seriously about training staff, in the case of doctors by offering approved postgraduate training. That would be expensive and might require some form of agreement with the NHS on the employment of doctors and other health professionals to prevent costly and unproductive competition between the two sectors. Such a non-market solution would not appeal to right-wing politicians but with the government largely controlling the supply of skilled staff a true market does not exist.

The independent sector will survive. In what form and in what size is hard to forecast at this early stage of the government's NHS reforms. To survive and expand, especially in the acute sector, independent operators will need to amalgamate since their success in an increasingly competitive health sector could depend on their economies of scale, which is the NHS's strong suit. It would also strengthen their hand in negotiations with NHS purchasers, who are themselves amalgamating into fewer and larger groups. While larger and more competitive independent providers would deliver the NHS a strong stimulus to improve its services, such a development is unlikely to result in the independent sector having realistic takeover designs on the NHS, at least not in this century. Competition and co-operation will shape a continuing symbiosis between the state and independent sectors. Bevan's 1948 compromise lives on.

REFERENCES

1. Parliamentary debates (1991). *House of Commons official report 1990–1, vol. 191, col. 413.* London: HMSO.

2. Secretaries of State for Health, Wales, Northern Ireland and Scotland (1989). *Working for patients.* Cmnd 555. London: HMSO.

3. *Laing's review of private health care* (1992). London: Laing and Buisson Publications.

4. McLachlan G, Maynard A (eds) (1982). *The public/private mix for health: the relevance and effects of change*. London: Nuffield Provincial Hospitals Trust.

5. Organisation for Economic Co-operation and Development (1993). *The reform of health care*. Paris: Organisation for Economic Co-operation and Development.

6. *Health Services Act* (1976). London: HMSO.

7. *Report of the Royal Commission on the National Health Service* (1979). Cmnd 7615. London: HMSO.

8. Anon (1965). An independent medical service. *BMJ* II 9th Oct. 831–2. (Editorial).

9. *Health Services Act* (1980). London: HMSO.

10. Beck E (ed) (1992). *In the best of health*. London: Chapman and Hall.

11. Independent Health Care Association (1993). *Acute hospitals in the independent sector: survey 1993*. London: Independent Health Care Association.

12. Nicholl JP et al. (1989). Role of private sector in elective surgery in England and Wales. *BMJ* 298: 243–7.

13. Department of Health and Social Security (1983). *Competitive tendering in the provision of domestic, catering and laundry services*. HC (83) 18.

14. *Health and Medicines Act* (1988). London: HMSO.

15. Department of Health (1989). *Income generation: a guide to local initiatives*. HN (89)9.

16. Prowse M (1989). *Competitors in white coats: the economics underlying public concern at the government's plans for the National Health Service*. Financial Times 22 August.

17. *National Health Service and Community Care Act* (1990). London: HMSO.

18. Propper C (1989). *Working for patients: the implications of the NHS white paper for the private sector*. York: University of York Centre for Health Economics.

19. Maude F (1991). *Private health insurance (tax relief)*. House of Commons official report (Hansard) November 5:198 C32W.

20. Petchey R (1993). NHS internal market 1991–2: towards a balance sheet. *BMJ* 306: 699–701.

21. National Association of Health Authorities and Trusts (1991). *NHS handbook. 7th edition*. Birmingham: NAHAT.

22. National Audit Office (1990). *The NHS and independent hospitals*. London: HMSO.

23. McKee M, Clarke A, Tennison B (1993). Meeting local needs. *BMJ* 306: 602.

24. Anon (1992). We need to see private figures. *Fundholding* 1 (8): 3.

25. Tomlinson B (1992). *Report of the inquiry into London's health service, medical education and research*. London: HMSO.

8

COMMUNITY CARE

—————— ◆ ——————

INTRODUCTION

Care in the community has a compassionate ring to it. It contrasts favourably with the forbidding echoes of institutional care and the Poor Law. Successive governments have espoused the cause of looking after more people in the community and fewer in hospitals or long-stay institutions. The reasons are understandable. Few patients receiving long-term care need an expensive hospital environment: sympathetic attention in friendly surroundings, with an emphasis on their social rather than medical needs, is more appropriate for many elderly, mentally ill or handicapped people. Institutional care too often depersonalises those in them, staff as well as patients. For governments, closing costly hospital facilities has been an attractive financial option, although it is doubtful whether they have realised the real cost of good quality community care.

The move towards community care started in the 1930s and for the past 30 years all governments have supported the concept. In 1957 a Royal Commission looking at the law as it affected mental illness and deficiency proposed transferring care from hospitals to the community.[1] The Mental Health Act of 1959[2] made this official policy and the government's Hospital Plan of 1962[3] set in train the wholescale closure of psychiatric hospital beds. The target was a cut in numbers from 150,000 to 75,000 by 1975. Public scandals about conditions in several long-stay hospitals in the 1960s added momentum to the change. They also prompted the Secretary of State, Richard Crossman, to set up the Hospital Advisory Service in 1969 to inspect long-stay hospitals and to make recommendations for improvements in how they were run. This led to better care, but it was a slow process since funds to improve buildings were scarce and staff found it hard to change old habits. Community care was seen as the right solution.

The transition to community care has not been, and will not be, easy. At the start of the 1980s the Black report[4] showed the immensity of the problems to be overcome in improving the health of all the nation. In particular, the report highlighted the contrasts in health status between social classes. Serious deficiencies in preventive medicine and in health care were identified among the lower social classes, whose social deprivation was designated as the prime cause. To make community care a viable alternative to institutional care for communities in which these social classes predominate is a formidable task. The government's inaction over the Black report, coupled with the effects of the recession and rising unemployment that has hit these communities the hardest, has not made it easier. Even the more affluent communities find caring for their ill and disabled members at home, in residential units or nursing homes a demanding challenge. From April 1993, however, when the final phase of the NHS and Community Care legislation comes into operation, with local authorities becoming the agents for purchasing appropriate community care, more and more people will be looked after in the community, most at home but an increasing number in independent residential and nursing homes, the rapid expansion of which has been a feature of the 1980s.

WHAT IS COMMUNITY CARE?

"The meaning of community care has evolved over time," declared the National Association of Health Authorities and Trusts (NAHAT) in its handbook.[5] "Originating from a concern that care for mentally ill and handicapped people should increasingly be provided in the community," the association explained, "it also embraced a switch from residential to home-based care, especially for elderly people—there was a growing emphasis on providing individual care in accordance with 'ordinary life' principles and thus organised around domestic housing rather than hostel settings." Community care should not be confused with community health services that have traditionally been run by health authorities, although the two spheres of activity do overlap—hence the need for co-ordination and collaboration. Governments have recognised that for many people care in the community for the vulnerable groups concerned—the elderly, the mentally ill, and the mentally and physically handicapped, including some children—means care by the community.[6] Indeed, the vast bulk of such care, particularly of the elderly of whom 95% live at home, is provided in the patient's home by relatives, friends and neighbours. Some of these carers are supported some of the time by such services as home helps, day centres, special equipment and respite admissions to enable them to cope with what is often an onerous emotional and physical burden.

Arguably, the so-called 'cost-effectiveness' of community care rests on its implied financial costs being shouldered by the informal carers who look after their partner, granny or a disabled relative at home, which is a largely hidden burden that has been estimated at about £25 billion annually.[7] This figure places in perspective the government's "key achievements" that were detailed in the 1989 white paper, 'Caring for people', of a rise in gross expenditure on core community services of 68% in real terms between 1979 and 1988: £1,168 million to £3,444 million.[8] Over a similar period spending on community health services, which have been the responsibility of district health authorities, rose by 35% in real terms. In sharp contrast social security support for people in independent residential care and nursing homes increased steeply, from £10 million in 1979 to over £1 billion in 1989. This state funded move into an expanding private sector was unplanned and the cost explosion helped to propel the government towards its reforms of community care. It also reflected the run-down by the NHS of its beds for long-stay patients. The figures must also be seen against the background of more people living longer, with the result that the magnitude of services needed have steadily grown. Great Britain has more than eight million people aged over 65 and the figure is rising, with over one million receiving some form of community care. Another 500,000 younger people receive care because of a mental or physical handicap or mental illness. All told, publicly funded community based care cost over £14 billion in 1989/90, a larger sum than was spent on the hospital service. This then must be added to the £25 billion of estimated costs being met by the informal carers.

Why, despite the claimed advantage of and support for the concept, has community care remained a cinderella service? First, there has been a history of neglect of these services and those they care for. Society has preferred to tuck the infirm elderly and those with mental illness or disability out of sight, often resisting attempts to move people from institutions into the home or into community units. The institutions were old and often isolated, their fabric was poor and their facilities a disgrace, with staff left to cope as best they could. Second, since 1948 community care has been provided by several statutory and voluntary agencies and has been the most visible casualty of the financial and administrative conflicts spawned by the tripartite structure of the NHS. The territories of hospitals, community health services, primary care services and community care have overlapped to varying extents, leading to confusion, conflict and gaps in care. There have been unproductive boundary disputes about who should pay for what, with each service beset by a lack of resources and identifying people's needs in terms of others' responsibilities. Even the local joint consultative committees and the government's joint financing initiative, launched in the mid-1970s and aimed at alleviating these tensions, have only partly succeeded.

A third reason has been that social workers, key staff in the provision of community care, have been buffeted by major changes to their profession following the Seebohm report of 1968[9] and the NHS reorganisation of 1974.[10] The former restructured the training of social workers and how they worked, while the latter brought them all within the ambit of local government. The demands put on them as a result of these changes and a stream of subsequent social legislation have left them underfunded, overworked, publicly criticised (often unfairly) and demoralised. Community care has often lacked the professional leadership that has existed in the hospital and primary care services. It has also lacked a political constituency among patients, relatives and carers: until the 1970s few effective pressure groups existed to speak up for those in community care. Finally, services in the community, while attracting some dedicated, professional and voluntary workers, did not have the glamour and kudos of high-technology hospital medicine or the traditions of family doctoring. Thus, they have rarely had sufficient staff of appropriate quality. What in 1979 were the government's priorities for leading community care out of this mess?

GOVERNMENT'S PRIORITIES
In 1979 the Royal Commission on the NHS identified the problems of community care but did little more than exhort those agencies responsible for it to improve their co-operation.[11] Two years later the government published 'Care in action', a handbook of policies and priorities for the health and personal social services in England.[12] In it the Secretary of State reiterated government policy, stating that he expected "authorities to give priority to the further development of services, both statutory and voluntary, for the needs as locally assessed of the following priority groups:

(a) *Elderly people, especially the most vulnerable and frail.* The number of people over 75 is increasing and those who need care have often been provided with unacceptably low standards of service, particularly in some aspects of long-term care;

(b) *Mentally ill people.* This group is frequently provided with services of inadequate standard and services need developing in more accessible facilities;

(c) *Mentally handicapped people.* This group is also often not provided with services of adequate standard and many services need development in more appropriate locations and on a different model; and

(d) *Physically and seriously handicapped people.* Services to meet the needs of this group are frequently inadequate.

Even the understated official prose showed the doldrums into which community care was drifting despite fine sounding policy declarations. Perhaps this operational drifting was understandable if not acceptable. The NHS had been gearing up for its second reorganisation in a decade, during which staff unrest had been a significantly disruptive factor. Local authorities, too, had been suffering from staff disputes and were under pressure from the new Conservative government to cut costs and improve efficiency. Cross-boundary services, like community care, were especially vulnerable to neglect and conflict over who paid for what in such a turbulent environment. The rise in unemployment, the extent of poverty and housing shortages, as the Black report had pointed out,[4] had contributed to ill health and so increased the pressures on community care services. The practical consequences of these pressures were illustrated in a report on community care for the mentally ill, published by the House of Commons Social

Services Committee in 1985, which stated that many people with mental illness being discharged from the large institutions were disappearing into the community but were receiving little or no care from it.[13]

FAILURES IN THE SYSTEM

Which are the agencies responsible for the complex web of services provided under the heading 'community care'? At a national level four government departments, those of Health, Social Services, Environment and Education, have direct responsibilities. National voluntary organisations, such as MIND and Age Concern, also provide an independent input at this level as well as making substantial practical contributions to care locally. At a local level social security offices, health authorities, local authorities, housing associations, local voluntary services and private sector establishments all have an interest in or provide the many care and accommodation services that are or should be available. These multiple services were clearly illustrated by a diagram prepared by the Audit Commission for its report, 'Making a reality of community care',[14] (see diagram 1).

This table shows the political, administrative and financial will (and goodwill) necessary to ensure that the complicated machinery delivers the right care to the right person at the right place at the right time. Indeed, the report from which this diagram was taken offered an incisive analysis of the system and some constructive proposals for leading it out of the doldrums. Community care, said the Audit Commission, is about "changing the balance of services and finding the most suitable placement for people from a wide range of options. It is not about imposing a community solution." That was a valid point in a decade when rhetoric championing consumer choice was soon deflated by the drive for cost-effectiveness. The gap between the run-down in hospital beds for the mentally ill and the build-up of community based services was highlighted. "No one knows what happens to many people after they are discharged," the commission admitted. Some undoubtedly ended up homeless on city streets, a sad failure of policy for a civilised society. Local authorities provided a "very uneven pattern" of services with care received being dependent upon

*Diagram 1

**PRINCIPAL AGENCIES INVOLVED IN COMMUNITY
CARE**

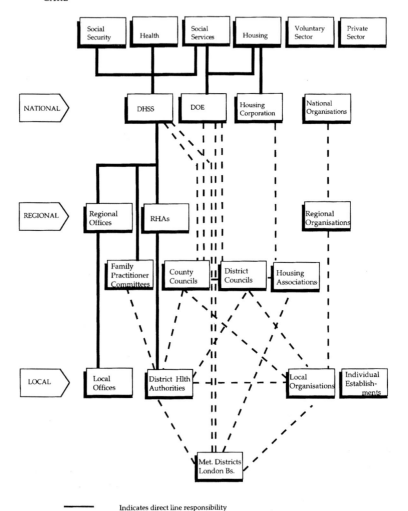

Indicates direct line responsibility
Indicates interrelationship

*This diagram is reproduced here with the permission of the Controller of Her Majesty's Stationery Office.

where people lived, reported the commission. Although 10% of the population consulted their general practitioners about a mental health problem, with 10% of these being referred on to a psychiatrist, many local authorities spent less than £1 per head of population on services for the mentally ill.

Referring to the 300,000 people still living in residential settings, the commission pointed out that the reduction in NHS beds for the elderly had been offset by the growth in private residential homes. Some of the residents had help with their fees through supplementary benefits, the cost to the social security budget rising from £200 million in 1984 to £500 million in 1986. That figure, as mentioned earlier, rose to nearly £2 billion at the turn of the decade and has continued to rise. At best, the authors argued tellingly, a shift had occurred from hospital based residential care to an alternative type of residential care, supported from a different state budget, "missing out more flexible and cost-effective forms of community care." At worst, the commission warned, the shortfall in service would grow with "many vulnerable and disabled people left without care and at serious personal risk."

This was a bleak scenario that typified the haphazard nature of the services provided for vulnerable groups. The commission did not lay the blame solely on a shortage of funds. "Although more money could always be spent to advantage, the current levels of expenditure from public funds could provide a community based service for elderly, mentally ill and handicapped people." To do this, declared the commission, meant remedying the underlying weaknesses:

(a) the failure to provide a mechanism to shift funds in parallel with changes in care;

(b) the straightjacket of the local government grant system prevented the funding of necessary building projects;

(c) inadequate funds for the difficult transition phase; and

(d) the way that supplementary benefits for elderly people in independent residential care were producing (inadvertently) an imbalance of residential homes, with some south coast areas having nearly ten times as many private and voluntary residential places as some urban areas such as Cleveland.

These unbalanced benefit payments frustrated the government's attempts to distribute public funds equitably since there was no proper assessment of those people entering residential care and those eligible for benefits. Responsibility for launching and running community based services was fragmented between agencies with "different priorities, styles, structures and budgets."[14] There were too few staff and their training and prospects were uncertain. Not all was gloom, however, and the Audit Commission described several local schemes where community care was working. These showed "radical departures from the established patterns" and were the result of local initiatives. They were characterised by having strong and committed local champions of change, and a focus on action not bureaucratic machinery by being locally integrated. The commission saw it as "little short of amazing" that any successful community based schemes had been introduced since the existing system was a "barrier to change." The focus was on services not clinics, whereas the management focus should be on local operations. That was a significant diagnosis that would motivate the government's plans for community care.

Finance was a fundamental problem and the commission came up with the radical idea of a lead agency to 'buy in' services as necessary from other agencies, a foretaste of the purchaser concept that featured in subsequent plans for the NHS as well as for community care. In the late 1970s the DHSS loosened the financial straightjacket on community care a little by providing the NHS with funds to pump prime joint projects with local authorities and by allowing transfer payments. The scheme was only moderately successful since local authorities were expected to take on the financing of the projects after three years, though this period was later extended, and many were reluctant to assume such a commitment. More radical changes were required to introduce the flexibility needed to make community care a real success.

Among several strategic options put forward by the commission were the speedier transfer of resources from the NHS to local authorities and the removal of financial disincentives for local authorities to take part in community care. Others included bridging finance for the change from residential to community care, an increase in the rate of change, the co-ordination of community care policies and supplementary benefit arrangements to remove policy conflicts and perverse incentives, and the identification of a system to deliver proper care to patients at the right place and cost. The commission also called for the co-ordination of manpower planning, including redeployment and training, and the most appropriate use of cost-effective voluntary organisations.

A SECOND GRIFFITHS INQUIRY

This was a formidable list but no less than was needed to break the log-jam over community care. In the same month, December 1986, that the Audit Commission's analysis appeared Sir Roy Griffiths, the Prime Minister's special adviser on health, was, according to the Lancet, instructed by Mrs Thatcher "to find a solution to the problems of community care."[15] Over a year later, in March 1988, the man whose management plan for the NHS had been accepted with such alacrity in 1983 presented his solution for community care.[16] This time the government's reception bordered on the insulting. "From the DHSS the silence was deafening," commented Carvel.[15] Released in the publicity slipstream of the 1988 Budget and when Sir Roy was still convalescing from a serious operation the report was said to have made the Prime Minister "furious."[17]

Her fury was such that she launched an interdepartmental review of her own, the provocation being Sir Roy's boldness in assigning local authorities a pivotal co-ordinating role for community care services. The alleged profligacy and inefficiencies of local government had for long made them the bête noire of Tory ministers. Sir Roy's pedigree was "not sufficient to win support for an idea which is heresy to the present administration," concluded the Lancet's Parliament watcher.[15] Griffiths' solution would have expanded local authorities' budgets and resulted in even higher levels of the already unpopular poll tax.

The Griffiths report was not alone in marking local authorities as key players in community care. In 1987 a report, 'Public support for residential care',[18] from a joint central and local government working party argued that local authorities should be responsible for the quality of private and voluntary homes. They should also, said the authors, be responsible for assessing potential residents and for financing care in the home. These ideas slotted in well with the broad range of proposals from Griffiths. How did he envisage a local authority centred community care system working? At the top Griffiths wanted a minister of state in the DoH to be made responsible for community care. The minister's responsibilities would include:

(a) publishing a statement of the government's community care objectives and priorities;

(b) deciding on those areas in which the government wanted to lay down standards of service delivery;

(c) arranging for a review of local social services authorities' plans against national objectives and linking that process with the allocation of resources; and

(d) ensuring that health authorities' planning and funding reflected community care objectives.

The key role he proposed for local authorities expanded on the report from the Audit Commission. It was to include an assessment of the community care needs of the locality with local priorities, service objectives and plans set in consultation with health authorities, housing authorities, voluntary bodies and the private sector. He called for individual needs to be assessed, taking account of personal preferences, to enable the consumer to live as normal a life as possible. Other proposals were for the necessary care to be arranged using informal carers, neighbourhood support, domiciliary and day services or, if appropriate, residential care. Local authorities would design, organise and purchase the non-health care services needed. While not acting primarily as direct providers they would appoint nominated 'care managers' to oversee all these changes. For all this to happen effectively local social services departments would need to conduct a comprehensive review of care needs and services.

His report did not examine funding as such, but Sir Roy proposed that central government should also arrange "for the necessary transfer of resources between central and local government to match the defined responsibilities." Warning that adequate money for community care must be provided he emphasised that the review was about cost improvements and not cost cutting. His plan was for central government to fund up to half the costs of care through charges, with local government taxation making up the rest of the resources required. A significant, and politically very sensitive, recommendation was that funds for community care should be ring-fenced within the central block grant to a local authority. Social security benefits would no longer be paid automatically to people in residential care: social services departments could 'means test' applicants and a residential allowance, lower than the present allowances, might be payable with local authorities judging whether to top it up. Vouchers, insurance, tax incentives and pension charges were other ideas he floated for financing care with the aim of encouraging people to plan ahead for their needs, thus permitting public resources to be concentrated on areas where they were most needed.

The report emphasised the importance of local accountability, though without detailing how, and its author argued for care being placed as near to the individual and his or her carers as possible. Staff would mainly come from a multi-disciplinary auxiliary workforce that would encompass social services and the voluntary and private sectors. The social work profession would not be available in the numbers required and he added that insularity among the professions and groups providing care led to failures in communication. Health authorities would continue to be responsible for the medical and community health services that would be required and general practitioners would be expected to ensure that local social services authorities were told of patients' needs for 'non-health care'.

Sir Roy Griffiths summed up his aims as follows:

"Implementation of the proposals will increase the ability of managers in all community care services to ensure that the right services are provided in good time to the people who need them most; the people receiving help will have a greater say in what is done to help them, and a wider choice; and people are helped to stay in their own homes for as long as possible, or in as near a domestic environment as possible, so that residential, nursing home, and hospital care is reserved for those whose needs cannot be met in any other way."

ENTHUSIASTIC, WARY AND CRITICAL RESPONSES

If the government greeted the second Griffiths report with near silence others did not. Local government organisations, not surprisingly perhaps, praised Sir Roy's emphasis on the core role for social services departments and urged the government not to pigeon hole his proposals. From the NHS side of the fence the National Association of Health Authorities and Trusts (NAHAT) greeted it with equal enthusiasm. While emphasising the contribution to care by health authorities NAHAT saw the appointment of a minister as ensuring a quicker and more effective implementation of policies for care in the community. The King's Fund liked the report but, noting the government's antagonism towards local government, warned that unless there was a political commitment to carry through the reforms they would fail. MIND disliked the proposal to means test people for services and claimed that the report had ducked the thorny issue of local collaboration.[19]

The Royal College of Nursing dismissed the report as fatally flawed, as exhibiting dickensian and paternalistic attitudes, and as failing to tackle the real challenges.[20] It claimed "that only a mass profession like nursing can meet this challenge" and pointed out that there were only 30,000 social workers in the field and 35,000 general practitioners. It argued that nursing provided a much better base from which to recruit and train the right staff and would tie in with the proposals on neighbourhood nursing published in 1986.[21] Furthermore, "local authority social services suffered chronic skill shortages and had a poor record of providing care for the elderly." Initially, the BMA reacted cautiously to the proposals but in May 1992 published a considered response to the government's eventual plans, which broadly supported Griffiths' original proposals, emphasised the importance of adequate and properly targeted funding, and warned against hasty implementation.[22] Meanwhile, an editorial in the British Medical Journal picked up the theme of the local authorities' poor track record:

"Far and away the most worrying feature," said the author, Professor Elaine Murphy, "is whether local authorities have the ability or the will to implement the recommendation... an appreciable minority have elected members whose priorities are concerned largely with the advancement of an ideology. Some councils refuse... to purchase private services... several... have so mismanaged their own social work departments that they no longer have sufficient staff to fulfil their minimum statutory responsibilities to children at risk and to mentally ill people."[23]

Another example of the poor track record of community

care providers was the failure of joint planning initiatives between local and health authorities, which did not augur well
for a plan that depended on collaboration. A letter in the BMJ
a few weeks after the Griffiths report appeared illustrated
this.[24] The authors had carried out a postal survey of directors
of social services and general managers of district health authorities, which from a 50% response rate showed that only a
minority held regular meetings, some only every six months.
Over 25% had either discontinued or never had a joint care
planning team, under 10% held ad hoc meetings and the rest,
29%, failed to specify a frequency. Many replies commented on
the difficulties of attempting to co-ordinate plans with other
organisations. The picture that emerged was described as "a
morass" by the authors, who were clearly sceptical about Sir
Roy's solutions, arguing that "fudging the issue of coterminosity of health authorities, social services authorities and family
practitioner committees precludes long-term improvement in
community care."

   The initial welcome, therefore, was not universally friendly.
An especially fierce criticism was launched by the voluntary
sector. The Director of MIND, as well as condemning means
testing, argued that the cash available would be "wholly inadequate to purchase good care" (though to be fair to Sir Roy the
amount of cash available was not in his remit). MIND's Director condemned the result as likely to be "the cheapest option
paid for by the poorest funded and delivered by the profit
conscious."[19] Perhaps the nutshell diagnosis came from Hudson, an academic in social policy, who suggested that "while
cash was short acrimony, not harmony, was likely to result
from the Griffiths recommendations."[25] Clearly, with primary
health care undergoing restructuring, the Prime Minister's
NHS review expected early in 1989 and with local authorities
under intense pressure to become more cost-effective government action was urgently needed to bring order to the border
areas between these sectors.

"TWO CHEERS FOR GRIFFITHS"

While Whitehall was busily searching for a viable alternative
to Sir Roy's local authority based plan the debate continued
outside the Department of Health. At a conference in May

1988, organised by NAHA and NHS managers, Sir Roy summed up the response to his proposals as "two cheers for Griffiths." He admitted the need for a lot more work but argued that the opportunity his proposals gave the NHS to concentrate entirely on health problems would be welcomed. He emphasised the key role for health professionals in assessment and said that valuable nursing time should not be spent on routine and non-specialised care, hence his recommendation for a new breed of carers. Sir Roy also underlined the fact that many different local solutions were possible within his vision of community care.[26] Let a hundred flowers bloom was the philosophy. A King's Fund survey reported that district managers and social services directors wanted urgent action, but whereas 90% of directors, not surprisingly, supported Griffiths only 46% of district managers did so.[27]

One suggestion (from the Association of Directors of Social Services) for circumventing this confusion was to set up a community care development agency. Such an agency would audit the available funds, oversee planning, monitor their implementation and ensure that budgets were ring-fenced. A more radical solution, aired in a BMJ editorial in December 1988 demanding action, was to combine the community health services and community care parts of the priority care services with family practitioner services and social services departments to create one primary health authority.[28] That, however, while theoretically elegant would have caused further upheaval in a health service already demoralised by constant change and threats of change. By and large the feeling in the agencies affected was that Griffiths had offered a solution which, while it might need modifying, should be put in place as soon as possible.

The government finally responded to the Griffiths report in July 1989.[29] Internal Whitehall consultations had failed to produce a viable alternative to making local authorities and social services departments the lead agencies. The Secretary of State for Health supported the distinction between health and social care but rejected the sensible idea of a minister of state for community care. Emphasising that existing community health services would continue to play an essential part in meeting the medical and nursing needs of people outside of hospital the Secretary of State for Health endorsed the Griffiths plan to make social services departments the main co-ordinating bodies for all social care in the community. A single budget would be handled by the local authority, which would take over the responsibility for the care elements of public support for people in private and voluntary residential care and nursing homes. Thus, the Department of Social Security would no longer contribute to the cost of people in private or voluntary homes.

Local authorities social services departments, in collaboration with others including doctors, nurses and other caring professions, would assess an individual's needs, design appropriate care packages and arrange for their delivery. The Secretary of State for Health emphasised the role of GPs in ensuring that the departments were aware of their patients' needs for social care. To widen choice and encourage innovation and flexibility local authorities would be expected to make the greatest possible use of the voluntary, non-profit and commercial sectors. Social services departments were to act in an enabling and not just in a providing capacity. Local authorities would have to make plans that would be inspected by a social services inspectorate.

The Secretary of State for Health promised to transfer resources to local authorities to cover the extra functions but rejected a key Griffiths proposal: the government would not ring-fence money for community care within the annual central grants to local authorities. An exception to this would be funds designated for severely mentally ill people leaving hospital for social care in the community. This rejection of earmarked funds was, as Sir Roy subsequently described, like taking a wheel off a vehicle designed to run on four wheels. At a time of financial stringency it would certainly aggravate the local strains engendered over providing services that overlapped the financial boundaries between health and local authorities. Fortunately, the government later changed its mind or more accurately the next Conservative government did so. After the 1992 general election Mrs Virginia Bottomley was appointed Secretary of State for Health and in October 1992 she announced that funds for community care would, to start with, be ring-fenced within a local authority's central grant, as Sir Roy Griffiths had suggested. This was universally welcomed. Griffiths had also proposed that local authorities should set up inspection and registration units "at arms length" from the management of their own services.[16] These units would check standards in local authorities' homes with the help of independent outsiders. The government endorsed this idea.

WHITE PAPER: CARING FOR PEOPLE

The government now had a community care policy that broadly matched the philosophy of its NHS reforms: greater consumer choice, more consumer sensitive services, a pur-chaser/provider split, more competition, the involvement of the private sector, a clear line of accountability and mecha-nisms to monitor performance. But it was to be some time before these policy aims were to be tried in practice. The next stage of policy making was a white paper and this appeared in November 1989. The white paper, 'Caring for people: com-munity care in the next decade and beyond',[29] covered England, Wales and Scotland—Northern Ireland's health and personal services were to be dealt with separately as these were already run by unitary boards. The white paper fleshed out the Secretary of State's July parliamentary statement. The key objectives set out in it were as follows:

(a) to promote the development of domiciliary day and respite services to enable people to live in their own homes wherever feasible and sensible;

(b) to ensure that providers make practical support for carers a high priority;

(c) to make proper assessment of need and good care management the cor-nerstone of high quality care;

(d) to promote the development of a flourishing independent sector alongside good quality public services;

(e) to clarify the responsibilities of agencies and so make it easier to hold them to account for their performance; and

(f) to secure better value for taxpayers' money by introducing a new funding structure for social care.

The magnitude of the task facing local authorities in imple-menting the changes was apparent from the figures in the white paper. These showed that in 1987–8 local authorities in England spent £2,350 million on community care—split roughly 50:50 between residential care and domiciliary and day care services. They employed 232,000 staff: 5,550 managers; 27,000 social work staff; 1,100 occupational therapists; 88,200 staff in residential care establishments; 59,500 home helps; and 27,200 day care staff. They provided 133,800 residential care places, 108,700 day centre places and 46.4 million meals on wheels. The pressure would increase as community services were asked to help more people with more complex needs. The transition to the new system would require time, a great deal of planning and commitment from the staff. Initially, the government intended 1st April 1991 to be the start-up date, which was the same date as the NHS reforms and the Children Act were due to be implemented. But by the time the proposals in 'Caring for people'[29] had been translated into the NHS and Community Care Act in the summer of 1990,[30] after a relatively trouble free passage through Parliament, an extended timetable had been announced by Mr Clarke. In July 1990 the Secretary of State for Health told Parliament that its introduction would be phased. April 1991 would see the introduction of the complaints procedures, inspection units and grants for tackling mental illness and drug and alcohol misuse. The first of the community care plans would be implemented in April 1992 and a year later would see the start of the transfer of social security funds to local government and the introduction of new assessment procedures.

DELAYED IMPLEMENTATION AND CONCERN OVER RESOURCES

The Lancet reported that anger at the delay "even on Conservative benches" had been intense.[17] "The Carers National Association declared itself angry, cheated and betrayed. The mental health pressure groups were contemptuous of the grant for the mentally ill (some £21 million as long as the local councils were ready to raise another £9 million). The National Schizophrenia Fellowship noted that the average cost of caring for a seriously mentally ill person was £10,000. The new grant would help 3,000 severely ill people, yet there were 250,000 schizophrenia sufferers alone." That would mean either patients staying in hospital or more mentally ill people on the streets. Mr Clarke blamed the delay on the state of unreadiness at the local level but Whitehall watchers had no doubt that the culprit was the politically embarrassing poll tax and the government's reluctance to do anything that would increase it. It was estimated that the community care changes would add at least £15 to the tax. The Secretary of State's reasoning was in any case confounded by a survey of social services directors, which reported that 94 out of 95 wanted the new system to start in April 1991.[17] This eagerness to start was understandable: waiting for Griffiths had become debilitating. Yet a year later the Audit Commission, in an analysis of how local authorities were progressing with their plans, suggested that there were problems even with the staggered timetable.[31] It claimed: "Progress is being made at different speeds in different authorities, and, on the surface at least, the deadlines for the government's timetable should be met in most places. But the fundamental changes to organisational culture required have still to work their way through. Big changes in policy and practice at all levels are still needed if the government's objectives of a user-driven, cost-effective system of community health and care services are to be realised, and it is likely to take years for this process to reach completion."

A more disturbing aspect even than the problems over money and local organisation was the government's attitude to the concept of community. This was encapsulated in comments by the Oxford social historian Professor AH Halsey, who spoke at a conference early in 1991 organised by the Joseph Rowntree Foundation. He was reported in the Lancet[1] as warning that the disabled, the mentally ill and the mentally handicapped were facing a government which was the "most anti-community administration since the Poor Law days of 1834." It was hardly surprising that those responsible for community care from family carers through nurses, doctors and directors of social services to the voluntary organisations were apprehensive about what would happen to their relatives, patients and clients in the 1990s.

Britain's deteriorating economic situation during 1992 did nothing to improve the confidence of those who would be trying to make the fundamental changes referred to by the Audit Commission. The critical question was: would the government be willing or able to provide local authorities with sufficient funding? The BMA, for one, had doubts. In a report,

'Priorities for community care',[32] published in April 1992, it pleaded for adequate resources. The association supported the government's philosophy behind 'Caring for people' but was worried about its translation into practice. It urged the Secretary of State for Health to monitor closure plans of long-stay hospitals to ensure that adequate services in the community were being developed.

Unless this happens hospitals will find their beds blocked when there are no suitable community care facilities available for patients, particularly the elderly. The primary care services are also vulnerable in that they will have to pick up some of the pieces if community care proves inadequate, as already happens to some extent. Close co-operation will be essential for the welfare of patients whatever the levels of funding. The resources earmarked for community care will be of special interest to the independent sector, which is making an increasing and substantial contribution to the facilities available. The role of independent nursing and residential homes is discussed in Chapter Seven.

A study published in October 1991 claimed that "a large group of people with chronic mental health problems will continue to 'slip through the net' into isolation and homelessness unless the government changes its funding policy... the majority were living alone in unsupported accommodation and were unemployed, and, of those eligible, most were not using day care or occupational services." These problems were recognised but it was claimed that they would continue in the short-term because of the funding mechanisms operating. Peter Reading, Lewisham and Guy's Trust Mental Health Unit General Manager, argued that there was no indication that the government would take the steps necessary to remedy the problem. The National Schizophrenia Fellowship said that the study findings raised serious questions about the government's community care policy. Mental health charity MIND said the survey highlighted the need for better employment opportunities and more imaginative support services.[33]

Despite taking a resolutely positive line about the opportunities offered by the 1993 changes, the Audit Commission's February report had warned that the "rebalancing" between service providers and the needs of users and carers would require "adjustments at every level which will in turn trigger further complications in an ever decreasing cascade of change." Promising to help with the implementation along with the regional health authorities and the new social services inspectorate (a sensible innovation that might usefully be emulated by the NHS) the commission said that the aim would be to assist authorities to "identify the most significant gaps and address the needed changes systematically."[31] Such assistance will surely be needed.

October 1992 saw Mrs Bottomley announce a community care budget of £539 million for 1993-4 for the payment of residential care in response to a demand for £600 million from local authorities. The Association of Municipal Health Authorities wanted more—£750 million. The allocation included a social security transfer of £399 million. The two year delay in introducing the reforms had resulted in implementation at a time of even greater austerity than that which had prompted the postponement. In the circumstances the outcome was better than might have been expected. One policy change she announced was widely welcomed—central financial support for community care would be ring-fenced, at least to start with. She also granted special protection for the independent sector and for clients—a substantial part of the grant would have to be spent in that sector and individuals would have the right to choose where and what type of accommodation they entered.[34] With the promise of consumer choice and greater use of the private sector basic Tory policies had, it seemed, survived intact. Not entirely, though, because at a fringe meeting on community care at the Tories' annual conference some nursing home owners expressed the fear that the assessment and funding role of local authorities could well mean some existing nursing homes failing to win contracts and thus going to the wall.[35] This was capitalism with a municipal face perhaps. Certainly, as 1st April 1993 approached many nursing and residential care homes were worried that town halls were dilatory in getting to grips with the community care market because many owners were still awaiting negotiations over contracts for the care of their residents. A survey by Laing & Buisson illustrated the confusion and inadequate funding to meet demand in the run up to the April deadline.[36]

CONCERNS OVER IMPLEMENTATION AND
EFFECTS ON NHS

After two years the NHS purchaser/provider arrangements were slowly, if unevenly, shaking down but were still causing strains throughout the service. The similar community care arrangements have to contend with the added complication of several varied providing agencies in the public and independent sectors. As the Audit Commission commented "... big changes in policy and practice locally are still needed if the government's objectives of a user-centred and cost-effective system of community-based health and care services are to be realised."[31] These changes will exert further pressures on the NHS. Early in 1993 the National Association of Health Authorities and Trusts drew attention to the gaps in plans for care between local government and the health service. Unless these gaps are closed it foresees patients having to stay in hospital while assessments are carried out.[37] Hospitals will certainly have to upgrade their pre-discharge assessment of patients needing community care, which will be 'purchased' by social services and not the NHS. This may well block beds in a hospital service already under pressure for beds. GPs claim that the new assessment procedures will mean more work for them, as will the consequences of blocked beds.

The varying levels of commitment to the reforms among health and local authorities, the belief amongst many staff and authorities that the government had allocated insufficient resources—a belief vigorously challenged by ministers—and the traditional boundary stresses between hospitals, primary care and local authorities signalled a rough launch for the government's plans. A further destabilising factor will be the changes resulting from the Local Government Commission, which could disturb existing boundaries between health and local authorities. Perhaps a lesson could have been learned from Northern Ireland where unitary boards have for 20 years been responsible for health and social services. Managers there are optimistic about the reforms, even if providers are not so sure.[38] There is, however, concern over funding, as elsewhere in the UK, which will be critical to its success. The new structures could probably be made to work if adequate resources are provided. The reported tight government guidelines on the assessment of clients, with assessors obliged to take into account available resources in judging clients' needs and in-structed not to tell them what their assessed needs are, suggest, however, that the government is nervous about its claim to have provided appropriate funds.

A potentially damaging fault line in the reforms is the pro-vision of financial support for elderly clients who need either institutional community care or expensive support to live at home. If social services departments are unable to meet all the demands what will happen to the unlucky clients who cannot fall back on long-stay accommodation in NHS hospitals or local authority establishments? Anxieties abound, too, among those responsible for the care of the mentally ill. A government task force has embarked on a two year drive to replace old mental institutions with up to date community facilities but events may overtake its work, as patients are discharged into communities unprepared to care for them: "into a vacuum" according to the National Schizophrenia Fellowship's Chief Executive.[37] None of this augurs well for a supposedly con-sumer sensitive service. Indeed, they are the makings of a social and medical crisis and possibly a political one as well.

The uncertainty among the groups responsible for operating the new structures was epitomised by Professor David Hunter who, three weeks before the April deadline, warned that "policy makers, managers and practitioners are already look-ing beyond the 'Caring for people' changes... to construct alternative configurations for the effective delivery of commu-nity care."[39] He highlighted a paper from the Health Services Management Unit at Manchester which forecast that the new infrastructure would prove defective and that obstacles to co-herent community care would remain unresolved. The report believes a fundamental rethink is unavoidable, suggesting that one solution might be to set up commissioning agencies for all the social, health and welfare needs of population groups of around 250,000.[40] The proposal has an attractive if idealistic logic. But to those struggling with the realities of the NHS and Community Care Act 1990[30] the prospect of yet more up-heavals will be as welcome as a cold bath to an Eskimo.

THE CHILDREN ACT 1989

The NHS and Community Care Act 1990 was not the only major legislation in the decade affecting the overlapping activities of health and social care. In November 1989 Parliament approved what the government described as the most comprehensive piece of legislation ever enacted affecting children. That description was reflected by the Department of Health issuing 35 consultation papers on the regulations to translate The Children Act 1989[41] into action in October 1991, when its provisions came into operation. The act, which is concerned with civil not criminal law, brought together and simplified existing legislation to produce a more practical and consistent code. It integrated the law relating to private individuals with the responsibilities of public authorities, in particular local authority social services departments, towards children. The new legislation struck a new balance between family autonomy and the protection of children, with the child's welfare paramount. Though primarily affecting local authorities' responsibilities the legislation was of significance to all sectors of the NHS and, of course, to the education authorities.

For many years successive governments have supported the idea of comprehensive integrated health care for children, in which parents have an important responsibility. Progress had been patchy but the government's continuing support for the policy was made clear by Baroness Blatch, its spokesperson in the House of Lords, who said that it would be the duty of district health authorities to promote comprehensive health services for children. She went on: "It has been the policy of successive governments since... the Court report in 1976 to encourage the integration of hospital and community health services for children, with close links to local authorities' childrens' services given to families with children."[42]

General practice also has considerable responsibility for child care, as the 1990 contract recognised. Regrettably, however, there had been prolonged demarcation disputes within the profession about where the boundaries should be drawn, especially for screening and surveillance services, primarily between the community health services and general practice. Nevertheless, as the health service moves towards more effective internal integration these differences should be resolved. Indeed, given the complexities of the child care services it is essential that they are.

Children are not just the responsibility of professionals, however, and the health service recognises the key role of the parents in their child's health and sickness. This parental responsibility is at the core of the new Children Act, which rests "on the belief that children are generally best looked after within the family with both parents playing a full part and without resort to legal proceedings."[43] This may not always prove possible and local authority social services departments have special responsibilities for finding the best possible alternative arrangements for the care of the child in the absence of the parents, either because the child has been abandoned by them, is an orphan or because the parents are incapable of caring properly for the child. In these circumstances the local authority accepts 'parental responsibility' and social workers usually try to settle a child in as normal a family environment as possible. All decisions about parental authority must, under the new act, be made by the courts. As well as care and supervision orders to determine parental responsibility courts now also have the power to decide with whom a child will live, determine what form of contact he is to have with other people, deal with any special problems he may have and prohibit actions not in the child's interests.

The legislation means more work for already overburdened social services departments and a greater workload for the health professions. As an article in the April 1991 edition of Archives of Disease in Childhood warned, "the courts are likely to require much more by way of expert assessment, and a significant proportion of this will be medical assessment."[44] The author also forecast the involvement of doctors in private law cases and in care proceedings, in which the guardian ad litem may need medical advice to draw up recommendations for presentation to the court. These activities would seem to have implications for NHS resources and in the same issue of Archives of Disease in Childhood Dr Miles warned that "assumptions have been made that there will be no significant health resource implications flowing from the implementation of the act. Clearly... this is not true. Even if health agencies wanted to restrict their contributions, it would not be possible to do so as Section 27 of the Children Act allows a local authority to request help from a health authority. Having received a request that authority must comply."[45] Although Dr Miles also made the point that co-ordination of health participation should be easier in districts with integrated child health services that will not reduce the need for more resources. Social services, education and health care are all operating with tightly controlled budgets. It seems more than likely that these restraints will handicap those trying to operate the Children Act at the sharp end, who in any case are experiencing legal and practical problems in translating the law into daily practice.

PUBLIC HEALTH

In its report, 'Priorities for community care',[32] the BMA called for community care planning to include input from all relevant branches of the medical and nursing professions. The association argued that the public health physician was "probably the doctor who would have the most continuous input into the needs assessment and service planning of an area, taking advice from appropriate specialists and liaising with... social services departments and the voluntary sector." Public health doctors have their roots in the community, originating from the great public health reforms of the 19th century. They became powerful figures in local government, exerting considerable influence on the health of the communities they served. When the NHS was set up medical officers of health stayed with local government, although some of their previous health responsibilities were spread throughout the health service. They continued to have a defined community role, dealing with environmental health, communicable disease control, health visiting, community nursing, midwifery and the school health service. Other responsibilities included the prevention of illness, health education, care and after care, some welfare services and advising the local authority on public health.

This split in responsibilities for health between local authority health services continued until 1974, when reorganisation of the NHS abolished medical officers of health and brought most of their health functions within the remit of the hospital and community health services, which were run by the newly constituted health authorities. Before this, however, in 1968 the Royal Commission on medical education had proposed setting up a new specialty of community medicine, and a faculty of the Royal Colleges of Physicians was duly established to oversee training and standards for the specialty.[46] Four years later the Hunter report on medical administration suggested that medical officers of health and their staff should be brought together in the new specialty along with administrative medical officers of hospital boards and the medical staff of academic departments of public health and social medicine.[47] Health authorities would get advice from specialists in community medicine on their responsibilities for the health of their populations, an echo from the days when a single medical team advised local authorities on the health needs of the local community. Community health services continued to be provided by the 5,000 or so clinical medical officers. They ran clinics and undertook pre-school surveillance of children as well as being involved in preventive medicine and health education.

The promising concept of linking medical management with the planning and development of health services for local people, which could have been a positive consequence of the 1974 reorganisation, unfortunately failed to develop satisfactorily in many areas. The inability of some community physicians to rise to the challenge meant that the new specialty never really established the professional standing that it merited. To be fair, the reorganisation had launched the holders of the new posts in community medicine on "largely uncharted waters and competition for the new posts created a great deal of bitterness amongst the unsuccessful candidates," the Royal Commission on the NHS subsequently observed.[11] The result was that the status of community physicians was uncertain and confused, with even their clinical colleagues often not understanding the contribution the specialty should be making to health care. As the Acheson report later commented, health authorities often "undervalued the contribution of their public health doctors, and failed to give sufficient emphasis to public health issues."[48]

Events during the first part of the 1980s did little to restore confidence in the specialty or among its practitioners. With the exception of a few beacons of academic enlightenment the specialty trundled along behind changes in the NHS, contributing little to the direction that it should take. The 1982 reorganisation dealt a further blow to community medicine, which lost 20% of its members when area health authorities were abolished and with them a managerial tier that contained community physicians. Once again this small specialty of around 1,000 doctors was the only medical group whose jobs were on the line as a result of organisational changes. Eighteen months later the Griffiths report[49] on management failed to revive them. It replaced consensus management by district teams, which included community physicians, with general managers and accountable line management. Though emphasising the importance of doctors participating in management, Roy Griffiths referred specifically to the contribution that practising clinicians could make. He also pointed out how little measurement there was of health output and that clinical and economic evaluation of medical practises were "extremely rare." Despite their experience in management and epidemiology and the importance of public health in planning health services, the report did not identify community physicians as having a special role in the new management structure. As Sir Donald Acheson, Chief Medical Officer, put it in his 1988 report on public health (see below): "The implementation of general management at a time when... the nature of the public health functions of health authorities was not clearly defined, and the credibility of... community medicine had in some places become compromised, tended unintentionally to confuse its image further and sometimes to weaken the position of community physicians." It was hardly surprising that the specialty had become so demoralised and recruitment difficult. The crisis facing community medicine was comparable to that experienced by general practice 20 years earlier.

ACHESON REPORT LIFELINE

Just as the Family Doctor Charter had rescued GPs so the Acheson report threw community physicians a lifeline and began a renaissance of the specialty.[48] The Committee of Inquiry, led by Sir Donald, had been set up in response to two major outbreaks of communicable disease, which had caused serious public and political concern. In the event, the inquiry became "the first major review of public health in England since the Royal Sanitary Commission report of 1871," as the Department of Health described it.[50] The report's main thrust was the resurrection of public health. The stimulus for the report, control of infectious disease, became part of a rather more important whole. There were, nevertheless, valuable practical recommendations for improving the inadequate control procedures, a failure that had been a consequence of the decline in the effectiveness of community medicine/public health.

The Acheson inquiry worked to a definition of public health as "the science and art of preventing disease, prolonging life and promoting health through organised efforts of society." Given the Tory government's known disdain for public planning and state interference in people's lives it was a commendable decision. The overriding objective of the report's 39 proposals was to ensure that the nation's health was constantly monitored and that the services provided, both for prevention and treatment, were evaluated for their likely impact on that health.

Among its main recommendations the report wanted:

(a) health authorities to be told of their public health responsibilities;

(b) a public health doctor, normally the existing district medical officer of health, to be appointed as director of public health and to be part of the authority's decision making machinery;

(c) a director of public health to produce an annual report on the health of districts or regions; and

(d) a small central unit to be set up at the DoH to facilitate the monitoring of the nation's health.

The inquiry proposed that the director of public health should be accountable to the district general manager and that the post should be held by a doctor. It also redefined the function of community physicians, emphasising their role in the prevention of illness and the promotion of health and in the planning and evaluation of health services. The report pointed out that the specialty's epidemiological skills were "relevant to monitoring the population's health and analysing the pattern of illness in relation to its causes... ." Epidemiology was also seen as important in evaluating services, which with its other benefits was helpful in making "the best use of finite resources," a phrase that would appeal to cost-conscious ministers.

Within six months the government had accepted the recommendations and a leading article in the BMJ saw it as "an opportunity for a radically new public health," with the new directors garnering information and using it to analyse health problems and to persuade those who wielded executive, political or professional power to take appropriate action.[51] As it turned out, the government's political agenda for the health service opened up an entirely unexpected avenue through which DPHs could influence the pattern of health care provision. In the past this had been done via the planning and management processes, which called for persuasion and, often protracted, negotiation. The National Association of Health Authorities and Trusts argued that the new contract mechanism, introduced as a result of the 1990 NHS Act, had made the "science and art of public health more explicit and visible... ."[5] In the purchaser/provider service the DPH assesses not only the volume of particular services to be purchased but how much health care can be obtained from the different ways of tackling particular diseases. He or she must then attempt to modify the use of resources to achieve the most effective pattern. By bringing together the various measures of the local population's health DPHs can advise on the nature of the care to be provided. Their medical background enables them to judge services on offer from providers and to negotiate on standards with the doctors providing the services.

The opportunities for public health in the wake of the Acheson report and the NHS Act 1990 have begun to revive the specialty's fortunes, although a note of caution is in order since concern has been expressed over cuts in posts when adjacent districts have merged. The opportunity to save money may be irresistible to managers but the public health needs of merged authorities are no less than those of the constituent parts. It is a false economy. That said, in its 1992 report the doctors' and dentists' pay review body noted that the number of consultants in the specialty had risen to 636 in 1990, with the government promising another 200 by 1998. The numbers of registrars and senior registrars had also gone up from 321 to 374 during the year, and in its evidence the BMA reported "that the increasing prominence of public health was attracting greater numbers of recruits."[52] The responsibilities of directors of public health in the reformed NHS will engage them across the whole spectrum of clinical and community care. This development should, if management permits, return to them something of the authority that their predecessors, the medical officers of health, had wielded in a very different political and medical environment.

REFERENCES

1. *Report of the Royal Commission on the law relating to mental illness and mental deficiency* (1957). London: HMSO.

2. *Mental Health Act* (1959). London: HMSO.

3. Ministry of Health (1962). *A hospital plan for England and Wales.* Cmnd 1604. London: HMSO.

4. Townsend P, Whitehead M (1980). *Inequalities in health.* London: HMSO.

5. National Association of Health Authorities and Trusts (1991). *NHS handbook. Seventh edition.* NAHAT.

6. Secretary of State for Social Services (1981). *Growing Older.* Cmnd 8173. London: HMSO.

7. Dean M (1991). Community care in a fog. *Lancet* 337: 225–6.

8. Secretaries of State for Health, Social Security, Wales and Scotland (1989). *Caring for people: community care in the next decade and beyond.* Cmnd 849. London: HMSO.

9. *Report of the committee on local authority and allied personal social services* (1968). (Seebohm report). Cmnd 3703. London: HMSO.

10. Department of Health and Social Security (1972). *National Health Service reorganisation: England.* Cmnd 5055. London: HMSO.

11. *Report of the Royal Commission on the National Health Service* (1979). Cmnd 7615. London: HMSO.

12. Department of Health and Social Security (1981). *Care in action: a handbook of policies and priorities for the health and personal social services in England.* London: HMSO.

13. House of Commons Social Services Committee (1985). *Community care with special reference to adult mentally ill and mentally handicapped people.* Volume 1. HC 13-I. London: HMSO.

14. Audit Commission (1986). *Making a reality of community care.* London: HMSO. P. 50.

15. Carvel J (1988). Lack of government enthusiasm for Griffiths report on community care. *Lancet* I: 8: 717–718.

16. Griffiths R (1988). *Community care: agenda for action.* London: HMSO.

17. Dean M (1990). Communities that can't care. *Lancet* 336: 235–36.

18. Department of Health and Social Security (1987). *Public support for residential care central and local: report of a joint government working party.* (The Fifth report). London: DHSS.

19. Heginbotham C (1988). Blinkered approach has missed the target. *Health Service* J 98: 329.

20. Royal College of Nursing (1988). *Press statement.* 16 March.

21. Department of Health and Social Security (1986). *Neighbourhood nursing: a focus for care.* (Cumberlege report). London: HMSO.

22. British Medical Association (1992). *Priorities for community care.* London: BMA.

23. Murphy E (1988). Griffiths on community care: potentially disastrous. *BMJ* 296: 876–77. (Editorial).

24. Baber SG,Haynes PW (1988). Co-ordinating community care. *BMJ* 296: 1467. (Letter).

25. Hudson B (1988). Storms that may blight a hundred local blooms. *Health Service J* 98: 327.

26. Crompton S (1988). Coming to terms with community care. *Health Service J* 98: 615.

27. King's Fund Institute (1988). *Community care—reacting to Griffiths*. London: King's Fund. (King's Fund Institute Briefing No.1).

28. Murphy E (1988). Government must act on community care. *BMJ* 297: 1558. (Editorial).

29. Department of Health (1989). *Caring for people: community care in the next decade and beyond*. Cm 849. London: HMSO.

30. *National Health Service and Community Care Act* (1990). London: HMSO.

31. Audit Commission (1992). *Community care : managing the cascade of change*. (NHS report no.6). London: HMSO.

32. British Medical Association (1992). *Priorities for community care*. London: BMA.

33. Anon (1991). Patients 'lack safety net'. *Health Service J* 101 (5276): 4.

34. Warden J (1992). Government squeezes care budgets. *BMJ* 305: 852. (Editorial).

35. Macpherson G (1992). Going great guns despite Essex man. *BMA News Review*, November. P. 18.

36. Laing & Buisson (1993). *Care of elderly people: market survey 1992/93*. London: Laing & Buisson.

37. Dobson J (1993). Space invaders. *Health Service J* 103 (5346): 16.

38. Tonks A (1993). Making progress—community care in Northern Ireland. *BMJ* 306: 262–5.

39. Hunter D (1993). A sticking plaster job. *Health Service J* 103 (5342): 28–9.

40. Health Services Management Unit (1992). *Caring for the community in the 21st Century: integrated purchasing of public services*. A discussion paper. Manchester: Manchester University.

41. *The Children Act* (1989). London: HMSO.

42. House of Lords (1990). *Hansard*. 7 June ,519, C1585–6.

43. Department of Health (1989). *An introduction to the Children's Act 1989*. London: HMSO.

44. Cretney SM (1991). Implication of the Children Act 1989 for paediatrics. *Arch. Dis. Child* 66: 536–541.

45. Miles M (1991). Implication of the Children Act for paediatricians. *Arch. Dis. Child* 66: 457–8.

46. Todd AR (1968). *Report of the Royal Commission on medical education 1965–68.* (The Todd report). Cmnd 35690. London: HMSO.

47. Department of Health and Social Security (1972). *Report of the working party on medical administrators.* London: HMSO.

48. Public Health in England (1988). *Report of the committee of inquiry into the future development of the public health function.* London:HMSO.

49. Griffiths report (1983). *NHS management inquiry.* London: HMSO.

50. Anon (1988). Return of the public health doctor: Acheson report boosts public health. *BMJ* 296: 303–304.

51. Gabbay J (1988). The new public health. *BMJ* 297: 371.

52. *Review Body on Doctors' and Dentists' Remuneration* (1992). Twenty second report. Cmnd 1813. London: HMSO.

9

FUNDING AND RESOURCE ALLOCATIONS

———— ◆ ————

THE CHRONIC DISEASE

The 1946 Act established the new National Health Service,[1] which has continuously generated fierce loyalty and pride amongst the people who have worked in it and genuine affection among those who have benefited from it. "It shall be the duty of the Minister of Health... to promote the establishment... of a comprehensive health service designed to secure improvement in the physical and mental health of the people of England and Wales and the prevention, diagnosis and treatment of illness, and for that purpose to provide or secure the effective provision of services in accordance with the following provisions of this Act."[1] The grand vision was of a comprehensive service for all where treatment depended on need and not ability to pay. A truly noble concept and a jewel in the crown of any civilised society.

At that time the attractive theory and government expectation was that in a few years the NHS would solve most of the nation's ills, and costs in turn would steadily decline. This hope proved ephemeral over the next decade as the medical perceptions of morbidity were extended, people's expectations of a 'free' service were raised, and the costs of comprehensive care became a running sore.

The government became increasingly concerned about health expenditure so it set up the Guillebaud Committee of inquiry into the costs of the National Health Service in 1956,[2] "to advise how a rising charge on the (Exchequer) can be avoided while providing for the maintenance of an *adequate* service." In future expectations would clearly have to be constrained by adequacy! The situation continued to deteriorate and by 1969 the first Secretary of State for the mammoth and unmanageable Department of Health and Social Security, Richard Crossman, stated that "the pressure of demography, the pressure of technology, and the pressure of democratic equalisation will always together be sufficient to make the standard of social services regarded as essential to a civilised community far more expensive than that community can afford... The trouble is that there is no foreseeable limit of the social services which the nation can reasonably require, except the limit that the government imposes."[3]

If ministers were increasingly concerned so also were the caring professions. The BMA undertook a wide ranging inquiry and in 1970 reported that "the NHS has never since the early years been able to fully cope with the rising demands that it and the parallel development of new methods of treatment were responsible for stimulating."[4] There was, therefore, agreement on the nature of the problem of rising demand and the need to restrain it between ministers and those who administered to the sick, but would there be an agreement over the solution?

Up to this time resource allocations had been based on the principle of incremental growth (a little more than last year) to make allowance for increased prices, nationally negotiated pay rates, and capital developments. There was the disastrous system of revenue consequences of capital schemes (RCCS), which guaranteed 'free' money from the department for new hospitals, causing there to be no restraint on medical ambitions and no management incentive for efficient, low cost revenue designs throughout the hospital building plan of the 1960s and the plethora of large and comprehensive district general hospitals (DGHs) which followed.

Next came the era of fixed cash limits—total budget allocations which had to contain not only all current expenditure but also planned and unplanned growth and development. This system was to offer ministers an iron fist in a velvet glove—more and more resources year after year but a rigid and inflexible control over total expenditure. The system proved extremely effective. The total NHS cash limit was never broken and the squeeze on public expenditure as a proportion of GNP was tightened.

In the 1980s government policy on financing the two bug bears—pay awards and RCCS—underwent a significant change. Part of the impact of the former, deliberate underfunding of pay awards, would be passed on to health authorities which had to take the strain through greater efficiency within their cash limits, while all of the latter would have to be met locally. The former brought new pressures and severe handicaps to health care as pay now had to compete with, and take precedence over, necessary clinical and service developments. The latter imposed a desirable discipline on management with major capital ambitions.

Throughout the 1960s and 1970s there still appeared to be evidence of gross inequalities in the provision of services in different parts of the NHS. It became clear that the government would have to fix the cash limits, distribute the resources in a different and differential way, identify the major clinical and political priorities, introduce the concept of rationing health care, and then seek to win the support of the professions and the public. But controlling total expenditure, within reasonable limits, meant not only rationing but also rationalising budget allocations and it became a politically desirable policy to be fair and to be seen to be fair.

In a little over 20 years after the establishment of the NHS idealism had given way to stark realism and the concept of rationing health care. The problem was both to contain the costs of rising expectations and to redistribute resources by devising a methodology which would regulate and differentiate the rate of growth across the NHS. All governments wished to solve the annual problem of resource allocation. Each year, however many additional resources were put in, they still appeared to fail to meet the criteria of adequacy. In 1976 the government thought that the report of the Resource Allocation Working Party (RAWP)[5] would give them an acceptable methodology and a policy for progressive moves towards the goal of equalisation, when it could be shown that everyone in the country had equal access to the same level of resources devoted to their health care. At first the somewhat elaborate system was accepted generally as a rational approach based on the best identification of need available, but during a period of national economic downturn its impact often appeared to lead to the deterioration of care in some places and extravagances in others. The speed of redistribution was crucial at a time of economic stagnation: some thought it too fast while others thought it too slow.

Where pressures on resources were greatest, in London and the south east, hospitals which were centres of excellence felt threatened during a period of 'negative growth'—departmental speak for cuts! Demand was demonstrably increasing: people were living longer and in Dr David Owen's words the ageing process was the "largest element of all illness in modern society,"[6] research and medical technological advances both cost more and could treat a wider range of diseases, and resources were not keeping pace. It was proving difficult to stand still let alone make progress.

In the face of increasing professional concern ministers searched for another guideline to help them. In responding to a report by the Centre for Health Economics at York University, commissioned uniquely by the BMA, RCN and IHSM, the Minister for Health, Barney Hayhoe, wrote: "I agree that as the report has suggested health authority services need at present to grow by about 2% a year in order to meet the pressures they face. It is the services and not expenditure that need to grow by 2%. Services are developed both by increased cash allocations and by greater efficiency in the use of resources."[7] Need would in future be met by a 2% growth in services from less than a 2% growth in cash through greater efficiency in the use of resources. This greater efficiency would also have to meet the increasing burden of the underfunding of pay awards that had become a chronic feature of the health service.

Ten years after RAWP, despite all health regions operating on a more or less level playing field, underfunding continued to be highlighted by the national press and make political headlines. In the run up to the 1987 general election the case of baby David Barber epitomised the problem. There appeared to be a shortage of intensive care nurses in Birmingham and the baby had his life saving operation delayed for weeks. When it eventually took place he died.

In the heated atmosphere of public anxiety over the state of the NHS the Prime Minister argued that NHS resources had increased during the Conservative administration from £8 billion in 1978/79 to £21 billion in 1987/88. But such explanations failed to convince the public who felt that they were being short changed!

RAWP

For the first 30 years of the NHS resource allocation methods had failed to address the nationwide inequalities which it was intended to eradicate. These inequalities were reviewed by minister after minister but still persisted, even through the period of the MacMillan years when we had never had it so good. There was a fear that the economic pressures following the oil crisis of the 1970s would exacerbate the position and this might well have happened had it not been for the RAWP methodology, which with all its shortcomings gave some hope of greater fairness.

Fairness was also an underlying principle behind the issue of the 1976 consultation document 'Priorities in health and personal social services in England'.[8] The time had come to try to bring the cinderella services out of the kitchen and on their way to the ball. The Secretary of State for Health, Barbara Castle, recognised that the NHS had always been not just institutionally dominated but also acute hospital dominated. She was determined that a fairer NHS, with equality for all, meant containing the ambitions of the teaching hospitals and Harley Street, and improving the poor, if not appalling, levels of care offered to the mentally ill, the mentally handicapped, the elderly and the chronically sick. This document was followed up with 'The way forward'[9] in 1977, and they together set not only long-term government priorities (valid until the internal market) but also specific development targets, expressed in financial terms, for the different care groups. Barbara Castle, together with her minister, Dr David Owen, developed and pushed forward both RAWP based allocations and plans for priority services, recognising that extra resources in one area or for one service meant less for another. There would be winners and losers but it was time, ministers believed, that the cinderella services started winning.

The RAWP methodology can claim to have had a significant and beneficial impact on the distribution of services across the country and to have changed the attitudes of both management and professionals. Ministers made it clear that "the underlying principle of RAWP, that of securing equal opportunity of access to health care for people in equal need" was here to stay.[9] There would be no turning back or lack of commitment. The only uncertainty about the implementation of the policy was the rate of redistribution, which would be for ministers to determine in the light of the economic circumstances of the time.

There was widespread agreement that relative need was best identified by measuring differential levels of morbidity, but because of the inherent difficulty of acquiring reliable and comprehensive data on morbidity, mortality was taken as a proxy and standardised mortality ratios (SMRs) were accepted as the best indicator available for need. However, questions were immediately raised about the importance of the relationship between socio-economic factors and morbidity, which seemed to be undervalued in accepting SMRs. The national formula, therefore, was population based, broken down by age and sex, and based on SMRs. As the legitimate and additional costs of medical and dental students' training and research were differential across the service and yet had to be accounted for in the formula a special allowance was included to recognise the service increment for teaching (SIFT). This formula was used to develop long-term target allocations and tables showing distances from target were published, which gave the relative position of all regions. The aim was to pursue a policy of 'equalisation' so that in about ten years every family, wherever they lived, would have equal access to similar levels of care.

In 1976 the recently established health authorities had to introduce fundamental changes to the methods of distributing resources. Part way through the implementation of the 1974 reorganisation of the service, a time of internal organisational turbulence and external economic crisis, they searched for ways to optimise the effectiveness of the new policy and minimise its disruptive effects on the recently developed strategic plans. Reservations about the sophistication of the formula were one thing but what was needed, and needed in a hurry, were guidelines for its immediate implementation. The burden inevitably lay with regional health authorities (RHAs), who had to determine their own internal 'sub-regional RAWP' from their regional allocations. In undertaking this task RHAs were given some discretion. They had to keep faith with the basic principles of the national formula but could make adjustments to take account of the peculiarities of their constituent areas and districts. In facing this task RHAs prudently took account of the following:

(a) the national policy showed the direction in which local health services and the distribution of facilities had to change. The blind application of the formula was clearly inappropriate and would have had disastrous consequences for local patient services;

(b) area and district targets had to be calculated, taking account of the statistical anomalies and other difficulties inherent in dealing with smaller populations. In many regions gross inequalities in resources were identified between health districts within the same area;

(c) 'the pace of change' within a region would be crucial. The sudden transfer of resources from an over-target authority to an under-target authority was likely to lead to a decline in the standards of care in the former without achieving value for money improvements in care in the latter;

(d) there were two major factors influencing the pace of redistribution. The first was the availability of capital money for new facilities. Regions had always used capital as the main vehicle for strategic change and the newly developed table of distances from resource targets led to the reappraisal of each regions' capital programme. New priorities had to take precedence over previous commitments. It takes time to plan and build a major hospital and the costs of abandoning schemes part way through completion can be considerable. For many months the strategy was in the melting pot;

(e) the second determinant on the pace of redistribution was the availability of staff, mainly but not solely doctors, nurses and other caring professionals. New services to patients are provided by professional people and most services are based in hospitals and health centres. Regional policies for changing the pattern and distribution of hospital doctors had to be reconsidered, with inevitable consultations and negotiations with the department, royal colleges and medical schools; and

(f) the politics of change were huge. Shifts in resources meant shifting entrenched attitudes. Endless consultations became necessary with local professional organisations, trade unions, local authorities, CHCs, and MPs. An anti-teaching hospital lobby developed and the costs of teaching and research were examined.

Every region had to abandon its strategic plan and develop a new one to take account of the movement of resources within its boundaries. In those regions gaining resources the new strategic plans were all good news because there was a general increase in the level of resources. Nevertheless, these plans caused arguments between the different authorities about the speed with which they got their better share of the cake. In those regions losing resources the new strategic plans usually consisted of bad news and less bad news. The bad news consisted of urgent cuts and closures forced on them by a reduction in resources for over-target districts, while the less bad news consisted of the inevitable delays before the new services could become operational in under-target districts. You have to take away from Peter before you can give to Paul.

Ministers, of course, were extremely concerned about the impact of the cuts and closures resulting from the policy, particularly in London and the south east where for historical reasons there was a concentration of expensive facilities and services. They announced that the policy was to be seen as a 'rationalisation' and not a reduction in services. Health circular HSC (IS) 207 (superseded by HC (81) 15)[10] set out the processes to be followed in which CHCs had the right to challenge any major change in provision. Where their demands were not satisfied locally their concerns were referred to ministers, who made the final decision. Local MPs were often prominent in fighting rearguard actions to defend a pet hospital project and in making direct representations to Whitehall for new capital expenditure. Regional management was under great pressure. They had to devise their own internal redistribution policy, rewrite their strategic plan in the light of these changes, renegotiate these changes with the Department of Health and satisfy the professions, unions, MPs, ministers and the public.

REVIEW OF RAWP

The RAWP system was central to all NHS policy for a whole decade and significant strides were made towards equalisation on a regional basis, although serious extremes of provision still existed at district level. The 1986 review[11] was intended to undertake "an analysis of the proxies for need for health services, including different forms of SMRs, social and other factors, carried out on a small area basis." For some years there had been a growing demand for the more effective use of socio-economic factors as measures of deprivation over and above the standardised mortality rates.

One critic identified the key issue as "whether an adequate model can be developed so that the allocation formula more closely reflects the 'need' for health services, defined in terms of characteristics of the population. Given the focus on small areas there are clearly severe practical constraints in the kinds of variables which can be included in a modelling exercise."[12]

The choice of appropriate data to reflect the variations in socio-economic conditions was limited to the 1981 census data.[13] It is true that the 1981 census provided data relevant to small area analysis but it was the general household survey which provided data substantial enough for the larger regions to offer reliable estimates for distribution purposes. The problems with the census data were that it was already out of date and some of the data it provided on key issues were limited. For example, in seeking ethnic minority data the census asked about the country of origin and not their membership of a particular ethnic group. This caused a distortion in the distribution of ethnic minorities between regions. Amongst the other shortcomings were first that there were no questions about income and second that the data about the proportion of people changing address within a year was meaningless as a guide to deprivation as it includes yuppies as well as vagrants!

It was the research undertaken by Professor Brian Jarman[14] that most significantly influenced the outcome of the review. He chose ten social factors for which census data were available—the under fives, unemployment, poor housing, ethnic groups, lone parent families, elderly living alone, overcrowding, lower social classes, mobility, and fewer married families. He examined the workload pressure on GPs and developed a 'GP under privileged score', which some people criticised for being biased towards London. By his scoring 12 of the 50 most under privileged health districts in England were in London and yet none of the 25 districts with the highest SMRs were located in London. Critics also commented on his inappropriate use of these social factors in determining equitable allocations to regions. The Jarman index was meant to reflect the need for GPs' services at local level, but with such wide variations in the weightings he used between adjoining electoral wards within the same local authority it was difficult to see how the data could be extrapolated and interpreted reliably for national allocation purposes.

Arguments continued, as they had done for many years, about the relationship between demand and supply. It seems logical that the population demands a level of provision required by their socio-economic characteristics (their needs) which is limited by any constraints on physical access. In turn, it is logical that the health professionals supply a level of service to meet that need. Yet logic does not appear to prevail. Most NHS managers will have had experience of predicting patients' flows prior to the development of a new hospital. Most know, however, that supply and availability influence the level of need. For example, the new Northwick Park Hospital in Harrow, a large district general hospital with a vast research capability, was expected to have a significant impact on patient flows to nearby hospitals in the London borough of Hillingdon. Waiting lists at Hillingdon hospital were temporarily reduced but the pressure on beds soon regained its former level due to additional population or GP demand, which had previously remained hidden due to the lack of available facilities. Morbidity in the community had apparently increased over the past couple of years and yet socio-economic factors remained unchanged. In reviewing issues of this kind the working party sought to make RAWP more sensitive to social deprivation and its report was as valuable in provoking further research and stimulating awareness of the issues as providing any clear solutions to the problem. The revision of RAWP would continue to dominate all allocation processes until the market arrived. Its success was, at a macro level, that it brought all regions closer to equalisation. Its failure was, at local level, that it did not adequately address the problems of social deprivation and the balancing of demand with supply. Perhaps that was too much to expect.

RAWP, of course, dealt not with determining the total volume of funding but only with its distribution. By the end of the 1980s the public perceived that the NHS was still suffering from underfunding. What was needed was new thinking on the provision of resources and the structure and style of delivering care: optimally a self-regulating means of handling supply and demand.

THE MIRAGE OF THE MARKET

Since the early 1970s the Institute of Economic Affairs had from time to time challenged 'the defenders of the most politically sacred of all sacred cows'—the NHS—and had attracted the attention of ministers searching in vain for an acceptable and reliable means of containing health expenditure, as well as retaining the founding values and principles of the NHS. The answer, according to the institute, was the power of market forces and in Hobart paperbacks Nos. 23 and 27 Dr David Green took to task Professor A J Culyer, of the University of York, for believing that "The marketeers' image of the market for health is a completely irrelevant description of an unobtainable utopia."[15,16] The market 'failures' of professional power, consumer ignorance and the uncertainty of demand for health care could all be overcome through a major element of private health insurance added to and co-operating with the NHS. The 'moral hazard', which is the change in attitude experienced by both the doctor and patient when the patient is insured and is said to lead to the doctor over-treating and the patient determined to get his money's worth, does not necessarily result in an escalation in costs. The situation in the US since the 1970s, Dr Green maintained, has genuinely resembled a competitive market, with hospitals reducing their costs and doctors cutting their fees to maintain their market share. Ivan Illich's contention that "the medical establishment has become a major threat to health"[17] was out of date. One by one the restrictive practices of the medical profession in America had been declared unlawful, so why could this not be the case in the UK? There was evidence that consumer power was increasing, with people being able to make choices between: (a) doctors, (b) the recommendations of one or more doctors, and (c) health insurance plans.

Dr Green did not accept that it was possible to create objective criteria for the non-market allocation of resources, arguing that "medical need cannot be objectively measured or predicted and resources allocated to match." Judgements about treatment are never purely medical and there are no experts other than the patients themselves and, therefore, he argued "it is the patients who must decide allocations through a means of offering them money with which they may buy services in the market." His theory was that the money should follow the patient. "Only a competitive market can reflect the increasingly complex character of medical decision-making."

The Institute of Economic Affairs developed a persuasive argument that it is possible to retain the framework of the NHS but improve its funding by ensuring that people who are dis-satisfied with the service "should be allowed to *escape* and to claim an age weighted voucher, representing the tax they have paid towards the NHS," if they agree to relinquish their claim to free services and take out private insurance to the value of the voucher. Those privately insured could receive care from the NHS if they wished as paying customers and "the poor could receive a voucher sufficient to buy a *specified* (not comprehensive) set of health care services." A two or three tier service!

The institute believed that there was plenty of evidence over the past 40 years to suggest that the government should not attempt to both finance and 'produce' health care services. It should finance only care for those in need to ensure that everyone has the power to buy insurance cover and it should not attempt to pay for it all from general taxation. It should develop a competitive market to service the interests of all, rich and poor alike, enabling people to make more effective choices and it should break the NHS monopoly. On the costs of health care "competition alone gives self-interested providers an incentive to serve their customers." On financing and taxation "centralised budgets allocated according to need fail to respect the individual judgements of the customer." On the incentives for improvement "private demand is preferable to government prescribed need." The planning of health care "stifles innovation" and "forces us to put up with inferior health services."

These views were undoubtedly taken into account as the government prepared its white paper for 1989. It did not, however, agree to such a radical voucher scheme but it was determined to create an environment for increased competition—its own kind of regulated market. It has as a result separated the financing from the production of health care services, not at the national level but within the NHS through the purchaser/provider split.

The experience of the market place in the USA is sobering. Our market, the typically British version of pragmatism and compromise, may well bring significant benefits to the service and the people it serves without destroying fundamental values and objectives. Times may be hard in the NHS but it is cheap at 6.2% of GNP and it is important to remember that 37 million Americans do not have access to health care because they lack medical insurance cover, do not qualify for medicare or medicaid, or because they are poor.

FUNDING THE MARKET

By 1989 the government's new thinking on funding and the style of provision had come to an end and it was time to test the market. Additional resources from voucher systems or extensive insurance solutions had been rejected and the conclusion reached yet again that the NHS had to continue to be financed almost wholly from general taxation. RAWP had succeeded because money had been evenly distributed across the country and no region could legitimately complain about unfair allocations. But at the local level incentives were being stifled and gross inequalities persisted. A new system of allocation needed to be developed to enable purchasers to buy services without the distraction of having to produce those services, which would ensure that money genuinely followed the flow of patients. This system was weighted capitation and was introduced progressively ten years after the introduction of RAWP.

In EL(90)MB/22[18] the department set out the new arrangements for resource allocation based on resident populations. A national model was developed to determine the regional allocations from 1990/91, which used a comparatively simple formula based on resident population, weighted for age and social deprivation, plus an allowance for the higher costs in the Thames regions—the London factor. The London problem of too many beds, too costly services and too few patients remained a major issue of political sensitivity. London needed a measure of protection. The market would not be allowed to savage its centres of excellence. The problem was kicked out of a level playing field and into touch before the 1991 general election through the invitation of a team, headed by Professor Sir Bernard Tomlinson, to come up with some solutions.

In implementing the new policy regions were given discretion to use the national formula unchanged for their sub-regional distribution or to make variations in order to take account of local factors, with the proviso that there should be a presumption against 'top-slicing'. This was intended to enable the greatest volume of resources to be allocated to the district level for purchasing care for their own resident population. The process which regions have generally followed has been:

(a) to use the regions' 1993 target fixed by the national formula as the starting point;

(b) top-slicing—the money required for central contracts and the RHAs' administrative costs, which could not effectively form part of the billing process between purchasers and providers, is taken out of the calculation at this stage. Top-slicing includes emergency ambulance services, SIFT, CHCs' administrative expenditure, AIDS, drug dependency and supra-regional services. As a result of the differential usage across the region what is left in the calculation is the capitation element for distribution to district purchasers;

(c) this balance is then distributed across OPCS population projections weighted for age and social deprivation;

(d) top-slice money is then added back;

(e) district target allocations are created; and

(f) they are compared with current allocations to establish the distance from the target.

The weighting for age is still based on the patterns of utilisation of inpatient and GP activity representing the acute and non-acute sector uptake. Social deprivation ratios by electoral wards include social variables like housing tenure, access to a car, socio-economic group, and metropolitan/non-metropolitan area of residence. Recent history suggests that it is these indicators rather than any strict measures of social deprivation that will increase sophistication and their impact on the allocation process, so that it becomes more sensitive to local needs. However, there may well develop a mismatch between the identified level of need and the availability of facilities and services. These will, of course, not be planned but will be subject to market forces, and who knows what options will be available to purchasers in five to ten years time when the market consists of large numbers of trusts trying to do their own thing and even larger numbers of GPs with their own budgets, each devoted to the small part of the local population on the practice list and to the professional and financial success of the practice.

THE OREGON EXPERIMENT
In the USA the medicaid and medicare programmes were intended to provide a federal safety net for the poor and elderly respectively. The federal government pays 63% of the cost of medicaid and leaves the individual states to make up the rest. In the early 1980s Oregon provided only a limited form of medicaid to those whose incomes were below 58% of the federal poverty level, but by the end of the decade the state government sought to extend medicaid cover to all those with incomes of 100% of the federal poverty level by rationing the range and number of treatments it would finance. It did this first through analysis undertaken by its health service commission (whose membership was primarily made up of professionals) and second through a dialogue with the community it served. The first part consisted of collecting data about health outcomes using Quality of Well-Being Scores (QWB) together with the cost of treatment and the duration of benefit, which determined the finance required to deliver 'a quality adjusted life year' (QALY). The public was consulted about the results of this work through random telephone surveys and public meetings.

In 1991 the state commission produced a ranking list of approved treatments totalling 709 items[19] of which the Oregon legislature agreed to fund only the first 587 items, although the proposal is still awaiting approval from an unsympathetic Washington.

Undertaking analysis of the comparative 'value' of treatments by the application of cost-effective criteria proved extremely difficult and as the magnitude of the problem has revealed itself so the emphasis has shifted towards community values and moral judgements. Thus liver transplantation for alcoholic cirrhosis was ranked 690th whereas liver transplantation for cirrhosis not involving alcohol was ranked 366th. This raises the question of what is the balance between clinical and moral judgements in the process of rationing health care and in deciding what to treat and how to treat?

Professional decision making will always dictate the priority of access to treatment and the way individual treatments are carried out. The community, however, can become increasingly involved in prioritising the allocation of resources in the main areas of health care, such as the cinderella services, and in commenting on the allocation of resources to individual treatment groups.

The Oregon experiment has stimulated a passionate argument between those who believe it is unethical to ration health care and those who are against rationing just one sector of society, such as the poor. There has also been a debate amongst those who criticise the absence of reliable data and contend that it ignores the fundamental political issue of cost containment. This experiment certainly ignores the 'need' level of overall funding and the adequacy of provision and it may stimulate the private sector to provide low priority treatments. But it does provide lessons for the purchasers in the NHS market. Rationing in secret is no longer an option. Having established the structures for purchasing teams and their alliances with various local agencies it will become increasingly important for purchasing authorities to open an honest and meaningful dialogue with the people they are there to serve. They should be honest in sharing the limitations of assessing relative health needs and health outcomes and in demonstrating the influence of the community's moral judgement on the pattern of provision of health services provided for them with their own money.

CONCLUSION

The funding of the NHS has proved to be a constant political problem and its apparent permanent underfunding a chronic disease. It raises fundamental issues about the kind of public morality which suits modern society. Can or should society continue to seek the ultimate goal of comprehensive health care for all, rich and poor? Can society afford such a goal and, if so, how can it hope to meet the costs of ever rising expectations? It is unrealistic to suggest that an increase in the percentage of GNP devoted to health up to the European average through taxation, a specific health tax or additional insurance would be the answer.

John Major's Citizen's Charter envisages a consumer democracy where you give the people what they think they want. But in health care consumer choice will always be ill-informed. Patients are better able to judge hotel services than clinical services and if asked to decide the latter will, with emotion, plump for 'high-tech' services, such as heart surgery and cancer research, with hernias, varicose veins and the care of the mentally handicapped coming low down on the list. Will the government persist, like its predecessors, with the paternalistic management of the NHS in which you give people what they would want if they knew better and in which major decisions are taken in an unholy alliance between professionals and politicians?

The Patient's Charter suggests that steps should be taken to enable the consumer to have a greater impact on the style and nature of the services provided, but in most market places it is the providers who persuade and bully the customer to take what is on offer. The Oregon experiment offered an innovation in the exercise of democratic power on health care in which the budget is fixed and rationing is explicitly approved of by the voters.

In Britain the internal market will be the new force for redistributing resources. It is intended that competition will optimise value for money, but if in the foreseeable future governments continue to allocate cash limited health budgets annually what will we get for our money? The hope is identifiable and measurable 'health gain'. But this can only come from greater efficiency and effectiveness in the use of fixed cash limits for the service directed towards priorities set both by government and by competent and sophisticated purchasers at local level. Government funding will continue to be on an incremental basis but if these hopes for improvements are fulfilled we shall receive an even better service from a comparatively small percentage of GNP and the people will increasingly get what they deserve.

REFERENCES

1. *National Health Service Act* (1946). London: HMSO.

2. Guillebaud Committee (1956). *Report of the committee of inquiry into the cost of the National Health Service* . Cmnd 9663. London: HMSO.

3. Crossman R (1969). *Paying for the social services*. London: Fabian Society.

4. Thwaites B (1988). *The grand dilemmas of a National Health Service.* Leeds: University of Leeds Nuffield Institute for Health Services Studies.

5. Report of the resource allocation working party (1976). *Sharing resources for health in England.* London: HMSO.

6. Owen D (1976). *In sickness and in health: the politics of medicine*. London: Quartet Books.

7. Anon (1986). Minister responds to professions' attack on NHS financing. *BMJ* 292: 426.

8. Department of Health and Social Security (1976). *Priorities for health and personal social services in England: a consultative document*. London: HMSO.

9. Department of Health and Social Security (1977). *The way forward*. London: HMSO.

10. Department of Health and Social Security (1981). *Community health councils*. HC (81) 15.

11. Report by the NHS Management Board (1986). *Department of Health and Social Security review of the resource allocation working party formula*. London: DHSS.

12. Carr-Hill R (1988). *Revising the RAWP formula: indexing deprivation and modelling demand*. Discussion paper 41. York: University of York Centre for Health Economics.

13. OPCS (1993). *General household survey 1991*. Series GHS no. 22. London: HMSO.

14. Jarman B (1983). Identification of underprivileged areas. *BMJ* 286: 1705–1709.

15. Green D (1986). *Challenge to the NHS: a study of competition in American health care and the lessons for Britain*. Hobart paperback 23. London: Institute of Economic Affairs.

16. Green D (1988). *Everyone a private patient*. Hobart paperback 27. London: Institute of Economic Affairs.

17. Illich ID (1977). *Limits to medicine*. Harmondsworth: Penguin.

18. Department of Health (1990). *District allocations*. EL (90) MB/22.

19. Oregon Health Services Commission (1991). *The prioritization of health services: report to the Governor*.

10

HUMAN RESOURCES

♦

INTRODUCTION

For decades central government and local management have both taken for granted and often abused their most valuable resource—the unfailing commitment of the vast majority of the one million people who work in and, more importantly, believe in the National Health Service. Since the establishment of the NHS staff have felt a strong motivation and deep loyalty not to their health authority, their managers, nor least of all to their ministers, but to their 'patients' and their 'NHS'. A sense of real ownership has always been strongly felt by the majority of staff who have found their jobs, poorly paid and unrecognised as they might be, personally rewarding and worthwhile, while also knowing that despite all the difficulties of funding, professional power and politics the NHS genuinely does its best to care for the sick and needy. It is in fact a hallmark of the civilised society in which we live and the staff are proud to be a part of it.

The development of an effective personnel function as an integral part of management was a slow process in the NHS as it was in British industry as a whole, where for years personnel was viewed as an 'add-on' function and often a job for the second class manager who had not succeeded in production, marketing or sales. In the NHS it was only as administration evolved into general management that the care of the work force was seen as a high priority and establishment clerks were transmuted into personnel managers. Even then this development was brought about not by an enlightened management which wished to seize the opportunity to harness so much commitment and motivation towards better quality care, but by a frightened management which was increasingly concerned about breaking its cash limit. Staff costs made up no less than 75% of hospital and community health services expenditure and annual pay settlements, nationally agreed but not nationally funded in full, put an ever tighter squeeze on local resources. It was the government's policy in the early 1980s of shrinking public expenditure, through such schemes as the value for money initiatives, the Rayner scrutiny, competitive tendering and cost improvement programmes, which consequently put a new emphasis on staff numbers and their most effective use. The fictitious statistical returns of 'whole-time equivalents', laboriously compiled and since 1948 submitted to the Department of Health and filed, were scrapped and Mr Clarke, as Minister, demanded accurate figures from each region and personally and arbitrarily set reduction targets. Undertaking at least the same amount of work, if not more, with fewer people in such a labour intensive industry put yet more pressure on management and forced it to take its personnel responsibilities more seriously than ever before. But Mr Clarke became the great divider. He divided the staff into sheep and goats, the 'front line' and 'non-front line' staff. The former might increase in number but the latter had to be reduced. Ministerial intention was strong and a wedge was driven through the NHS, which succeeded in disrupting staff cohesion in a way no less disastrously than the splits created by the union and professional association rivalry and battles of the mid-1970s.

The 'non-front line' staff, the ancillary groups of porters, cooks, cleaners and laundry workers, and the administrative staff (the admin and clerical grades) were all put under the political hammer. Their numbers, structures and ways of working were changed radically and they wilted under extreme pressure. 'Front line staff', 50% of the total, blossomed in comparison and did not undergo such a sharp appraisal of numbers and working practices. More doctors and more nurses was assumed to mean more patient care, irrespective of their efficiency. Gradually this split was reflected in the negotiating arrangements at the centre. The nurses and some professional and technical staff joined the doctors and dentists in having their pay determined through independent review bodies, a reward for agreeing not to strike. Those professional staff, like speech therapists, who chose not to join were left in the Whitley system, singled out for second class treatment.

Between 1979 and 1992 nurses' pay increased by some 260%, while ancillary workers, whose numbers had been drastically reduced as a result of competitive tendering, could achieve only 220%.[1] While in society as a whole the 1980s saw the rich get richer and the poor get poorer so in the NHS the gap between review body pay and Whitley council pay widened. It would not be until the reforms began to be implemented in the 1990s that the problems created by this gap could be addressed and old style central pay systems could be tested by the NHS trusts, who were to negotiate in an internal market.

When the Conservative party was elected in 1979 it was faced with an NHS in which many staff felt undervalued, underpaid and demoralised and their commitment to the patient had been sorely tested. The 'winter of discontent' that preceded the election had seen nurses, ancillary staff and ambulance crews taking prolonged industrial action in support of pay claims. Junior doctors were (and still are) disenchanted with their long hours of work and uncertain career prospects, and consultants had been arguing with the Labour government for the previous three years about their contracts and the amount of private practice that they could undertake. The reorganisation of 1974 had seen a steep rise in union membership amongst NHS staff, particularly nurses and ancillary workers. Even the professional associations had registered as unions in order to represent their members more effectively. At a time when unions were still a powerful national influence there was brisk competition among those representing health workers to increase their membership. Rivalry for nurses' loyalties between the professional Royal College of Nursing and the TUC-affiliated unions (the Confederation of Health Service Employees (COHSE) and the National Union of Public Employees (NUPE)) was particularly strong.

NHS staff had turned to militancy to combat a deterioration in their pay and conditions of employment in a service which they saw as exploiting the low paid.[2] The fact that senior and junior doctors had taken limited industrial action over their contracts had signalled to the public that the NHS was no different from any other employer and for the first time put to the test the ethos of vocational service to the community. So the incoming Tory government was faced with a health service that was not only absorbing an increasing amount of resources and likely to frustrate declared public sector policy, but which also comprised a restive work-force prepared, albeit reluctantly, to put patients at risk to improve its lot. If the government were to restrain public expenditure without a politically damaging restriction of services it would have to find ways of improving the productivity and morale of staff. That would mean changing working practices and negotiation procedures that stretched back to 1948.

WRESTLING WITH WHITLEY

The sheer bureaucracy and laborious procedures of the Whitley council system, which had changed little over the first 30 years of its existence, had been reviewed in 1976 by Lord 'Bill' McCarthy, a respected academic with NHS connections.[3] The General Council, the negotiating forum for general and common issues, and its eight satellite councils, each of which considered the pay of different staff groups, were the statutory channel through which national negotiations were conducted. These negotiations were ostensibly between representatives of NHS management and trade unions but in reality took place within such tight constraints set by the government that the union bosses knew where the buck stopped. They grew accustomed to by-passing Whitley and going straight to ministers when they wanted or threatened action.

In theory the system allowed the representatives of management and staff to have meaningful negotiations and to agree national pay scales for different groups of staff, with the Department of Health providing a co-ordinating link through the management side secretaries of all councils. These secretaries were junior career civil servants who were not usually experienced in the skills of negotiating and yet were in positions of considerable authority. They often used that authority behind closed doors or in corridor communications with national union leaders, which occasionally pre-empted the formal Whitley negotiations. They were clearly seen by both sides, management and staff, as ministers' men. Their negotiating shenanigans and back door agreements did nothing to gain the confidence of either the management representatives or the NHS in general. As concern increased, speculation grew about the advantages of creating an independent secretariat to run the Whitley system, staffed by skilled negotiators properly briefed by the department, the unions and management. This would have the confidence of all sides and would distance the process from ministers, who always complained of being drawn into the negotiations. Over the years there was much talk but no action. Ministers reluctantly concluded that it was better to be sucked in than to be frozen out!

The department, therefore, set out to mastermind the whole annual round of negotiations. The General Council, however, exercised little influence over the other councils, which frequently acted and negotiated in comparative isolation. The pay round began early in the year with the government setting in secret the limits on the total cash available for all pay settlements. The unions prepared their opening bids for pay rises and submitted them to the different councils. Although the staff side was fragmented and made up of representatives from no fewer than 47 trade unions and staff associations they usually managed to settle their differences and fix what was regarded as the 'going rate' for the year. On the subject of the acceptable minimum pay increases the staff side could often speak as one and thus make a better job of marshalling their arguments than the management side, which always appeared to be in disarray. This was not entirely surprising since the management side was large and consisted of NHS representatives who were almost all members of health authorities, many of whom knew little about negotiating and often little about the NHS itself. Their briefing arrangements were poor and fragmented. Management representatives, therefore, were often either not briefed at all or in a partisan fashion by their local administrator or matron! NHS managers as a body felt ignored and emasculated. They were rarely nominated for membership and were never appointed to the administrative and clerical Whitley council but senior nurses, for example, often found their way onto various councils and were suspected of 'grinding their own axes'.

Nevertheless, it was the managers who had to interpret the settlements and make sense of the increasingly complex conditions of service. They were prohibited from having any direct say in determining pay levels and conditions of service or in advising on whether they were workable or affordable in the local environment. So far as their own pay was concerned managers had traditionally looked to the administrative and clerical Whitley council. Their future, therefore, lay in the hands of NALGO, whose priorities were naturally focused on the vast majority of their union members—the lowly paid clerks and secretaries. Too often, it was argued, the unions main negotiating objective was flat rate increases across the board. Inevitably, over time such objectives affected differentials to the disadvantage of senior managers.

Lord McCarthy identified many of the problems and made clear proposals for streamlining the system and rationalising staff representation. His report stimulated a great deal of discussion and some promises were made, but little action followed. On 30th January 1979, during the 'winter of discontent', an answer to a parliamentary question in the House of Commons reported that "special attention was to be paid to training personnel officers and local managers in the skills and techniques of industrial relations."[4] Ministers were determined to shut stable doors after the unions' horses had bolted. For 30 years the Whitley system had been slow and ineffectual and at times had appeared almost to promote industrial unrest. By 1979 it could have been hoped that the handling of human resources would have reached the top of the political agenda.

The Royal Commission on the NHS also commented on pay and personnel policies.[5] Its report strongly criticised staffing policies and reiterated the warning that certain reforms of both constitution and procedure (tinkering with Whitley) were urgently needed. It accepted the argument in favour of some local negotiations to reflect varying circumstances and market forces but because the dividing line was hard to draw it supported the Whitley system in principle. "Standardized, centrally negotiated terms and conditions promote the unity of a national service." That 'unity' had almost been destroyed during the 'winter of discontent'. Some thought a unique opportunity for restructuring had been missed and for the next 15 years Whitley staggered on.

On the question of the right to strike the commission was equally unhelpful. It emphasised the special responsibilities of all NHS staff to patients but categorically dismissed the proposal that staff should forego the right to strike in return for compulsory arbitration. Sadly, although the report was pre-

pared during a period of increasing union unrest it offered few
original and helpful proposals for improving personnel and
industrial relations policies. It did recommend a TUC-led review of NHS industrial relations but this was hardly a
recommendation which would find favour with the new Prime
Minister, Mrs Thatcher, who as soon as she entered office had
the TUC in her sights.

Throughout the 1980s the pay negotiations followed the
same tedious pattern every year causing delay, frustration
and inefficiency. First, the cabinet agreed public sector pay
policy and fixed the likely levels and limits of acceptable increases in the NHS. Understandably, every effort was made to
keep these decisions secret to prevent unions treating them as
the 'going rate' and a starting point for the negotiations.
Second, regional health authorities (RHAs) were notified
about their allocations towards the end of the financial year,
sometimes so late that it did not give regions sufficient time to
allocate budgets to district health authorities (DGHs) before
the beginning of the new financial year. Every year the department responded to protestations by agreeing to make earlier
announcements and therefore allow more time and thought to
go into the sophisticated sub-regional allocation process.
Every year, however, it failed to happen. Third, the staff side
put in exaggerated claims that everyone regarded as tactical
opening bids, always related to the level of inflation and the
concept of catching up on previous low settlements. Fourth,
the effective date for pay settlements was 1st April but serious
negotiations did not get underway until well into the new
financial year. Fifth, delaying tactics were influenced by the
fact that all sides were aware that the eventual settlement was
going to depend on the cabinet's decision on review body
awards and on the level of increase agreed by the first Whitley
council to settle. These decisions would inevitably affect the
'going rate'. Sixth, a lengthy game of cat and mouse followed
in which the health department's management secretaries
sought in confidential corridor discussions to pick off the
weakest staff side and the group of staff least likely to cause
industrial disruption. They tried to keep that first settlement
below, if possible, or at least as close as possible to the maximum percentage increase allowed for in the Treasury's
calculations.

WHITLEY BY-PASSED

These covert negotiations by-passed the formal Whitley councils and often took months to complete. The first settlement to be agreed was so crucial that the individual management side secretaries discussed tactics for weeks at a time, trying to assess the comparative service risks of strike action against the financial risks of conceding to requests for high awards. The building and engineering workers were always given special attention. They had traditional links with workers outside the NHS, whose pay increases were beyond the control of ministers, and this comparatively small group could literally 'pull the plug' on the NHS pay negotiations. They could, and did at times, bring the service to its knees by 'going slow' in the boiler house, which provided heating for the wards, cooking for the kitchens and air conditioning for the operating theatres. This prolonged and clandestine series of negotiations were outside Whitley and quite often took place in parallel to the Whitley negotiations. At times the official management sides found themselves going through the motions of negotiation in ignorance of the real negotiations taking place behind the scenes between their own management side secretaries and union representatives!

This long drawn out process, conducted by junior civil servants who were undoubtedly bright but rarely had any training or experience in negotiation, meant that pay settlements were often not agreed until well into the autumn, which is half way through the financial year. Only then were NHS managers able to assess the impact of pay (75% of hospital and community health services' costs) on the cash limit for the year. By this time half the budget from April to September had already been spent, half the patients had already been treated and all health authorities had a statutory duty to keep within their cash limit by 31st March. It is little wonder that for years health authorities ran out of cash and started to close wards in the winter months, a time of great clinical emergency pressure. Management had the key role of balancing its books each month and this responsibility came to be significantly influenced by a guessing game. Each spring it had to estimate or guess the likely eventual level of pay settlements for the year and create an appropriate reserve, which health authorities were only able to release when the final agreement on pay had been reached. This guessing game became more complex when ministers introduced a policy whereby health authorities were expected to finance part of the pay bill through efficiency savings. Managers were then put in a position of having to guess not only the likely level of pay settlements in Whitley and the cabinet's decisions on the review body awards but also the percentage of pay rises which the government would underfund. These would have to be met locally through increased efficiency and other cash savings.

The annual pay round became a manager's nightmare, with there also being a real possibility of disruption to patients' services. At the heart of the problem was the Whitley system, which cried out for reform or dismemberment. But neither Patrick Jenkin, the first Secretary of State for Health and Social Services, nor his successor Mr Fowler implemented any strategic reforms. Even Mr Clarke failed to put an end to the unions' most cherished beliefs, although he did succeed in putting the management sides into better shape. He agreed that its unwieldy membership should be radically reduced in number and that regional chairmen should determine the selection criteria for management representatives and then undertake a selection process to pick the best nominees from across the NHS, from which he, the Minister, could make the final choice. He also connived at the Chairman of the General Whitley Council regularly meeting with regional chairmen for discussions on negotiating tactics. He supported the notion that that Chairman should take a leading role in co-ordinating the work of the eight councils within negotiating limits previously agreed by ministers in consultation with regional chairmen. At the end of the 1980s this involvement of the chairmen led to an annual private and confidential meeting which was staged in early winter. At this meeting the Management Executive and regional chairmen would be addressed by a minister and the next year's cash limits and pay negotiating tactics would be discussed, if not agreed. This was a significant step forward in making Whitley work but NHS managers knew that ministers were accustomed to playing their cards close to their chest and at times found themselves later in the year being trumped or pre-empted! Cynics might argue that regional chairmen and general managers were not necessarily

the best spokespeople for the NHS. Nevertheless, it was their
management initiatives and their increasingly close relationship with government ministers and the NHS's Chief
Executive that enabled them to have a more effective input into
pay policy than at any time over the previous 40 years.

THE 1982 PAY DISPUTE

The Callaghan administration had pursued the concept of pay
relativities in the public sector as part of a deal to settle the
widespread unrest during the 'winter of discontent'. Professor
Hugh Clegg produced his report in 1980.[6] The new Conservative Secretary of State, Patrick Jenkin, therefore inherited an
NHS staff who had become disaffected and the knock-on effects of the Clegg report on comparability, a policy of which
the new Conservative administration was highly suspicious.
Comparability had far reaching consequences and would almost certainly limit ministers' discretion.

   The nurses accepted an interim award of 9% for 1979, which
was subsequently and reluctantly increased as a result of the
Clegg proposals. In 1980 Mr Jenkin made a concession to senior hospital doctors by settling the long running, almost
theological, battle with the Labour government over private
practice by agreeing that all full-time consultants should be
permitted to work privately up to a limit of 10% of their NHS
income. This proved to be a significant concession, which as
time went on was very difficult to monitor and control. This
gesture ensured comparative peace with the consultants over
the coming years because when NHS pay was progressively
squeezed most consultants had a financial safety net in private
practice, thus lessening the likelihood of their being involved
in any industrial action. The new Secretary of State, therefore,
appeared to have taken steps to buy off both the doctors and
nurses without accepting the concept of comparability or any
other change of principle.

   In 1981 NHS staff covered by Whitley councils reluctantly
accepted a 6% pay rise, which was in line with cash limits,
having asked for 15%. Nurses had settled for 6% partly because the DHSS had also earmarked £116 million, equivalent
to a further 6% rise, to fund the shorter 37.5 hours working
week. For the 1982 pay round the Royal College of Nursing

(RCN) and the TUC-linked health unions claimed an increase of 12%. This time they all rejected the government's divisive offer of 6.4% for nurses and 4% for other staff, the cabinet having set a cash limit of 4% for increases in total NHS spending. The doctors, however, were offered a higher award and, with inflation in double figures, the RCN and health unions reacted angrily. The low offer and fears for the future provoked militancy among nurses as well as ancillary and clerical staff, and there was a short-term, unprecedented unity among the bodies representing them.[2]

May 1982 saw COHSE, NUPE and the National Association of Local Government Officers (NALGO) link up to form the TUC Health Services Committee and organise a series of one day strikes and other forms of disruption. The RCN, though rejecting the government's offer, did not take part since its constitution forbade its members from striking. The college did, however, run a high profile publicity campaign on nurses' pay. In June a one day strike was called by the health unions in which many thousands of ancillary, building, engineering, clerical and administrative staff took part as well as some nurses who were not in the RCN. There was a call for an 'all out strike' from COHSE, whose membership was wholly within the NHS, but this was not supported by the other unions. The industrial action continued and proved to be a major political challenge to the government. Nurses in particular attracted strong public sympathy and the wide media coverage and debates in Parliament fuelled public anxiety about 'their' NHS.

The Secretary of State for Health, Mr Fowler, kept his nerve. He was supported by the new Minister for Health, Mr Clarke, who was known for his refusal to be intimidated by vested interests. Ministers gambled on splitting off the RCN, which represented over 250,000 qualified nurses, from the other unions.[2] The college held the balance of power on the nurses' and midwives' Whitley council and with its no strike policy was seen, no doubt, as a more vulnerable target. But the RCN proved to be no walkover as a marginally increased offer was rejected by all staff, including college members, who held a ballot.

In June a commentator in the BMJ warned that the "Longer the present dispute drags on the more likely it will be that the

NHS unions will set aside sectional differences and operate as a unified body. Not," he added, "quite the outcome the government would want... ."[7] The unions, however, failed to settle their differences and the government offered further small improvements, resulting in a 12.3% pay rise over two years and, more importantly for the RCN, ministers offered to set up an independent review body for the nurses and the professions allied to medicine. It was proposed that the review machinery, which was to be run on similar lines to that for the doctors and dentists, would include the unqualified nursing assistants. The RCN was unhappy about this 'dilution' of professional skills but with the government wanting to influence the skill mix within the NHS's nursing work-force its determination to include the assistants was unsurprising and not a sufficient reason for the college to refuse the offer. The other unions that represented nurses, COHSE and NUPE, were also unenthusiastic as it would deny them the public sympathy generated by seeing protesting nurses on television and, equally importantly, reduce their bargaining power with ministers.

The review body appeared to be the long-term solution that the RCN had wanted. For the first three decades of the NHS the inability of the Whitley council to reach agreement on nurses' pay had often led to arbitration, recourse to the industrial court, or the setting up of special reviews. These latter actions were seen as essentially catching up exercises and what the RCN wanted was a genuinely independent annual review, which would demonstrate the intrinsic worth of nurses and maintain pay levels with the rate of inflation. A review body would also lessen the likelihood of regular confrontations with the government over pay. Doctors and dentists had shown that generally the system worked satisfactorily for them despite the occasional modifications of awards and staged implementation forced through by the cabinet in the 'national economic interest'.

At its annual meeting in November 1982 the RCN reaffirmed its no strike policy, accepted the review body and pay offer, and declined to become affiliated to the TUC. The unions were unhappy because non-nursing staff had fared worse out of the proposed deal but they were "caught between an (almost) unyielding government and a membership whose enthusiasm for militant action is fraying badly,"[8] while public sympathy for them was also waning. The cost of the dispute cannot be overstated. The cost to the NHS had been three million working days lost throughout eight months of disruption involving many thousands of staff. It had also been a traumatic time for health authorities and their personnel departments as well as for those staff who broke ranks trying to keep services to patients going. The cost to the public was, first, anxiety about what might happen if they needed emergency hospital care and, second, longer, painful delays in admission caused by a waiting list increase to more than 750,000.

TUC RULES—NOT OK

What had the strike gained for the government? Although it had compromised to end the dispute its determined resistance showed that even in the politically sensitive health service it was willing to confront the unions head on. The dispute was, consequently, followed by an industrial relations watershed in the service. The concession of a nurses' review body still left the government with the final card since it was free to modify and stage awards if it decided that the state of the economy warranted such a step. Ministers had also reserved the right to exclude from the review body recommendations "any groups that resort to industrial action"—yet another deterrent to militancy.[2] Apart from the six months dispute about restructuring and pay in the ambulance service in 1989–90, when Mr Clarke at some political cost faced down the ambulance union's leader, Roger Poole, who led an emotive public campaign for more pay and against restructuring, nothing compared during the rest of the decade with the 1982 disruption.

The government's determination to force industrial discipline on the NHS should be seen as an early manifestation of its policy to curb the overweaning power of the unions. The 1980s were to see the Conservative government transform industrial relations legislation. The decade was dominated by the miners' strike, and by the end of it the power of the TUC had been broken, the age of fixing government policy over beer and sandwiches at Number 10 had come to an end, and union membership was in sharp decline.

The effect of the government's desire to impose industrial discipline on the NHS was a significant change in attitude throughout the service. Management gained considerably in confidence and started to take the initiative in 'managing' industrial relations where previously it had been reacting to union sponsored crises. Shop stewards were less bullish in their negotiations locally, recognising a sea change in their relations with weakened union headquarters. The majority of health service staff had had enough of disruption and progressively came to see that job security was vital as the economic situation declined and unemployment rose. Even when provoked by government policies specifically aimed at improving efficiency through the 'privatisation' of services NHS unions had lost the will and stomach for a fight.

The policy of compulsory competitive tendering for catering, laundry and domestic services[9] had as its primary objective improvements in cost-effectiveness through a reduction in the number of staff employed by health authorities. Had it been introduced before the 1982 dispute it would have caused chaos. It would have been vehemently opposed at national level as the first step towards privatising the NHS, with strikes and general disruption across the country. Local shop stewards would have thwarted managements' best endeavours through endless, time-consuming consultations, and there would have been no co-operation from staff over submitting in-house tenders because in order to be competitive these would inevitably have meant job losses. In the event, the intensive programme of testing all these services by tender over three years, rigidly and personally monitored by ministers, was completed with minimum union disruption. In fact, regional managers had more difficulty with errant health authorities and their chairmen, who resented ministerial interference in local operational issues, than with the unions, which, except for isolated pockets, kept their opposition to a minimum. Within a decade the ancillary work-force had been decimated. The number employed by health authorities in the UK fell from 219,000 whole-time equivalents in 1980 to 137,000 in 1989, a drop of 37%.[10] Some staff were, of course, re-employed by private contractors (often on worse, yes worse, pay and conditions) but the majority lost their jobs either because a private company moved in and did not employ them or because the successful in-house bid was achieved only through slimming down the local work force. Most of these losses affected domestic staff who were one of the lowest paid groups of all NHS workers. This policy might have shown initial cash savings on paper, and might have improved management by forcing them to prepare detailed specifications and to monitor results, but it also drove the low paid lower and widened the gap between frontline and non-frontline staff. It also exacerbated communication problems with patients. The in-house ward domestics used to take the time to talk to patients as they went about their work. Staff from private firms were too busy watching the clock!

VALUING THE BEDSIDE NURSE

As with the pay comparability of NHS staff with workers outside the service, the notion that internal relativities should be maintained was not attractive to the government. Both would result in straightjackets being imposed on negotiations and would limit ministers' freedom and flexibility in addressing the demands of particular staff groups and in controlling overall costs. Pay differentials and relativities shifted during the 1980s to the advantage of nurses, partly due to the recommendations of their new review body and partly due to the introduction of an entirely new clinical career structure. The first major restructuring of the huge nursing work-force took place in the mid-1960s with the implementation of the Salmon report,[11] which set out to reduce over 200 pay grades for senior nurses down to 10. This was not enthusiastically welcomed by clinical nurses, who were happy at ward level and did not wish to climb the management ladder. The next restructuring was more comprehensive as it affected all grades of qualified nurse and was aimed at suitably rewarding those nurses who wanted to spend their entire careers in clinical care. This structure was designed by the Whitley council, which still negotiated conditions of service for nurses, after both the staff and management sides had found proposals from independent management consultants unacceptable. It was priced by the independent review body and introduced in 1988.

For years managers had complained that too many young nurses became disillusioned soon after completing training and left the NHS because of poor pay prospects. In 1987 a survey showed that nurses' dissatisfaction was extremely high as no fewer than 20% admitted to 'moonlighting' and 75% said that it was imperative for them to supplement their NHS salary.[12] The government decided to act and showed its determination to address this long standing problem of recruitment and retention by announcing some £800 million of additional resources for the clinical regrading exercise. It soon became clear, however, that the implementation of such a fundamental change affecting so many people in so many grades in so many different locations in over 200 district health authorities was a mammoth task, the like of which had not been tried before.

This worthy endeavour seemed doomed from the outset because the task of implementation was Herculean for the following reasons. First, the exercise was underpriced. The Department of Health had not consulted senior management about the costs and complexities of implementation and the lengthy processes that would be involved. Second, there was an inherent difficulty in seeking to guarantee comparable interpretations of national criteria for all grades across the NHS, and the RCN and the unions were understandably anxious to quote an apparently generous regrading by one health authority as a precedent for generous regradings elsewhere. Third, the Department of Health appeared to change its mind on the criteria as the exercise continued and as the high costs of implementation became more apparent. They issued further 'clarifications' and improved definitions of the criteria, which was not helpful and which provided additional opportunities for disagreement and delay. Fourth, an unrealistic timetable had been arbitrarily set by ministers without referring to those who would have to implement it. The period allocated to meet and agree a new grade with each of the 250,000 staff involved had been grossly underestimated, and the inevitable delay caused ministers a great deal of irritation and nurses frustration and disillusionment. Fifth, the number of personnel officers and middle managers who had the necessary skills and time to undertake this kind of comprehensive review was insufficient. Although the most strenuous efforts were made to apply the criteria fairly and quickly it was a substantial workload which distracted them from their core business of running local services. Sixth, the Whitley council appeals machinery was old, out of date and had been designed during an earlier era of industrial calm. Appeals against the local manager's decision on grading had to be heard first at district health authority level and then if the complainant was not satisfied the matter could be referred to region for a second hearing and hopefully a resolution.

At the start of the exercise nurses' expectations were unrealistically high as they hoped that clinical regrading would wipe out historical anomalies and reward clinical nurses according to responsibility, experience and expertise. They also expected the whole nursing work force to receive an average 15% increase in pay (placards held by protesting but arithmetically naive nurses outside the South Western RHA headquarters in June declared that "no nurse should get less than the average 15%"). However, the uncertainty and complexity of the regrading criteria, the perceived unfairness of their application from place to place, and the long delays in decision making for large numbers of staff brought new industrial controversy and widespread discontent. What had started out as a major boost to nursing morale ended by having precisely the opposite effect. As one commentator observed, "Applying differential pay increases to individual nurses at local level caused discontent, and differences in interpretation of criteria or in application of grading created varying patterns of grading outcome in different employing units. The result was that many nurses appealed against their grading outcome and entered an appeals procedure not designed to cope with the actual numbers of appellants."[13]

As time went on the exercise became a political and management running sore. The government realised that the cost of the changes had been underestimated and that it had to find a further £110 million to launch the exercise. The total bill of nearly £1 billion alarmed the Department of Health. The concern percolated down to local managers, who instead of introducing the scheme by objectively assessing the responsibilities of clinical posts were interpreting the new structure in terms of the old nursing hierarchy with seniority counting for more than skills and responsibilities.[14]

By the end of 1989 around 100,000 nurses had appealed against their gradings, throwing a heavy burden onto the local industrial relations machinery. Many thousands were still out-

standing in the spring of 1990 and even 30,000 appeals remained to be heard by the end of 1991.[15] In 1993 appeals still
outstanding were referred to a specially appointed independent appeals panel. Regradings also provoked divisions
among nurses in hospitals and in the community. The scheme
applied to community nurses but not to nurses working for
GPs, an outcome inimical to raising morale or standards of
nursing at a time when the emphasis was on greater teamwork
to improve services to patients. It was another example of
centrally negotiated and imposed change being translated into
action with great difficulty by local managers and under the
tightest financial constraint. Despite the huge disruption
caused the scheme improved career prospects for nurses and
by October 1992 the Secretary of State for Health was able to
claim that the average length of time that nurses remained in
the NHS after qualification had doubled from seven years at
the start of the decade to 14 years by the end. To what extent
this reflected the poor national employment situation or their
improved pay and career prospects is arguable.

FLEXIBILITY AND PERFORMANCE PAY—
A SPINELESS SYSTEM?

Throughout the decade minister after minister professed dislike of the annual process of central pay bargaining in Whitley
and the need for them personally to be dragged into the negotiations, certainly in the television studios if not in Whitehall
itself. The government's declared intention was progressively
to separate management (the running of the NHS by the Management Executive) from policy and politics (the proper
business of ministers). But everyone knew that it was ministers
who held the purse strings and so it was inevitable that they
would be dragged into the pay negotiations. One approach
which seemed to offer some hope and at the same time address
the need to provide local managers with discretion in pay was
the introduction of some flexibility into settlements. If central
agreements could fix base rates and the amount of the cash
limit available for pay to be distributed to health authorities,
then local managers could use it to combat the effects of

market forces in their locality by paying higher or lower additions as required. Such a system might be applied successfully to the lower paid staff, such as clerks, cooks, and porters, but did market forces really have any effect on the key professionals working within the NHS?

What opportunities might exist for flexibility in nurses' pay? Unlike doctors there has never been a centrally enforced limit on the number of student nurses, who have always been trained in numerous small schools throughout the country. In fact, ministers' objectives had always appeared to be that the employment of ever more nurses was an advantage in itself. The system of training had always been based on locally managed schools run within cash constraints and geared to provide a work force to meet the needs of the local health authority. When a school failed to provide sufficient staff nurses additional ones were hired from elsewhere through the offer of enticements, which were often more in the way of conditions of service, such as comfortable accommodation or seniority payments, than any real pay flexibility. Ministers did not contemplate flexibility for nurses' pay until the health departments' evidence was presented to the review body for the 1992 award. They then envisaged an annual recommendation for a target average percentage pay increase (TAPI), of which a proportion would be recommended as a basic increase for all staff with the balance available for local flexible awards and performance related pay (PRP). Members of the review body were sceptical, arguing that local flexibility and PRP were managerially separate exercises and so the suggested change did not form part of the 1992 award. They pointed out that without central monitoring of pay and of the supply of and demand for staff the Department of Health could not provide evidence of the effectiveness or otherwise of pay strategy.[15]

As for the doctors, the BMA had often warned ministers and review bodies that "market forces could not operate where the demand for medical manpower is controlled through, for example, limits on hospital and GP appointments, and the supply of manpower is constrained by the government's recruitment policy for medical and dental schools."[16] This had generally been true but extra payments had been offered for many years to attract GPs to areas of difficult recruitment, such as the unattractive parts of the north and east of London. In the future market orientated NHS could trusts use their freedom from central control to provide differential rates of pay and employment packages to attract senior doctors from other trusts and thus introduce an increasing market element?

Of course, one element of flexibility in pay had operated since 1948 and that was the distinction award scheme for hospital consultants. This scheme operated outside management and ministerial control and behind closed professional doors. It was run by a series of professional committees, some might say cabals, which voted their colleagues large additional payments. It had originally been intended that these additional payments should be made solely for exceptional professional excellence but the criterion of performing a useful managerial role was added later. The system has naturally attracted a great deal of criticism from other NHS staff and outsiders. A report by the Centre for Health Economics at the University of York argued that "The distinction award system should be targeted to reward consultants for the efficient allocation of the resources they use. 'Excellence' should be rewarded, but this must be done in an explicit and efficient way rather than behind closed doors and with unknown efficiency. It is surprising that tens of millions of pounds are spent without accountability and these practices run counter both to the goals of the Government's health care reforms and to good management practice in the public sector. Clinicians and NHS managers need to reform the "black box" distinction award system to ensure that scarce NHS resources are used efficiently."[17]

The scheme has certainly substantially enhanced the pay of over one third of all consultants and in 1992/93 it cost more than £13,000,000, when the awards ranged from £9,790 for a C award to £46,500 a year for an A plus award. Regional chairmen and general managers feared that the system had lost sight of its original objectives as it became clear that an increasing number of consultants were being given distinction awards shortly before their retirement, which of course significantly improved their pension benefits!

The NHS review was seen by ministers and the review body as an opportunity to implement some beneficial changes and to ensure some element of accountability. After discussions with the profession and the Advisory Committee on Distinction Awards the government instituted several reforms. All new and increased awards were to be reviewable every five years and age limits were placed on recipients. Awards could be cancelled or downgraded, with some salary protection provided, and doctors were given the right of appeal. The Chief Executive of the Management Executive would serve on the Advisory Committee and representative managers were tentatively and reluctantly introduced into the assessment process of candidates at local level. The award committees for C awards would be chaired by regional chairmen.[18]

These welcome changes were aimed at making the system more open and subject to managerial influence. Some hoped that it would become more like a PRP system for doctors. In its evidence to the 1992 pay review the department proposed, and the review body acknowledged, moves in this direction. The Secretary of State for Health suggested that any future reports "might recommend a minimum percentage increase, together with an average increase, leaving a margin to enable management to take performance into account."[19]

Such a move would certainly be a major cultural change for the profession. But like the nurses' review body the doctors' and dentists' review body (DDRB) had reservations about PRP and flexible pay. "Our collective experience is that performance related pay schemes present fundamental challenges to pay systems which limit overall earnings. When services are provided free to the consumer within a fixed budget increases in earnings are not funded by sales of increased output or reductions in manning. The incentive of PRP would be weakened if increased pay for improved performance was automatically set off against future pay rises." The review body suggested that PRP supplements, on a group basis within the hospital and community care services, should be considered and that general, medical and dental practitioner payment systems should be reviewed to see if they are compatible with PRP.[19]

In the early 1980s the government seized the opportunity of introducing competitive private sector practises into the NHS by responding swiftly to the Griffiths report.[20] They had intended the service to be managed, not administered, by a new breed of general manager who would be appointed on a fixed term contract (normally three years) and paid according to performance, which would be assessed annually. Managers had to forego their job security. Until then most hospital staff believed that they had been given a job for life. This was certainly true of hospital consultants for it seemed that only the General Medical Council or the Secretary of State could get rid of one, however unsatisfactory his or her performance. Most other staff were given a fairly free rein and attempts by a local manager to sack an unsatisfactory member of staff frequently led to appeals or threats from unions or professional associations, to a hearing by the health authority, and to reinstatement.

The introduction of general management broke new ground and changed the NHS culture as well as the Whitley system. First, it affected culture by breaking with the assumption that pay scales provided increases year after year without reference to performance. Under the new system if you did not perform well you would receive no pay increase and would eventually lose your job. This change occurred at a time when some Whitley pay systems had actually provided perverse management incentives. For example, chief medical laboratory technicians/ medical scientific officers in pathology laboratories had been paid according to the number of technicians they supervised. Therefore, during a period of technological change when there was increasing sophistication and the development of faster labour saving machines for performing tests the overmanning of laboratories persisted because of the need to maintain pay relativities between the Chief and the Indians.

The development of general management took one group (small at first but fast growing) out of the Whitley system. This was done arbitrarily by ministerial fiat and without consultation with the staff side of the Administrative and Clerical Council. It was clearly inappropriate for general managers, with a chain of command reaching up to the Department of Health, to have their performance pay negotiated by NALGO. It was regional chairmen who took on the role of the 'RGMs' shop stewards' in advising ministers on fixing the annual pay scales and performance rates for all general managers personally. At a stroke the most senior managers were prised out of the Whitley system and found themselves in the 'tender loving hands' of ministers for their future pay.

At first these arrangements applied only to some 800 general managers but by 1988 agreement had been reached in the Administrative and Clerical Whitley Council to extend the fixed term contract system to more senior managers who worked directly to their general manager. A 'pay spine' of 16 points was devised onto which all senior managers could be placed. By transferring to the new system, receiving higher rates of pay and qualifying for PRP they were required to give up security of tenure, early retirement benefits and to accept rolling contracts. This assimilation created a number of problems. First, many senior staff were most reluctant to give up early retirement benefits in the new authoritative 'hire and fire' culture of general management. Second, the new pay scales on the spine were fixed so that the maximum never encroached onto the top general manager's own salary. Third, the department, as always, was wary of giving too much discretion to local managers in the implementation of change in case it cost the Treasury too much. The implementation process was, therefore, closely monitored by departmental officials who argued with RGMs about individual cases in their region—yet again second guessing from their 'ivory tower'. They seemed to be particularly concerned about two points. First, that no senior manager should receive a significant pay rise for undertaking the same job. This attitude completely missed the whole point of introducing a new contractural relationship with no security of tenure and payment according to performance. It also meant that some personnel directors remained comparatively undervalued. Second, there was a belief that some groups of staff should not be seen to lose out during the transition. In particular, the Chief Nursing Officer in Richmond House was warned that if nurse managers at region, district and unit level had their 'management' jobs evaluated they might lose in pay relativities compared with their colleagues on the same board. They might also see disadvantages in future review body awards, refuse transfer to the new contracts and thus frustrate the desire to get as many professionals as possible onto the general management ladder. The result was that the Management Board Personnel Director sent 'confidential' messages to RGMs saying that they should place regional nursing officers or their equivalents onto 'acceptable' points on the pay scale, which was higher than initially proposed!

In the early years of general management a tough stance was taken on pay and performance but this was later relaxed. In order to retain good managers at all levels and in various disciplines the application of performance criteria became less strict and the offer of additional responsibility benefits meant that the actual pay received was usually considerably more than the basic pay offered. The history of general managers' pay is one which began with tough ministerial strictures (job security and extra pay only for good performance whereas poor performance meant the termination of the contract and the sack at short notice). Some five or six years later the situation changed when ministers withdrew and there was connivance between the Chief Executive of the NHS and regional chairmen and RGMs over adaptations to the national system to create a high degree of flexibility, which in time was able to meet each and every local eventuality.

The reforms of 1991 brought substantial changes to general managers' pay. NHS trusts were able to use their discretion in their pay of managers. The Chief Executive of Guy's Hospital, a first round politically up-front trust, was reportedly paid £90,000 a year in addition to a one or two car allowance and other benefits. Other trusts of less managerial and political significance followed in its wake, which sent shivers down the managers' pay spine! Differentials were erased overnight and general managers in the rest of the NHS feared that they would fall behind. What would happen to the pay of RGMs who were the ministers' shock troops for implementing government policy? What about the pay of managers who took over the all important commissioning role of identifying health needs, addressing ministerial priorities and using their purchasing power to improve the health of the nation? Something had to be done and in a hurry. But trusts were naturally possessive about their new found freedoms. Were the Chief Executive of the Management Board and ministers having second thoughts? Might the freedom of trusts to fix pay be constrained? The Secretary of State for Health wrote to all trust chairmen advising reason and restraint and the Chief Executive sought new imaginative ways of fixing the system, which as time went on was to prove the general managers' truly 'flexible friend'.

THE DOCTORS—CONSULTANTS AT THE CUTTING EDGE

When the NHS was established Mr Bevan bent over backwards to gain the passive involvement, if not support of, the medical profession. They were allowed to have a different status to the rest of the service, undertake private practice and administer a merit award scheme for consultants which the government had little involvement in except in deciding how much cash overall to make available. There would have been no NHS without these special concessions. Then ten years later they were allowed to have their pay settled by an independent pay review body with minimum political interference. Throughout the NHS's history governments have realised that the doctors have a special if uneasy relationship with them that necessitates 'kid-glove' treatment.

Like bishops NHS consultants are appointed for life, or at least it always seemed so. Consultants were given professional style contracts but, despite their salaried status, they have always had a freedom of clinical action and working practices probably unrivalled in western medicine. Until comparatively recently they have worked alongside management but been independent of it. For the vast majority their contracts and conditions of service have been administered by a doctor at region (senior administrative medical officer/regional medical officer/director of public health), an arms length involvement which has guaranteed minimal interference and virtually no control. The profession and the BMA have consistently argued that this arrangement ensures an even spread of well qualified specialists across the hospital service and also freedom from local political and management pressure. Most consultants have undoubtedly given more in terms of professional commitment and hours worked than their contracts have required, but some have abused their special privileges and attracted silent contempt but few strictures.

To dismiss a consultant, even for grossly unsatisfactory behaviour or professional service, has meant invoking a Byzantine procedure on which regional health authorities have embarked on few occasions and then with extreme reluctance. This is because of the lengthy delay (months if not years), the cost (tens of thousands of pounds), and the almost certainty that should he or she invoke the full rights of appeal to the Secretary of State for Health, to be heard by a committee of doctors chaired by the Chief Medical Officer, the outcome would be fudged and lead either to reinstatement or, in exceptionally serious cases, to retirement on grounds of ill health. Over the first 40 years of the NHS very few consultants have been dismissed from the service, which has led some cynics to conclude that either the NHS must be particularly lucky in the quality of its consultants or that it is virtually impossible to be sacked as a consultant.

Since 1979 consultants have had a more work sensitive contract and the ability to engage in private practice up to the value of 10% of their gross NHS salary. Since then private practice, and with it the earnings of some consultants, has continued to grow leading to concern in the media and among politicians over whether private practice is being undertaken at the expense of NHS responsibilities. A survey undertaken for the review body by the Office of Manpower Economics in 1988 showed that on average consultants devoted some 10 hours a week more to the NHS than their contracts required.[21] Nevertheless, by 1990 the 12,000 consultants who practised privately in the UK were estimated to be receiving on average an additional annual gross salary of some £40,000.[22] In the same year a National Audit Office report[23] warned that any further expansion of private practice would be at the expense of NHS commitments, unless either consultant numbers were allowed to increase or their contracts were changed. This came at a time when the government had already heralded changes in 'Working for patients',[24] which was intended to make consultants more accountable by tightening up job descriptions, bringing managerial influence to bear on appointment committees, and modifying merit awards and disciplinary procedures.

Consultants' relations with their employing authorities would also undergo a significant change with the establishment of self-governing trusts since the latter would be able to negotiate contracts with consultants as with all other staff. In 1990 a departmental circular, HC (90) 16, stated that "NHS trusts will be responsible for arranging the duties of the consultants they employ whether under existing contractual provisions or under such arrangements as the parties may agree."[25] All local managers, whether in trusts or directly managed units, were to agree detailed 'job plans', which would specify for the first time not only their main duties but also a work programme for each session (outpatient clinics and operating lists), participation in medical audit, rota commitments, and budgetary and other management responsibilities. HC (90) 16 also stated categorically that "there is no requirement for NHS trusts to take account of national agreements. They are entirely free to offer their new employees whatever form of contract and whatever employment arrangements they choose." Gone was the traditional and cosy long distance relationship with regional bureaucracy when the fulfilment of centrally negotiated contracts was largely left to self-monitoring. Now, for the first time, local management on the spot would be able to monitor work in wards and departments on a regular basis and would be firmly in the driving seat.

Contracts for junior doctors, however, were not to be left to the new trusts and management orientated NHS. Their terms and conditions were to be 'protected' in order to meet national agreements on medical manpower and teaching requirements. The unacceptably long hours of duty, which at times clearly affect clinical judgements, and uncertain career prospects of young doctors in training have long been bones of contention between the BMA and the Department of Health and, perhaps more importantly, within the profession itself.

As medicine has become more technical, treatment more intensive and greater numbers of patients are admitted every year into fewer beds the burden on all staff has intensified and none have been more affected than the junior doctors. The pressure placed on them has created a situation that is often dangerous to patients' well-being and a threat to their own health and domestic lives. The review body undoubtedly provoked a great deal of anger amongst junior doctors by steadfastly refusing to treat their out of hours payments on an industrial basis and recommending 'time-and-a-half', but instead insisting that extra payments should be calculated in terms of percentages up to 100% of the equivalent rates of a full-time basic salary. The BMA's Hospital Junior Staff Committee has argued that until health authorities are forced to pay penal rates of overtime long hours will continue. In 1990 the situation became so bad that Mrs Bottomley, faced with intense media criticism of apparent government inactivity, forced through the 'new deal'—an agreement to reduce hours to 83 a week by April 1993, with a final target of 72 hours a week by December 1996.[26] Additional staff would clearly be required and the government agreed to fund an extra 200 consultant posts and 50 'staff grade' posts, which were introduced in the wake of 'Achieving a balance'.[27] A National Association of Health Authorities and Trusts (NA-HAT) discussion paper on medical manpower reported on the rate of progress: "the reality has been that whatever targets are set, the most important factor in determining the rate of consultant expansion is the money available to pay for new posts."[28]

The real heart of the problem, however, is not to do with government inactivity or local management weakness. It is to do with hard cash and the need for hospital consultants radically to change the habits of a lifetime. Some consultants have been known to complain that they worked long hours as a house officer so why shouldn't their junior doctors. Some juniors have claimed that their consultant was not there when they needed him—at best he was at the end of a telephone, at home, at a party, or at a private hospital, if only they could trace him. The real issue is to try to resolve the internal conflict within the profession itself. Junior doctors' hours can only be reduced in any significant way through an increased number of consultants offering to be on duty or on call for longer periods and to be physically in the hospital for longer. This is understandably seen as a loss of privilege and a deterioration in their lifestyle, and presumably can be achieved in the future not through altruistic motives of a better quality of service to patients being given by better trained and experienced doctors but through financial incentives. Meanwhile, the junior doctors are aiming at the wrong target. They want to strengthen their resolve for tackling local management through penal rates of overtime, but are reluctant to strengthen their own resolve for tackling their consultants because they depend upon them for good references and for future career prospects. There are signs of change and improvement but the problem still persists.

MANPOWER PLANNING—THE SIZE OF THE PROBLEM

Until recently, the NHS has always been a politically planned organisation. The planning responsibility of all governments has been to fulfil the fundamental principle of equity of access to a good service across the whole country. This objective was at the heart of the 1974 reorganisation—to integrate health services across administrative boundaries to provide continuity of care—and guided the development and implementation of the Resource Allocation Working Party (RAWP) policy to redistribute resources in an attempt to re-dress historical imbalances in the provision of services. This responsibility has always caused particular difficulty when it comes to staffing the NHS. The size of the problem seems to be too big to comprehend.

First, there are the issues of timing. Political timescales tend to last the period of office of the Secretary of State for Health, anything from two years until the next general election which is a maximum of five years. The time required for strategic manpower planning clearly extends over longer time periods and it takes some seven to 15 years to train the doctors upon whom the quality of medical services depends.

Second, is the question of size. The NHS employs a million people from a variety of ethnic groups. Half of the work force are nurses, of which the qualified ones are trained in a large number of comparatively isolated schools that comply with the nationally required standards. All the professional bodies set their qualifications almost irrespective of management con-siderations, the availability of young people, or future service needs. Staff are employed by independent statutory authori-ties, which can frustrate national policy and intentions. To add to the problem NHS staff are also represented by over 40 trade unions and staff associations, each of which has objectives for its own members.

Third, are the fast moving service requirements, which are not just determined by the rapid medical and technological changes in clinical care but also by demographic shifts. In-creases in the size of the elderly population create new demands, reductions in the number of school leavers bring new pressures, and society's new perceptions of priorities and acceptable standards of care have major implications for forecasting need. An excuse for inaction has often been that planners are aiming at a rapidly moving target.

George Bernard Shaw believed that all professions are conspiracies against the laity and over the years many secretaries of state have felt the force of this epigram. The caring professions, whether they be doctors, dentists, dietitians, nurses, radiographers, physiotherapists or pharmacists, have all continuously sought to raise their qualifications and thus restrict entry and protect and enhance the power, independence and pay of those who achieve qualifications. The medical 'mafia' is a long established cliché but others of the caring professions have progressively sought to follow suit. Each profession tends to look inwards and often interprets the needs of the world around them in terms of what its members can provide. In an age of increased specialisation internecine professional rivalry has always brought problems to job definitions. So far as some nurses are concerned 'tender loving care' seems to have been downgraded and they want to prescribe, or at least become, technicians in intensive care and move further away from the patient's bedside. In the 1960s and 1970s more discussion took place on defining non-nursing duties than nursing duties. All those essential Florence Nightingale tasks of cleaning, feeding and recording were removed from nursing responsibilities in the cause of functional management, only to be reinstated in the 1980s when nurses discovered that they were ward and departmental managers of all patient services.

On medical manpower arguments had long persisted about the right number of doctors required to match long-term service needs. Various major inquiries have been established from Willink in 1957, two Royal Commissions on medical education in 1968 and on the NHS in 1979 up to the Advisory Committee on medical manpower in 1985 and the Campbell Committee in 1992. No agreed criteria have emerged and final decisions on numbers required have usually been determined by what the country can afford. The number of students entering medical school was set at 4,087 in 1974 and has changed little since. Over the past 20 years there have been major changes affecting the number of available doctors to which a sophisticated manpower planning system would have been sensitive. The emigration (the 'brain drain') and immigration of doctors, particularly from the Indian sub-continent in the 1970s and more recently—but in modest numbers—from the European Community, have ebbed and flowed. The increasing number of women qualifying from medical schools, now reaching over 50%, has had an impact since their availability is punctuated by family commitments and necessary retraining. Most of these developments have been ignored by the politicians and planners and yet the NHS has managed to cope, often by overworking junior doctors and exploiting overseas doctors who came to Britain for training.

In the internal distribution of doctors to fill jobs and to provide real career opportunities there have been some chronic mismatches. Shortages of recruits to certain specialties and the over-popularity of others have brought distortion to hospital career structures. A mismatch between training and career posts (the numbers of which were strictly controlled by a combination of tight government funding and the profession's fear that diluting the main career grades would adversely affect standards) meant that not all junior doctors could achieve consultant status, even when they had the necessary higher qualifications and training. Where there was no satisfactory alternative career and as general practice was no longer an easy option frustration and anger developed amongst junior staff. As early as 1979 the Royal Commission on the National Health Service suggested that the training pyramid should be modified and that a new career grade should be introduced below that of consultant. Again nothing happened. In 1981 the House of Commons Select Committee on medical education (the Short report)[29] recommended a rapid increase in the number of consultants to ensure that they 'provided' the services instead of just 'leading' them. Nothing happened. The next attack on career bottlenecks came in 1985 when the professions and the health departments set up a Joint Planning Advisory Committee to recommend quotas for senior registrars (subsequently extended in 1987 to include registrars), the aim of which was to match them directly to future consultant vacancies. This was a serious attempt to bring about a fairer redistribution of senior training posts. Those regions which were to gain in senior registrar appointments applauded the plan, while those regions which were to lose posts went out of their way to frustrate it.

The most positive attempt to make the most effective use of medical manpower came with the publication of 'Hospital medical staffing: achieving a balance'.[27] This suggested measures to promote consultant expansion, which would be financed centrally, to control registrar and senior registrar posts with specially designated registrar posts for training doctors from overseas, and to introduce a new career service post, the 'staff grade', the numbers of which would be limited to no more than 10% of consultant numbers. The proposal caused a great deal of controversy but eventually in 1987 the profession supported the agreement, the government promised sufficient additional funding and detailed plans were agreed for its implementation.

The fulfilment of the objectives of 'Achieving a balance' became interlinked with the implementation of the NHS review even before a positive attempt to distribute and redistribute doctors got out of step with the policy of redistributing resources across regions. The aim of RAWP had been a fairer distribution of resources and to provide equal access to good care. It is doctors who provide that good care and so it was a mistake not to ensure harmonisation between medical manpower changes and total cash allocations. By 1991, when some extra consultant posts had been filled, the NHS reforms had already moved the goalposts, because the more hospitals that became NHS trusts the freer they were to settle their own medical requirements and the less reliant they were on central intervention. Trusts would have to comply with the teaching and research requirements of national policy but if they wanted additional consultants and could afford them then they were free to employ them.

If mismatches between training structures and career structures had detracted from the most effective use of doctors other mismatches brought serious problems for the nursing service. "Few groups have so obviously found themselves in the midst of recurring mismatches in the supply of and demand for staff as nurses."[30] Until 1982, when the DHSS initiated reports, there had been no national manpower planning for nurses and local health authorities had been left to devise their own projections linked to their plans for service developments. Some 200 health authorities managed hundreds of nursing schools, which although professionally run and professionally inspected operated outside any kind of strategic co-ordination. It appeared to be adequate as long as there was a supply of young women, and more recently young men, willing to enter nursing, and the NHS somehow managed to carry on with a combination of learners, unqualified nursing assistants and large numbers of agency nurses. The situation was always precariously balanced and there would be problems if the supply dried up. Advances in technology, more patients being treated intensively for shorter periods in fewer beds, more elderly people needing care, and more nurses working in general medical practice have all fuelled the national demand. The demographic 'time bomb' was a phrase devised to indicate the dangerous situation which would arise at the end of the 1980s when the number of teenagers leaving school and looking for employment would fall dramatically.

A shift from learners to trained staff was the only way to cope and so there was an urgent need to optimise the use of whatever nursing work force became available. Between 1979 and 1989 the number of registered nurses in hospitals in England and Wales increased from 175,000 to over 190,000, with trained staff forming about 55% of all nurses which was a rise of 7% since the start of the decade. The reduction in the length of the nurses' working week in 1983 and the phasing out of enrolled nurses contributed to this increase.[31] The skill mix was clearly changing but what should be done to put the meeting of nursing requirements on a more stable and professional footing than the hit and miss system which had previously operated?

PROJECT 2000

In the NHS most hospital care has traditionally been provided by the unqualified and least experienced nurse learner. The perceived misuse of learners, the professional desire to raise entry qualifications, and the need to raise standards of training led to a programme of reform by the United Kingdom Central Council for Nursing, Midwifery and Health Visiting (UKCC), the professional board responsible for education and standards. Designated Project 2000 it arose from increasing dissatisfaction with the patchwork quality of training provided by so many health authorities, each of which had a vested interest in using the students simply as extra pairs of hands. In addition, nurses were seeking greater professional status and independence. For years nursing culture had been stuck in a time-warp with a rigid hierarchical organisation, which did little to dismiss the persisting image of nurses as the doctors' handmaidens. While direct patient care remained the central focus of nursing work—nurses are the only staff in 24 hour contact with patients—an ingrained characteristic had been the difficulty of specifying precisely what they did. Their duties overlapped those of other staff, including doctors, therapists, secretaries and porters. Their work was task orientated rather than patient orientated. "Traditionally one of the most valued attributes of the nurse has been her ability to cope and to get work done... they tend to be the ones to cope with the absence of other staff."[14] A nurse was not so much Jack but Jill of all trades. With nurse training still locked into the apprenticeship tradition Project 2000 had the formidable task of trying to bring it up to date. The report was published in 1986[32] and following consultation was accepted by ministers in 1988, who promised pump priming money from the centre. The primary objective was to make the learners full-time students, like students at university.

Innovators in the profession had previously persuaded some universities to run undergraduate and postgraduate courses for nurses (albeit the number trained in this way was small) and academic research into nursing was gaining ground. Project 2000 was aimed at furthering these developments by basing nurse training on institutions of higher education. The expectation was that instead of the student nurses spending 80% of their time on the wards, simply as pairs of hands, this would be reduced to only 20%. The three year course, modelled on a degree course, would start with 18 months of foundation teaching in an institution of higher education, followed by 18 months concentrating on one of the following: general nursing, children's nursing, mental illness or the mentally handicapped.

Despite the government's formal endorsement of Project 2000 and the promise of funding its introduction provoked a great deal of controversy and delay. Its supporters warned that without these changes recruitment and retention would become harder still and argued that better quality recruits would be attracted because of the integration with other courses of further education. For too long nursing schools had been small and isolated. The objectors argued, first, that the proposals were very expensive and would require immediate injections of substantial resources; second, that the NHS would be deprived of a substantial contribution towards departmental work and that learners would have to be replaced by other pairs of hands, maybe at greater cost; and, third, that a practical occupation like nursing was most effectively taught as an apprenticeship and that the timing was wrong as fewer and fewer school leavers were coming onto the market.

Once again the Department of Health, acting in good faith, costed Project 2000 without the sufficient involvement of NHS management, as in the clinical regrading exercise, and called for proposals from each region and drew up an experimental list of sites for investment. The money proved to be insufficient, the approval criteria was changed, the numbers of sites were reduced, the expectation and motivation of senior nurses were adversely affected, and progress was inevitably slow.

At the end of 1992 the National Audit Office raised serious concerns about the whole project's financial planning. Its head, Sir John Bourn, said that with £209 milion spent since 1989 it had proved a "radical and costly" change to education.[33] Health authorities and colleges had faced serious "uncertainties" because of constraints on the public expenditure planning process, failure of the implementation group to get a consistent policy for funding the cost of inflation, and the fact that the first schemes had to enter the 1992–93 financial year without knowing how much they would receive from the centre. Another sorry tale of central mismanagement. Judgement must be reserved on whether Project 2000 will achieve what its inventors intended.

The government had not only supported the new style of nurse training but had also endorsed improved training for non-professional support staff. 'Working for patients' stated that: "As part of this initiative local managers in consultation with their professional colleagues will be expected to re-examine all areas of work to identify the most cost-effective use of professional skills. This may involve a reappraisal of

traditional patterns and practices."[24] The key to the effectiveness of any changes in skill mix is in finding the right balance,
with for example trained nurses seeking to expand into work
customarily done by junior doctors or GPs while other staff
take on more basic nursing duties and routine clerical work.
Even in obstetrics, where for years midwives have practised
partly autonomously and partly under medical supervision,
inter-professional tensions still persist. In the future
boundaries of responsibility will have to be more clearly
defined and legal liability established, particularly important
in an era of greater patient litigation. But most important of all
the quality of patient care must be protected. Some professionals fear that in the search for a more cost-effective skill mix
management may be tempted to choose the cheaper option.
Some research in the North Western RHA suggested that like
the move from institutional care to caring in the community a
move towards the greater use of unqualified staff might both
raise costs and lower standards. A larger study commissioned
by the Department of Health and undertaken by the Centre for
Health Economics at the University of York examined the links
between inputs into the nursing process and the output, in
terms of quality and outcomes of care. The authors found that
the higher the grade/skill of the nurse providing the care the
better was the outcome, as might be expected. They concluded:
"Investment in employing qualified staff, providing post-
qualification training and developing effective methods of
organising nursing care appeared to pay dividends in the delivery of good quality patient care."[34] The NHS will
undoubtedly get the quality of patient care it pays for, with the
implication that if nursing skills are too diluted by non-professional support staff quality will fall. Patients value nurses
above all other staff: it is they who give the personal, 24 hour
a day service. Purchasing authorities would be well advised to
seek quality first and competitive prices second and pay special attention to the nurse mix contribution to care. Attempts
by providers, in a search for cost-efficiency, to lessen the cost
of nursing care may prove to be a false economy and lead to
the loss of contracts.

Between September 1990 and September 1991 the proportion of qualified staff fell from 61.4% to 58.75%, while the
proportion represented by unqualified workers rose from

24.1% to 28.4% and that of the learners was reduced from 14.5% to 12.9%. Clearly, the nursing juggernaut may be slowly altering course but good sense and good management will be needed to determine the professional boundaries and skill mix balance to the patients' advantage. These changes must be introduced sensitively by general management with appropriate professional advice. But the problem is still that "nursing management and the quality of nursing advice available to general managers within the NHS are commonly agreed to leave a great deal to be desired in terms of both content and effectiveness."[35]

DON'T FORGET THE PAMs

The supply of qualified staff for the professions allied to medicine (PAMS) has often been ignored and, like that of the doctors and dentists, has been influenced by the professional bodies which set the curricula and examination standards for students. Most of these professions have training linked to the hospital for which students provide a service element. These staff can, of course, work in the private sector and many do. Over 40,000 work in the NHS, of whom 32,000 have professional qualifications. Physiotherapists and radiographers each make up a third of the professional group with dietitians, chiropodists, orthoptists and occupational therapists making up the remaining third. The work force has a number of peculiar characteristics: it is young, 80% of them are women and over a third of them work part-time.[36]

The training of PAMs has always been fragmented and unco-ordinated and demand forecasts have received little study. In 1987 the National Audit Office criticised the inadequate attention given to ensuring that the numbers entering training were sufficient to provide an "adequate and appropriate supply of new blood into the service."[37] It also condemned professional bodies for unilaterally increasing the minimum qualifications required for entry, thus adversely affecting the manpower position. This was a further example of how neither the department nor health authorities had much direct control over the numbers constituting a group of staff, most of whom they would be training and employing.

There have never been any useful criteria devised for determining the number of PAMs staff that are needed in the NHS and because of their lack of political influence due to their small numbers the matter has never been a management priority. Recruitment has always been difficult nationally but particularly in London, where in 1992 30% of qualified PAMS staff left their posts annually compared with the national figure of 18%.[38] In the reformed NHS GP fundholders may well find it an attractive proposition to employ more of their own physiotherapists instead of buying services from trusts and DMUs, and this, combined with the attractions of the private sector, add to the uncertainty over the numbers available for the rest of the NHS and future forecasts of need. Some shortages could be made up in part by the use of 'generic health care assistants', who are trained within the framework of the National Council for the Vocational Qualifications, but trusts and DMUs will need to develop dynamic employment policies and packages if they are to attract and retain their share of PAMs to maintain services as they become increasingly in short supply.

CONCLUSION

What is the position of human resources within the NHS in the 1990s, 45 years after its creation? Even though for more than a decade the government has extolled greater devolution pay bargaining is still centralised under the direct control of ministers at Richmond House. Perhaps this is inevitable because the staff cost almost three quarters of the £35 billion a year spent on the NHS, but one can hope that the reforms will progressively lead to fewer pay settlements being determined from the centre and for more flexible packages being developed at the local level.

In recent years NHS staff have clearly become divided into two distinct camps. The frontline staff have their pay settled by cabinet decisions based on independently assessed review body awards. The non-frontline staff have their pay fixed in the old Whitley councils, where in theory management and staff representatives fight it out but in reality ministers dictate negotiating limits and junior civil servants try to fix deals behind the scenes. The only link between the two different systems, to see that there is fair play, is the Secretary of State in the cabinet.

Proposals for the closer involvement of professionals in management and for optimising the cost-effectiveness of their skills have not been successful. First, fewer doctors and nurses have become general managers than hoped for. Second, the development of the resource management initiative has had an uneven impact at hospital level, with too little commitment and support from the medical profession. Third, the divide between doctors and managers has narrowed but it has been a postponed marriage of convenience. Fourth, attempts to re-structure nursing and create improved rewards for staff who wish to remain at the patient's bedside backfired, while the clinical grading exercise demonstrated the near impossibility of satisfactorily influencing by edict from the centre the pay and promotion opportunities of such a large work force. In terms of training the centre has tried with only limited success to change the very concept of professional education and the training of nurses. It has facilitated and financed more of the former than the latter and received few plaudits for its efforts.

To improve management training the NHS Training Authority was established as an independent special health authority and subsequently became a directorate of the Management Executive. It was intended to give a sense of direction, to create a national training strategy, and to provide a cohesive force for the integration of programmes developed by health authorities, universities, business schools and independent bodies, like the King's Fund and the Nuffield Trust. Despite the fact that the old special health authority and the new directorate have generally failed to gain the confidence of NHS senior managers its success might well come from the new management development strategy for the 1990s and the development of employment related vocational qualifications as part of the work required by the National Council for Vocational Qualification. This positive push from the centre may yet stimulate local management into recognising that "major investment is needed in management education and training to bring about the changes required and to secure the delivery of high quality services."[10]

Ministers have wisely stayed clear of direct involvement in details of professional training, with the exception of Project 2000, but here again, like the clinical grading exercise, the motivation was good and the intention was clear but the means of implementation proved too complicated to obtain quick and effective delivery. There appears to be too many nurses, working 24 hours a day, in too many locations and with too lengthy a chain of communication for there to be an effective translation of policy into real changes in local practice.

There has always been a tight control on medical student numbers but more recently strenuous efforts have been made to goad the profession into accepting new grades, new work patterns and new career opportunities to optimise their input into patient care. Disciplinary procedures have been simplified and the merit award system has been made more acceptable and more accountable. Despite the independent and privileged position of the profession central attempts at manpower control have proved to be more effective with the doctors than with any other NHS staff.

Few attempts have been made with other types of staff to forecast need and plan the recruitment and training required to meet that need, which is probably wise. Ministers have usually singled out a particular group of staff as a target and have acted obliquely through a particular policy. The competitive tendering exercise set out to obtain better value for money and was particularly successful in saving cash in the short-term. It was uniquely successful in reducing staff numbers by partial privatisation and in doing so further weakened the power of the NHS unions. Another policy of cutting management costs and reducing the administrative bureaucracy had some success in the early 1980s when the numbers of administrative and clerical staff (a vague heading) fell, but this trend found itself in conflict with another policy—the introduction of the reforms. Administration had always been a dirty word. Improved management to achieve ministerial objectives was politically acceptable even if it did result in a huge increase in the numbers of 'admin and clerical' staff.

Since 1979 ministerial policy and intervention on personnel matters has generally failed to meet the policy objective. It has failed to cut the gross costs of the NHS and failed to reduce the overall numbers of staff working in it. It has, however, shifted the balance between staff groups with the emphasis now being placed on direct patient care. Today there are more doctors and dentists in the hospital and the community than ever before and amongst them there are many more female doctors.

The nursing work-force has shown the largest increase to over 400,000, and professional and technical staff have shown a sufficient increase to keep in step with technological demands and opportunities being offered by modern medicine. This may sound like a success story but to Eric Caines, Personnel Director on the NHS Management Executive, it was not. On retiring in 1993 to a post in academia he claimed that the NHS's one million staff should be cut to 800,000 and he targeted the health professions as possessing the greatest potential for productivity gains—gains that ministers, senior civil servants and the management have failed to achieve "for fear of offending" the professionals.[39]

Attempts to improve management and the management of human resources have had a mixed success. The development of general management following the Griffiths report has been spectacularly successful in creating a strong management chain of command from hospital to the department and ministerial level. Ministers can issue general policy, rely on its implementation and monitor its effectiveness as never before. The success of the 1991 reforms owes much to a handful of committed and loyal general managers.

But has the management of human resources kept pace? A survey by questionnaire which was sent to all NHS personnel directors and deputy general managers in May 1992 suggested that it has not. The report by Professor David Guest of Birkbeck College and Richard Peccei of the London School of Economics[40] provided an "effectiveness index" and identified both strengths and weaknesses. The strengths included industrial relations policy and recruitment systems but those areas that are crucial in the new market culture—negotiating pay and reward packages, staff appraisal and manpower planning—were in a cluster of topics near the bottom of the index. If the growing numbers of trusts are to take advantage of devolved powers and local freedoms there is still much to be done in the development of personnel skills as a central feature of improved management. After 45 years the personnel capability is still weak. The committed and loyal NHS staff deserve better.

A lesson learnt slowly over the decade is that better management means better communications, better use of human resources and better patient care. The NHS is essentially the people who work in it, giving care to those who need it: a personal service by a committed staff. The changes introduced by government policy over the past decade, culminating in the 1991 reforms and the internal market, will only succeed if they have the understanding, support and goodwill of the workforce. Too often intervention from the centre has failed to capitalise on that goodwill upon which the future of quality care depends.

REFERENCES

1. Department of Health. *Health and personal social services statistics for England 1979*. London: HMSO, 1979 et seq.
2. Salvage J (1991). *The politics of nursing*. Oxford: Butterworth-Heinemann.
3. Department of Health and Social Security (1976). *Making Whitley work*. (McCarthy report). London: DHSS.
4. Anon (1979). Questions in the Commons: industrial relations in the NHS. *BMJ* 1: 562.
5. *Report of the Royal Commission on the National Health Service* (1979). Cmnd 7615. London: HMSO.
6. Standing Commission on pay comparability (1980). *Report 3: nurses and midwives*. (Clegg report). London: HMSO.
7. Anon (1992). The week. *BMJ* 284 : 1885.
8. Anon (1992). The week. *BMJ* 285: 1669.
9. Department of Health and Social Security (1983). *Competitive tendering in the provision of domestic, catering and laundry services*. HC 83(18).
10. National Association of Health Authorities and Trusts (1991). *NHS handbook. 7th edition*. Basingstoke: Macmillan.
11. Ministry of Health and Scottish Home and Health Department (1966). *Report of the committee on senior nursing staff structure*. (Salmon Report). London: HMSO.
12. Waite R, Buchan J, Thorcas J (1989). *Nurses in and out of work*. IMS report 170. Brighton: University of Brighton Institute of Manpower Studies.
13. Buchan J (1992). *Flexibility or fragmentation? Trends and prospects in nurses pay*. Briefing paper 13. London: King's Fund Institute.
14. Beardshaw V, Robinson R (1990). *New for old: prospects for nursing in the 1990s*. Research report 8. London: King's Fund Institute.
15. Review Body for nursing staff, midwives, health visitors, and professions allied to medicine (1992). *9th report on nursing staff, midwives and health visitors*. Cm1811. London: HMSO.
16. *Review Body on doctors' and dentists' remuneration* (1992). 22nd report. Cmnd 1813. London: HMSO.
17. Bloor K, Maynard A (1992). *Rewarding excellence? Consultants' distinction*

awards and the need for reform. Discussion paper 100. York: Centre for Health Economics, University of York.

18. Central Consultants and Specialists Committee (1990). *Consultants' guide for the 1990s.* London: BMA.

19. *Review Body on doctors' and dentists' renumeration* (1992). Twenty second report. London: HMSO.

20. Griffiths report (1983). *NHS management inquiry.* London: DHSS.

21. *Review Body on doctors' and dentists' remuneration* (1989). Nineteenth report 1989. London: HMSO.

22. Laing & Buisson (1992). *Laing's review of private healthcare 1992–93.* London: Laing & Buisson.

23. National Audit Office (1990). *The NHS and independent hospitals.* London: HMSO.

24. Secretaries of State for Health, Wales, Northern Ireland and Scotland (1989).*Working for patients.* CM555. London: HMSO.

25. Department of Health and Social Security (1990). *Consultants' contracts and job plans.* HC(90)16.

26. Department of Health (1990). *The heads of agreement on junior doctors' hours of work.* London: HMSO.

27. A report issued on behalf of the UK health departments, the Joint Consultants Committee and chairmen of regional health authorities (1987). *Hospital medical staffing: achieving a balance.* London: DHSS.

28. National Association of Health Authorities and Trusts (1992). *Medical manpower training and hospital career structure.* Birmingham: NAHAT.

29. House of Commons Social Services Committee (1981). *Fourth report of the session 1980–81: medical education.* HC31.

30. Long AF, Mercer G (1987). *Health manpower: planning, production and management.* London: Croom Helm.

31. Department of Health (1992). *Health and personal social services statistics for England.* London: HMSO.

32. United Kingdom Central Council for Nursing, Midwifery and Health Visiting (1986). *Project 2000: a new preparation for practice.* London: United Kingdom Central Council for Nursing, Midwifery and Health Visiting.

33. National Audit Office (1992). *Nursing education: implementation of Project 2000 in England.* London: HMSO.

34. Carr-Hill R, Dixon P, Gibbs I et al. (1992). *Skill mix and the effectiveness of nursing care.* York: University of York Centre for Health Economics.

35. Schong P, Robinson J (1988). *New model management: Griffiths and the NHS.* Coventry: University of Warwick Nursing Policy Studies Centre.

36. Buchan J, Pike G (1989). *PAMS into the 1990s. Professions allied to medicine: the wider labour market context.* IMS report 175. Brighton: University of Brighton Institute of Manpower studies.

37. National Audit Office (1987). *NHS: control over professional and technical manpower*. London: HMSO.

38. Seccome I, Buchan J (1992). *Health care labour markets: supply and change in London*. London: King's Fund. Initiative working paper 10.

39. Caines E (1993). Amputation is crucial to the patient's health. *Guardian* 11 May, 20.

40. Personnel Division, NHS Management Executive (1992). *The effectiveness of personnel management in the NHS*. (Unpublished).

11

MANAGEMENT AND ACCOUNTABILITY

————— ◆ —————

INTRODUCTION

The political strategy pursued by successive administrations since 1979 has been driven by a number of political objectives with direct relevance to the NHS:

(a) decentralisation, devolution and deregulation (lessening the control of Whitehall and limiting the power of, and the central support for, local government);

(b) stimulating the business enterprise culture through low taxation, low inflation, lower interest rates and less political intervention; and

(c) testing the efficiency and costs of the public sector, reviewing public services, and, through the Citizen's Charter and its multifarious programs, seeking to introduce a new sense of dynamic responsiveness to people's wishes and needs.

Although these are consistent themes of government policy it appears that its attitude towards the NHS has not been based on any clear strategy or vision for the future but rather has manifested itself in a process of frequent interventions, often to meet political expedient. The service has been subjected to a large number of central initiatives to improve the efficiency (and later the effectiveness) of management within the NHS. The 1970s was a decade characterised by a belief in the value of comprehensive planning, such as the 1974 reorganisation with its standardised administrative structures (the Grey Book).[1] The 1980s placed an emphasis on improvements in management to deliver value for money services. The 1980s saw considerable achievements in increased productivity and improvements in management efficiency. The 1990s have begun with a belief in the market to provide management incentives for greater effectiveness through the competition for customers between providers, and to ensure the efficient (but not necessarily equitable) distribution of resources across the country.

The NHS has been consistently stimulated, provoked and reorganised, with more sticks than carrots, and often with no prior testing of the proposals for change nor any monitoring of the outcome. This has meant that although the changes have revolutionised management style and practice this has had until recently only a limited impact on professional attitudes and behaviour and on the nature of the services provided for the sick. The changes proposed for the 1990s are aimed not only at improving management within the service but also at breaking the mould and introducing new dynamics into the system.

CHANGING ADMINISTRATORS INTO GENERAL MANAGERS INTO CHIEF EXECUTIVES

The government's key objectives in implementing the recommendations of the Management Inquiry by Sir Roy Griffiths[2] were to create a new business management culture at all levels in the NHS and to improve the management leadership role of the centre. The former was aimed at breaking the bureaucracy, with its professional autonomy, and placed the emphasis on cost-effectiveness to get better value for money from the huge slice of public sector expenditure devoted to health care. The latter was part of the policy of 'cutting the civil service down to size' and making it a more willing tool of government and less an independent and loose player in the game. Governments come and go but the influence of the civil service is ever present.

The speedy introduction of general management raised both concerns and expectations throughout the administration of the NHS. The concerns were about yet another reorganisation and scramble for new jobs and about conditions of service and loss of security following the requirement that administrators should give up their rights to early retirement and sign new fixed-term contracts. The expectations were about local freedoms, increased management authority and new opportunities for taking local initiatives to improve services. Administrators had always acted as co-ordinators and were increasingly held unofficially accountable when things went wrong, but complained of responsibility without power. The DHSS's circular HC(80) 8 had made it clear that administrators had personal "responsibility to see that an account is provided to the authority on how its policies and priorities are being implemented."[3] Many hoped that as general managers they would be given authority and influence commensurate with their personal responsibility.

Concerns had been heightened by bullish statements by the Minister of State, Mr Clarke, who frequently not only questioned the management competency of administrators but also their loyalty and political affiliations. There were, he feared, many reds under the bed, or at least sitting around the committee table. He wanted a new breed of general manager. Doctors would be given every encouragement to take up the new appointments under favourable and less threatening conditions of service. The Minister hoped that 40% of general management posts would be filled from outside the NHS by dynamic managers from British industry. However, the businessmen who were attracted by comparatively low NHS salaries were often those who had failed to make the grade in industry and were looking for a soft option on their way to retirement. The colonels who had taken early retirement applied for jobs with the advantage of the apparent glamour of Falklands War service, although it was feared that the complex nature and ill-discipline of the NHS environment might prove puzzling and debilitating. Doctors in general were not seduced by the attractive general management package and hid their nervousness of becoming identified with difficult decisions over resource constraints behind the avowed need to remain in continuous touch with clinical activity. Whereas the administrators were well trained and generally competent in fulfilling a demanding and sophisticated management role.

In 1986 it was revealed that of 188 district general managers appointed 113 had an administrative background, 38 were from outside the NHS, primarily from business and the armed services, only 15 were filled by doctors and sadly only five were nurses.[4] Administrators had clearly won out in the scramble for jobs because of professional competence and the lack of competition. But questions were asked: were they up to it, would they simply be better paid bureaucrats, would they respond to the challenge, and could they provide a new style and much needed visible leadership?

The development of general management was given a mixed reception in the NHS. It was perceived by many to be the introduction of macho management into a multidisciplinary and professionally dominated environment. Fears were expressed that the emphasis would be on quick, not necessarily sound, decision making and that individual accountability would lead to an autocratic style of management with little or inadequate time for consultation with professionals. Concern was also expressed that all those who cared for patients would lose their essential influence in determining local affairs. In June 1984 Mr Norman Fowler, Secretary of State, stressed the value of modified consensus, although this did little to stem a hostile reception. "There is no question of throwing consensus out of the window. Consensus is vital to the management of any organisation. But this should not mean that decisions are ducked or avoided."[5] The professional organisations were not persuaded and their attitude remained at best one of suspicion.

The BMA had responded to the publication of the Griffiths report by supporting team management, rejecting a non-medical chief administrative officer (for had not Griffiths himself described doctors as the natural managers), and by complaining about the lack of adequate consultation—only ten weeks. If management in the NHS was in a poorly condition the right prescription was in the hands of the doctors. The nursing profession, on the other hand, was more concerned about the lack of recognition of its status and importance in direct patient care, the failure to guarantee its representation on the Management Board at the centre and at top management level in health authorities, but above all it was concerned about the breaking of the tradition that nurses could only be managed by nurses. After all, Griffiths had written that "in short, if Florence Nightingale were carrying her lamp through the corridors of the NHS today she would almost certainly be searching for the people in charge."[2] The role and authority of the matron and nursing administration had been undermined by functional management and the Salmon report[6] in the 1960s. The profession had gained in management confidence by being given equal status in the consensus teams of the 1974 reorganisation, but 10 years later the Griffiths recommendations might cause the profession further and irreparable harm.

The Royal College of Nursing, the Royal College of Midwives and the Association of Nurse Administrators contributed voluble criticism of the proposals in general, stressed the need for a trial period to see if they worked, fought to keep the direct management line relationship between district nursing officers and directors of nursing at unit level, and embarked upon a Griffiths advertising campaign. In this battle they were joined somewhat embarrassingly by their odd bed fellows, COHSE and NUPE. However, this campaign did achieve some modifications of the proposals. The Chief Nursing Officer was appointed to the Management Board, a little late in the day to provide real central nursing leadership, and health authorities were required to include in management arrangements a named senior nurse, who had direct access to the health authority and could advise them on professional matters. The profession, however, remained concerned about the long-term threat of general management to its status and influence at local level, a concern which with hindsight seems fully justified.

CLINICIANS IN MANAGEMENT

Sir Roy Griffiths had written of doctors that "their decisions largely dictate the use of resources and they must accept the management responsibility which goes with clinical freedom... the nearer that the management process gets to the patient, the more important it becomes for the doctors to be looked upon as the natural managers. This should be more explicitly recognised: in the doctors' training... and in constructing the system of management budgets in a way which supports this work and meets the medical requirement and interest."[2]

It was generally hoped that the improvements in management would change the traditional reluctance of clinicians to get their 'hands dirty' and become compromised in the eyes of their colleagues and patients by taking on management responsibilities. The manager deals with uncertainty while the doctor deals with certainty in the validity of his own clinical judgement. The manager sees the wood and not the trees, while the doctor sees only the trees and then only one tree at a time. The manager lives by multifarious relationships, the doctor lives for the one to one relationship, which is with his patient. The manager is trained to compromise in the interests of the organisation, whereas the doctor is trained to prescribe the best possible treatment for his patient. The manager is part of the system, has loyalty to it and is committed to making the system work. The doctor appears to be outside the system and has loyalty only to the individual patient. The doctor has no scruples about complaining to the press against his employer to obtain better patient care. The manager may not 'spill the beans'.

The uneasy relationship between managers and doctors has changed significantly over the past ten years. Doctors now recognise that managers make decisions under resource constraints, which directly affect their work, pursue policies that are imposed from above, often with purely political justification, and monitor outcomes, which progressively concern not just finance and administration but also clinical practice. This role often involves ethical, legal and safety matters and increasingly impinges upon clinical behaviour and decision making. Doctors must be free to determine their own policies and individual clinical decisions that can be reviewed only by their peer group. But the way these policies are implemented collectively must involve the managers: it is here that the doctors have the choice of whether to become part of the management action.

In the 1980s many large units, particularly large acute hospitals, followed the lead given by Guy's Hospital in developing a network of clinical directors, each of whom manages, with varying levels of administrative and nursing support, a particular specialty or group of specialties. To be effective the director needs management skills, the support and trust of his clinical colleagues, a great deal of administrative support, accurate budgets, timely information and financial analysis of his clinical activities. Encouraging the doctors to not only become involved but to actively and enthusiastically take part in the management of the unit has produced better value for money services, better internal staff communications and more patient orientated decision making. It is, however, expensive in both money and time and in some hospitals has got out of hand, producing excessively complex structures of clinical directors running divisions and sub-divisions, each with a support team whose costs are impinging on the undoubted benefits—cost savings and the more effective use of resources.

It is a cliché that nurses have traditionally acted as the doctors' handmaidens. Only recently have they been accepted as crucial team players in patient care, capable of making clinical decisions themselves and having an increasingly direct impact on the nature of the services provided at or near the bedside. If some managers were uncertain of how to handle doctors they had no such qualms about the nurses. The sister was clearly the general manager at ward level. He or she assessed the nursing needs of patients, met them through nursing procedures, nurse training, and through the development of good professional practice. But above ward level it was maintained that any competent manager, whatever their background and training, could manage 'a nursing service'. This meant that in the early 1980s many unit management structures downgraded the nursing role in senior management, while managers with the wrong background and training were appointed to jobs at the former director of nursing services level and thus were ill-equipped to control the nursing budget, to manage the work force to meet the fluctuations in nursing demand, to cost and evaluate clinical nursing developments, and to provide the necessary local leadership.

In some districts the unit and district manager felt this need could be met by a district nursing adviser, whose role was often unclear as it included some element of direct management or professional management of nursing services at unit level. At region, although no practising nurses were employed, there was a need to recreate the post of regional nursing officer/regional nursing adviser (RNO/RNA). This post not only had a major professional leadership role for half the total staff employed in the region, some 30–40,000, but also a vital strategic role with crucial operational consequences of developing and restructuring nursing education across many districts. The RNA, however, was often a very lonely role. There clearly had to be a professional link with directors of nursing education and a frequent dialogue with district nursing advisers. The main problem was that the roles and relationships of DNAs within districts varied widely and some saw the RNA as the best chance of settling local scores with an unsympathetic district or unit general manager. The RNA had to exercise strong leadership to stimulate and develop the profession throughout the region while also avoid being dragged into local management and operational issues. At the department effective leadership was lacking and one RNO, when asked to whom the profession looked for national leadership, replied with a note of uncertainty "perhaps Trevor Clay"—the general secretary of the RCN!

NEW LEADERSHIP

By implementing Griffiths the government had set out to change the style of management throughout the NHS and the decade can be said to have achieved a great deal. There has been a change in the status, role and relationships of general managers throughout the service, a change in the contractual terms and conditions of service which now relate security and pay directly to performance, a change in the way in which managers are perceived by the work force and the public, and a change in management style and management ethics.

In 'Patients first'[7] the government had argued strongly against the concept of a chief executive but within only five years it had begun transforming the NHS organisation, which is still being worked through and needs time and space (from further central management initiatives) to develop and prove its worth. On being appointed the Secretary of State for Health, following the April 1992 general election, Mrs Bottomley called for a period of stability. Some might think this odd following a year of 'steady state' but stability is what is required to reap the benefits of the general management development.

When the reforms began individual ministers had their objectives. Mr Clarke said that he wished to recreate the house governors of the pre-1974 reorganisation, who had status in the organisation and whose staff had loyalty to their hospital and pride in the excellence of the services it provided. House governors were outside the bureaucracy of hospital management committees, regional hospital boards and executive councils, and negotiated for resources directly with the Department of Health. A job similar to that of the trust chief executive of later days. Mr Clarke wanted the best paid management jobs to be at unit level where most people were treated, most staff worked and most resources were consumed. In the euphoria of the day he wanted to develop a cadre of general managers who would take risks, 'stand up and be counted' (be one of us), who would be willing to 'put their heads above the parapet', and would become subalterns in the inevitable political battles over the NHS which lay ahead.

Today, Mr Clarke must be satisfied that there is a clear, visible leadership at all levels in the service to give a sense of direction to the organisation, create its 'mission' and agree the values by which that mission can be achieved. Accountability is unified and personal, the general manager is increasingly becoming the organisation personified to the world outside and progressively to the people who work in the service. Wise and mature general managers are engaging in strategic management and avoiding the day to day operations, are developing its purpose and values, and are employing others to undertake the trouble-shooting role which previously took up so much time. A shift is occurring from keeping the show on the road to improving the quality of the show and determining the direction in which the show heads. The NHS is moving from being an introverted and professionally led organisation to being an extroverted and patient orientated service. There is also a shift occurring from competent administration to pro-active leadership in which the commitment of staff, added to their undoubted competence, will deliver a better, more people orientated service that will improve the health of the nation.

The reforms of 1991 have created a decentralized structure and a freer environment in which originality and initiative can flourish. Mr Clarke, like Chairman Mao, wanted to 'let a thousand flowers bloom'. Chief executives of trusts have now been given a singleness of purpose. The providers' role is clear cut and they are relieved of the pressures and distractions of ministerial and departmental guidance on day-to-day operations and the frustrations of having to comply with regional policies, not all of which are flexible enough to recognize the variable needs of the local situation. The chief executive stands or falls by his ability to work the market and to deliver the quality services which people will pay for and, therefore, make his unit financially viable. The effective chief executive gets close to his staff with the attitude that they are all in it together and requires each of them to contribute to the contract and be committed to its effective delivery. The contract binds man-

agers and staff together and determines their success or failure. Its very existence creates a positive environment in which
creative energies are released and directed towards the ultimate objective.

The developments over the past decade have begun to create
a new breed of NHS manager: one who is more confident in
the value of his/her own role and in his/her relationships,
both within and outside the organisation. NHS managers are
coming of age, mastering a sophisticated environment to deliver   improved   services   and,   through   demonstrable
competence, will increase public confidence in the NHS and
lessen the negative and debilitating effects of political back-bit-
ing at the local and national level.

PUBLIC SERVANTS, PERFORMANCE AND PERKS

Fundamental objectives for general management were the development   of   a   business   orientated   ethos,   the   more
cost-effective use of resources, more attention to the demands
of market competition, and paying greater concern to the
needs of customers who now had a real choice. However, three
unattractive features of the business culture have begun to
show themselves in recent years. The first is the 'Sword of
Damocles', which hangs over general managers and is at the
sole bidding of the manager's superior. The second is the conduct of business in secret and the absence of local public
debate. The third is the company perk syndrome.

All general managers accept that their performance has to be
monitored by superiors through a system of target setting and
all believe that promotion and pay should be linked to satisfactory performance. In fact, since the introduction of general
management, following Griffiths's proposals in 1983, short-
term contracts and performance related pay (PRP) have
become the norm for senior managers in the NHS. PRP has
undergone a number of changes since its inception, culminating in Health Circular HC (91) 10,[8] including the introduction
of individual performance review (IPR). Management targets
and objectives are set by line managers and chairmen and then
reviewed on an annual basis. Initially, targets were set in a
practical and realistic management context but over the years
they, first, acquired an increasingly political complexion and,

second, some were set not by the local superior at the health authority level but directly by the Chief Executive in the NHS Management Executive. For example, the minister determined the objective of specific reductions in waiting lists and waiting times. From the start it was obvious that there would be difficulties in measuring their success in meeting objectives and their all-round performance and that most ultimate judgements would have a highly subjective content. It was also clear that some targets set in good faith at the beginning of the year would become unachievable during the course of the year due to reasons outside the control of the manager, such as the loss of cash against the fixed cash limit caused by the underfunding of wages. In some cases these developments made senior managers increasingly vulnerable. Situations arose where even with a previous history of success in meeting target dates, achieving IPR objectives and with a consistently high overall rating for pay managers were 'fired' abruptly by a senior manager or chairman, either because their 'face did not fit' or they were not appreciated by 'the powers that be' at the centre. Such sudden departures had repercussions throughout the service by creating an air of uncertainty and a wall of suspicion about the legitimacy of the appraisal system. In any organisation there needs to be confidence and trust throughout all levels of management and this is particularly important in the NHS with its complexity, its fast rate of change, and its highly volatile political environment.

The second negative consequence of moving towards a business culture in the NHS is that more decisions about local health services and facilities are now made in secret. Health authorities have always been subject to the Public Order Meetings Act. There was an element of representation in health authority membership, including local authority members elected by their community. Uncomfortable though it might be for chairmen, members and managers to face the press and limited numbers of the public at monthly meetings it seems right that if the authorities are spending public money in determining local levels of services they ought to demonstrate some degree of local accountability. At times of severe resource constraints, such as during the impact of RAWP on 'over provided and over privileged' regions, and at times of cuts and closures it was not unknown for members and managers to be physically abused during the course of meetings, which were often disrupted and then brought to order with or without the assistance of the police. At times it was dangerous to serve the public face to face, but the danger of conducting too much business behind closed doors in meetings of small health boards, with no representative element, is potentially worse in a democratic society.

In recent years, with the development of trusts which have legal obligations to conduct only one public meeting a year, 'the annual general meeting', local communities have become separated from the decision making bodies. They may not be less well informed, however, for trusts sell their services to the public to generate their needed workload. The problem is that the public now hears what the trust wants them to hear, which is naturally only the good news. Previously, the public had the opportunity to examine their local service with its warts and all.

The third unattractive feature of attempts to generate a business orientated culture in the NHS has been the company perk syndrome. Effective leadership has to be 'visible leadership', visible both to the work force and the customers. Many NHS managers have consequently had to step out of their offices, where they used to hide behind piles of paper for protection. The need for them to be up front, however, has been unnerving for many. To engage in face to face dialogue with staff, to talk honestly and openly about strengths and weaknesses, to inspire them with the organisation's mission, purpose and values, and to listen and be seen to act on their ideas and initiatives undoubtedly builds trust in positive leadership. This is a risky business and one which requires confidence and clear understanding of the direction in which the organisation is going. Some insecure or arrogant managers have mistaken visible leadership for image making and presentation. In the NHS some general managers and chief executives have used resources on designer offices and public relations to project an image, which is intended to sell the excellence of their service to both competitors and customers but in many places, regretfully, the medium has become the message.

Managers in business receive various incentives and inducements to improve performance, only some of which are legitimate in a public sector context. The most common perks include the company car, the mobile telephone, the FAX at home (all for private use), travelling and accommodation expenses without too many questions asked, corporate entertainment, the free lunch, the free trip abroad, and the suppliers' 'gifts'. Everyone who reads the Sunday 'tabloid' press remembers the trust chief executive in 1991 who was said to have received in excess of £90,000 a year and whose two 'company cars', his and hers, were photographed outside their new house. Other stories did not reach the press of senior managers taking trips to the USA, paid for by computer companies to see their equipment in action. In one case the invitation was extended to a second member of the family. Or of the chief executive who, anxious to please his chairman, was reluctantly persuaded that he should make a token payment towards the cost of his own car in case the auditor should show an interest at a later date. Chief executives and permanent secretaries of the health service in England, Scotland, Wales and Northern Ireland have also allowed their names to appear as patrons of a health service 'charity golf classic' tournament sponsored by the main supplier of incontinence towels to the NHS!

Any or all of these actions might well be justified as entirely natural in the business environment. It is a matter for debate as to whether moves in this direction are acceptable or unacceptable in the public service. It is easy to be 'holier than thou' but public servants, whether they are general managers, chief executives, or directors of corporate affairs, remain public servants spending taxpayers' money. Bringing business principles into the NHS was intended to make it more cost conscious and more customer responsive but not to enable its management to acquire some of the less attractive features found in the private sector.

THE ROLE OF THE CENTRE

All who were involved in the general management developments in the 1980s hoped to achieve improved efficiency through greater decentralisation and clearer accountability. Ten years later, however, it could be argued that the NHS has experienced a period of increased centralisation with less influence for representation in local health services, increased government patronage, and an effective and severe line management accountability system that guarantees the delivery of ministers' objectives right through the hierarchy up to the Management Executive at the Department of Health. One of the major problems of moving towards a market environment has proved to be the need to free local management of central control and genuinely decentralise but at the same time retain sufficient control to ensure the implementation of fewer but equally stringent government priorities. The old tensions between the centre and local health management have had to be re-examined as the centre now has to relate differently to purchasers and providers. The successful operation of the market system depends on the effective management of purchasers and the regulation of the market through assessing the performance of providers. In theory, the centre has a direct line management relationship with purchasers to ensure that there is an adequate arrangement for identifying the needs of local communities, for determining local health priorities, for combining these effectively with national priorities, and for monitoring contracts to ensure that central and local health objectives and outcomes are achieved.

In its role of regulating the market the centre must agree principles, rules and procedures (which govern the interaction between purchasers and providers and which monitor provider performance) to ensure the acceptability of its behaviour and to provide incentives for desirable market practices. The centre must also make changes to the structure of the market as it thinks necessary through purchaser and provider mergers, and it must allocate revenue and devise appropriate capitation strategies. It must resolve key service location issues and the distribution of high technology and major capital investments. It must also set standards and ensure that outcome objectives are achieved.

Some systems and regulations will be constant, such as the educational and research responsibilities of the health service, but other systems will vary from year to year according to the costing and pricing systems and the pace of development of real competition.

The centre must, therefore, ensure that there is clear management through the purchasing chain and minimal regulation of providers. It will have an on-going direct management relationship with purchasers, but only an intermittent regulatory relationship with providers. The frequency of its interventions will be determined by the need to deal with political issues and to avoid crises. Regulation by the centre, therefore, will remain a feature of the market system to ensure that publicly owned providers give value for money services and that there is effective stewardship of the NHS.

Never before has there been such a need for a sophisticated tight/loose relationship between the centre and peripheral units. It must be tight on minimum standards of service, on safety and legal requirements, and implementation of ministerial policy. It must be loose on the means used to optimise the use of resources in the implementation of ministerial policy. The NHS Management Executive has to balance its central role of managing the NHS with the political accountability of ministers to Parliament. It not only has to develop new tight/loose relationships with the NHS but also within the DH at Richmond House. How much freedom can ministers allow the Chief Executive who, after all, is a top civil servant? How far will ministers be able to stand back and not be sucked into day to day hospital issues, which may be raised through MPs' inquiries or Prime Minister's Question Time? The horizontal tight/loose relationship between management and politics at the centre has to be harmonised and integrated with the vertical tight/loose relationship with managers in the NHS working at patient level. The history of the early 1980s shows that both sets of relationships became tighter. The hope of the 1990s is that both will get looser.

THE POLITICS OF CENTRAL MANAGEMENT

At the end of the 1980s, before the market was launched, the new Secretary of State, Mr Clarke, accepted the need to give central management sufficient 'space' to exercise discretion in its control of NHS services and expenditure. He was more emotionally attuned to management culture than traditional civil service culture. He wanted to give the Management Board and its successor, the Management Executive, a distinctive and separate role from the rest of the department and to be seen to back decisions made by the Chief Executive on his behalf. Mutual confidence existed between the two and hopes were high. He was determined to work towards a clearer separation of management and politics and this wise objective eventually led to the foolish decision to create space by despatching the Management Executive to Leeds!

The Chief Executive's earlier attempts to distance himself from ministers began badly due to an unlucky turn of events. The long union dispute over the pay of ambulance men and women in 1989 raised fundamental questions. Was this a management matter for Duncan Nichol to resolve? Could ministers keep out of it? The answers were yes and no. The Chief Executive strove manfully on television and radio to appear to be dealing with management issues by negotiating with union representatives to seek a solution. The Secretary of State, with tongue in cheek, said it was a matter for the management side of the Whitley council and for Duncan Nichol to resolve. Those within the NHS knew that Whitley was not a free agent in its bargaining but was constrained by the politically determined maximum level of cash available. The public became confused but expected the Secretary of State to cut the Gordian knot. It eventually became clear to all that ministers remained firmly in control not just over policy objectives, like pay restraint in the public sector, but also over detailed management arrangements, like the level of overtime payments for ambulance men. So what new structures and changes were required at the centre to give the Management Executive real authority, and to create space between it and ministers and then between it and the rest of the Department of Health?

Sir Roy Griffiths had hoped to achieve the separation of management and politics through the creation of the Supervisory Board (later the Policy Board) to formulate health policy and objectives and to give strategic direction to the Management Board. The Social Services Select Committee in its report[9] on the Management Inquiry endorsed this structure and recommended that the Supervisory Board should include a regional chairman among its members to provide experience of local practical problems in implementing policy. It commented on the tight/loose relationship in the following way: "it is also important that authority is not unduly drawn upwards to the Supervisory Board and that specific powers be delegated to the Management Board. We recommend that such instruments of delegation be laid before the House so that the degree of managerial independence of the Management Board is made known to Parliament." A regional chairman was appointed to the board but such specific instruments of delegation were never agreed.

The Select Committee's report also commented on the relationship between the two boards at the centre and the NHS. It was clear that regional chairmen would continue to be appointed by the Secretary of State and have access to and remain accountable directly to him. But how were they to relate to the Management Board? "They would therefore seem not to be directly responsible to the Management Board, although it will presumably be from the board that management directives will come. The Board Chairman emerges as a sort of full-time supraregional chairman."[9] This was an interesting interpretation and the report continued: "there is an inherent contradiction between regional chairmen continuing to be responsible to the Secretary of State and the projected role of the Management Board and its chairman. This will have to be resolved." This was impressive foresight from a select committee but this 'apparent contradiction' persists to this day.

The Chief Executive is in fact 'supra' to the regional chairmen who have continued to lose influence at court ever since. It is true that they meet the Secretary of State and contribute to ministerial thinking but a more pragmatic involvement of the NHS in central policy making and priority formulation comes through the Management Executive and its increasingly close working relations with regional general managers.

The past decade has seen a steady decline in the influence of regional chairmen on ministers and civil servants. In Mr Fowler's day the 14 chairmen, over half of whom had been appointed at the same time and all of whom had the best possible political credentials, acted as his health cabinet. They were often consulted on new policy initiatives and always acted as a sounding board between the Whitley councils, which did the 'negotiating', and the department, which fixed the national pay limits. The chairmen submitted independent evidence to the review bodies, which was usually, but not always, in tune with departmental thinking. Chairmen can rightly claim that their evidence influenced the review bodies' attitudes to the merit awards system. They also played a key role in negotiating with ministers over the pay and conditions for general managers as there was no one else to speak on their behalf. On one famous occasion chairmen working closely with regional treasurers and Ian Mills, the Management Executive's Director of Finance in whom they had great confidence, brought new evidence to John Moore on the worrying state of NHS expenditure. The Secretary of State was taken aback to discover the gap between the reassuring messages he had received from within the civil service about the NHS's finances and the reality presented by the regional chairmen. Unfortunately, in this regard there was a change of Secretary of State soon after.

But gradually the 'supra' regional chairman gained a stronger grip on the pay and performance of their general managers. Although the IPR objectives were set by regional chairmen they had to be ratified by the Chief Executive. The 14 chairmen found themselves in no-man's land between ministers who became progressively less inclined to share confidences and the Chief Executive who did not regard a close relationship with the chairmen as a top priority. The chairmen themselves became less cohesive and more disgruntled. They were not happy at being told that they should withdraw from management issues and concentrate their efforts on policy through the briefing of the two chairmen on the Policy Board, who had been appointed not as representatives but in a personal capacity. As a group they also lacked the strong leadership that had been provided in Mr Fowler's day by an ex-permanent secretary, a sophisticated businessman embedded in the Conservative party network and a political warlord from the Welsh Marches. Their influence steadily declined until it reached a stage of extreme anxiety and insecurity. It was suggested that they should send an emissary to the new Permanent Secretary, Graham Hart, to seek guidance as to which of their number should be elected to lead them out of the wilderness!

The House of Commons Social Services Select Committee had not been particularly helpful to the government over the Griffiths report but its views and recommendations had generally been treated with polite indifference. It continued to be unhelpful in the following years and this was partly due to the politically ill disciplined behaviour of its Chairman, Nicholas Winterton. Mr Winterton was a member of long-standing who would challenge policy and speak out in the patients' best interests. He was, in fact, appointed as Chairman of the committee in the first place not through the insidious influence of party whips, who favoured Sir David Price (a safe pair of hands), but through an unholy alliance with Labour members who thought that Mr Winterton was their best chance of putting the executive to the test.

Mr Winterton was recognised and respected by backbenchers not as a good party man but as an outspoken rebel with some 18 years service on the committee and its predecessors. His reputation was such that when it came to the appointment of committees in July 1992 the knives were out. Sir Marcus Fox, the Chairman of the Selection Committee and of the 1922 Committee, announced a new rule to the House of Commons that no member should continue to sit on a select committee for more than three government terms. This new rule meant that Mr Winterton could not be re-appointed and had to continue his one man crusade from the backbenches.

THE MANAGEMENT EXECUTIVE AND THE REST OF THE DEPARTMENT

From 1989 a great deal of work went on in Richmond House to try to separate the roles and responsibilities of the two Permanent Secretaries, Sir Christopher France (in charge of the Policy Group) and Duncan Nichol (Chairman of the Management Executive). Rules for separation and 'instruments of delegation' were pursued both conceptually and in practice. This was achieved in the case of the former through two studies undertaken by consultants and by Sir Christopher's former private secretary, and in the case of the latter through an investigation which led to the decision to move the Management Executive to Leeds. Some feared this was not simply a decision to create space between management and politics (200 miles) but would eventually mean transferring the executive to outer obscurity.

The autumn of 1989 saw work being conducted on the policy and management functions in the centre and the need for clear rules of engagement, such as the relationship between the Policy Board and the two executive structures, the Management Executive and the Policy Group, and in turn between these groups and the NHS regions. The objective was to establish clear roles, agreed communication principles and improvement in practice. It was clear to all that the department was responsible for far more than just the NHS. Its functions included health promotion, social care, environmental health, food safety, and hygiene regulations. It was the Policy Group that undertook this wide range of functions and also had to ensure that the NHS gave ministers value for money in achieving health outcomes. The Policy Board, supported by the Policy Group, found itself almost in the position of a 'commissioner', contracting with the Management Executive to achieve the results which would fulfil the government's health strategy. Management by contract rather than management by command, by outputs rather than inputs, had to apply both within Whitehall and between the department and the Management Executive and the NHS as a whole.

The Management Executive's remit was to 'run' the NHS by entering into annual contracts with regions for the delivery of agreed objectives. The system was intended to be flexible. The regions were supposed to influence some of these objectives and the way in which they were to be met. To take account of different regional needs and circumstances a contract had to be agreed by both parties and the RGMs had to acquire a new style of managing their regions. The challenge was for them to move from a position only recently acquired of tight line management control over their constituents to one of greater delegation to districts and units and to negotiating contracts with them. This was being done at a time when the Management Executive was flexing its muscles. The regions were placed in the middle: suffering a sense of loss of authority downwards and manifesting concern about the increasing authority of the Management Executive upwards. The RGMs' temporary uncertainty about their new role was diminished by the knowledge that the Chief Executive understood the NHS and its needs, and was surrounding himself with directors and others who had management experience in the service and who were former colleagues of the RGMs. The role of the Management Executive was being redefined. It was there to discharge management functions on behalf of ministers and, so long as mutual confidence existed between the Secretary of

State and the Chief Executive, the latter spoke with supreme authority. Each year, after consulting the Policy Board, the Secretary of State issued annual key objectives for achievement within the 'resources available', including performance targets covering quality, outputs and value for money. The Policy Group made its formal input into the management of the NHS through the Policy Board and in developing policy and resource guidance directly for ministers. The Permanent Secretary, the Chief Executive and the Chief Medical Officer each had separate commands with their own budget within a single administrative vote and each had an interconnected set of objectives.

The total staff working for the department in 1989 was huge. It totalled 8,600 people, although this included in excess of 3,000 working in the special hospitals, over 1,000 for the Disablement Authority and smaller numbers employed in the NHS Superannuation Division, the Statutory Audit, the Social Services Inspectorate, and the Medicines Control Agency. The staff working directly to the two Permanent Secretaries totalled 860 for management executive functions, 680 for policy functions and over 1,000 for common analytical, advisory and support services. One of the department's internal objectives was to achieve major staff 'savings' and this was done by transferring work to the NHS, such as the National Disablement Authority, and devolving other functions to agencies. This objective was part of the policy of reducing the size of all central government departments but also derived from the need to rationalise the split of the former DHSS into two departments. It was clearly important to take stock of the collective impact of these changes on the future shape of the department in light of the decision to achieve separation by operating from two locations: Leeds and London.

The Heather Gwyn report was a confidential internal review, which was never published, of the purpose, functions and structure needed to accommodate the different roles of the Management Executive and the rest of the department, and which analysed necessary changes in both management arrangements and the number of staff required. It began as a separate but parallel exercise to the Management Executive's own review but after some months the two programmes were changed and integrated. The outcome of the Gwyn report was a tripartite or trefoil relationship:

(a) the Health and Social Services Divisions' (HSS) Policy Group and associated professional divisions responsible for advising ministers on health care policy and for "executive action as necessary in respect of the social care and wider health businesses";

(b) the NHS Management Executive Divisions responsible for operational matters; and

(c) Central Resource Management Divisions (CRM)—the common services for Leeds and London.

On some specific issues it was obvious that certain operational functions, like the waiting list unit, should clearly physically cross the boundary from the Policy Group to the Management Executive, but there remains a great deal of uncertainty about that part of the spectrum where policy development shades into operational and management considerations.

In an attempt to reduce this uncertainty it was suggested from within the Management Executive that because 'policy' was a catch-all there would be an advantage in differentiating between management policy, such as industrial relations or communications, for the NHS; operational policy, such as waiting lists, and admission to hospitals; health priorities and the relative resourcing and priority of different services, which was the old Barbara Castle priorities document; and health strategies, such as long-term issues involving prevention and promotion. In the first two the Management Executive had the predominating role whereas in the second two categories, the last of which extended outside the boundaries of health, the lead was taken by the Policy Group. The report was a step forward in clarifying roles and relationships, in redrawing the boundary between the HSS and Management Executive Divisions, and in developing new ways of working at that boundary through what was called a 'policy to implementation cycle'. The intention was to minimise duplication and to contribute to a constructive, 'no surprises' regime. The Departmental Management and Policy Group (DMPG) was to be the official forum and determining influence on the integration of work into one agreed agenda for the department as a whole. The objective was to be clear about the roles undertaken within a department that operated from two HQ locations. The tensions that were increasing between the career civil servants and the NHS managers, who worked for the Management Executive, were to be resolved by new manpower planning, new management development and unified career opportunities for all.

THE MANAGEMENT EXECUTIVE'S NEW ROLE

On 27th February 1991 the 'Review of the functions and organisation of the NHS Management Executive' was issued.[10] Over a number of months it had been put together by Mike Malone-Lee, the Director of Operations, to define the core work of the executive and the most appropriate style and structure to meet their strategic goals, which had been set by the Policy Board to reflect the NHS reforms. The new management style was to be one of corporate and integrated working as previously many directors had done their own thing. The Management Executive needed to develop a stronger, credible leadership. It was particularly important to be credible with managers, professionals and all other staff working in the NHS. It needed to be rigorous on outputs and outcomes and there had to be stronger personal accountability at every level of the organisation.

The core functions were agreed as:

(a) research and development (until now very much a Cinderella service);

(b) defining a strategic framework for the NHS;

(c) developing health care operational policy;

(d) objective setting and performance review;

(e) support for ministers in their dealings with the NHS and their accountability to Parliament for its management;

(f) resources and resource management;

(g) organisational and people development; and

(h) corporate management (managing the management).

It was proposed that these functions should be carried out by the Chief Executive and six directors and that certain secondary and support functions, like estates, procurement and information, should be considered for status as executive agencies. The six directorates were:

(a) Research and Development Directorate;

(b) Health Care Directorate responsible for developing operational policy and working closely with the Health and Social Services Group;

(c) Performance Management Directorate responsible for objective setting and reviewing the performance of the NHS;

(d) Finance and Corporate Information Directorate responsible for resources and resource management and analysing the Management Executive's corporate information needs;

(f) Personnel Directorate; and

(g) Corporate Affairs Directorate responsible for Management Executive communications, developing the strategic framework to reflect ministers' policies, managing the Management Executive's own resources, and managing the intelligence units that would give support to ministers in the same way as the previously much maligned Regional Liaison Division.

The report made it clear that the Management Executive should include medical and nursing directors. It was clear already that the Health Care Directorate might be run by a doctor but it was not so obvious which directorate might be run by a nurse. The report, therefore, hedged its bets by saying that the medical and nursing directors would either be one of the six or an add on!

These reviews of the two sides of the Department of Health were being finalised and made ready for publication at the time of a change of Secretary of State. Mr Clarke went to Education to take on the teaching profession and William Waldegrave arrived at Health, bringing with him a more conciliatory and less combative style in dealing with the professions and in ensuring that the reforms headed for a smooth take-off. The Management Executive's review took the Secretary of State by surprise. He would not be bounced into agreeing to its publication. It had not been shown to the Policy Board, which set objectives for the Management Executive and monitored its performance. Publication, therefore, was delayed for weeks.

Senior managers in the NHS were also taken by surprise. During a period of close working relations between Management Executive directors and RGMs the review had been completed without their direct involvement or consultation. What was meant by partnership asked senior NHS managers? Did the senior partner decide all the rules of the game?

BRIDGING THE GAP
The gap between NHS management and the centre had always been wide. It was a gap based on an ignorance of the different cultures operating in Whitehall and at patient level and an absence of mutual respect. NHS managers too often saw civil servants as good on paper, strong on theory but slow in action. Middle grade civil servants viewed NHS managers as over-paid administrators and an underlying jealousy developed over rates of pay. This led to an increasing number of them seeking better paid jobs in the NHS, which they invariably found both more demanding and more rewarding than they had expected. There was, as a result, greater respect and trust at the top. RGMs began to realise the relentless pressures which are placed on permanent secretaries, who work long hours at their ministers' whims. Top civil servants knew that managing multi-million pound cash limited budgets, with fluctuations in both clinical and political demands, was no sinecure. The creation of the Management Executive to im-prove both the management performance at the centre and the management control of the NHS had led to an increasing num-ber of NHS managers being transplanted into Whitehall. This had raised certain rivalries and suspicions but had also in-creased the opportunities for generating mutual respect and greater confidence. Duncan Nichol moved from the service and increasingly relied upon its senior managers and his for-mer colleagues to help him. Many were transferred to the centre and RGMs in the field also undertook joint working with him.

Joint working meant an RGM working closely with a Man-agement Executive director on the development of a particular aspect of policy or a particular element needed to implement the reforms. At the Management Executive and RGMs' annual meetings in Ilkley and Baslow a strategic agenda for joint working was agreed and full commitment to it was freely given. In theory, if senior managers were involved in the de-velopment of policy and in interpreting it for practical implementation the new management programme would be more likely to achieve a smooth take-off. The six big issues, which became known as the 'Baslow agenda', were:

(a) The health of the nation: an attempt to shift attention from the provision of better services for individual patients to better health for the community (health outcomes);

(b) purchasing: developing the identification of need and purchasing strategies to meet those needs (a crucial role to be undertaken by disillusioned and insecure district general managers (DGMs) and district health authorities (DHAs), in which organisational schizophrenia was rampant);

(c) operating the market: devising the minimum constraints and regulations to enable the market to operate in the public interest;

(d) empowering the patient: developing mechanisms to give consumers a greater influence and to promote responsiveness among NHS staff to ensure that the patient is central to the planning and delivery of care;

(e) community care/primary care: stimulating co-ordination, crucial for achieving the objectives in 'Caring for people',[11] developing the role of RHAs at the key interface with the Social Services Inspectorate, and developing the opportunities for better integration of primary and secondary care; and

(f) management development programmes for the new breed of providers: new skills for devolved pay bargaining and remuneration strategies for dealing with the demographic 'time-bomb'.

The concept of joint working in partnership has been very successful in using the experience and expertise of the NHS in the development of national policy. The system has achieved joint commitment, mutual appreciation of each other's different roles and responsibilities, and is developing a greater identity of purpose. It has certainly done much to make the Management Executive more credible in the eyes of the service and to demonstrate that regional managers are part of the new strategic centre.

THE CENTRAL MANAGEMENT OF THE MARKET

How to manage the old NHS was a constant concern. Many critics have said that it was unmanageable and that it created its own momentum, or lack of it. How to manage the new NHS in a market culture is bound to prove more difficult and more complicated, but also more urgent. Long and careful thought has been given to alternative management models that allow the NHS to operate a market without too much intervention and which balances this requirement with the need to protect ministers' interests in Parliament. The initial problem was the direct management of a very large number of self-governing trusts. The quick and easy solution was for the Management Executive to have outposts in the regions to establish local communications and information flows, but it did not offer an effective solution to the larger problem of managing the market.

The fundamental role of central management is to meet NHS objectives and ensure the delivery of a system which tries to improve the health of the population (the purpose), and which guarantees the long standing values of equity, access and efficiency. There are also the more recently acquired values of effectiveness (the achievement of intended benefits), appropriateness (meeting the needs of individuals and of the population as a whole), and responsiveness (a style of service to meet the reasonable expectations of the public). The centre must operate through a model of management that delivers the health care system in a free environment with minimum regulatory intervention. The centre must always set the strategic framework, the direction of change, and health improvement targets and priorities. It must continue to allocate resources and exercise accountability because the NHS is publicly owned, funded and managed. There will always be public and political concern about the distribution, levels and style of services. Central management must seek to turn this public interest and concern away from the closure of uneconomic units and the loss of jobs towards the appraisal of effectiveness through health outcomes. Central management must ensure change and development in the service but must control the rate of change to retain public support. It must regulate and intervene when things go wrong but for much of the time must allow the service to respond to pressures from the local level rather than from the political centre. In the past the centre has envisaged a change programme and implemented it in a uniform, inflexible and bureaucratic way. It has too often failed to stimulate local initiative, provide incentives and stand back in its monitoring role to observe the way in which imaginative managers run their own show.

The style of central management must be determined by the scale of the enterprise. In Scotland, Northern Ireland and Wales the strategic centre has always operated from one place. In England, because it is so much larger, the strategic centre needs to be distributed around the country with a common purpose, values and sense of mission. If decentralisation is to become a reality and if the market is to be allowed to operate freely so that local management responds to local needs and develops local priorities then central management must tolerate local variations in method and style.

What is coming to be called the local expression of central management is being operated in embryo form by both Management Executive outposts and RHAs. They are fulfilling different functions for purchasers and providers. With purchasers they are helping to set their strategic direction through strategic service planning, allocating resources, ensuring compliance with key national purchasing and health care policies, and monitoring the implementation and development of purchasing organisations and people. With providers they are helping to monitor financial viability, assist with investment appraisals, ensure effective communications, review business plans and annual reports, and monitor compliance with policy. The change in style of central management needs to be from one of centralised, line management accountability for the whole service to one of continuing management accountability for purchasers through the achievement of national health objectives, but to a very different form of accountability for providers. This becomes clear as more trusts are established and fewer district managed units remain. Trusts are accountable to the Secretary of State through the chairmen and non-executive directors appointed with the specific duty of ensuring the trust's success. While the Management Executive should continue to exercise accountability, as it did with the old health authorities, it should refrain from using IPR and personal target setting, as it did with the old health authorities and their general managers.

Trusts are accountable to the public through their annual general meeting and the publication of an annual report. This is thought by some to be theoretical accountability, like that of a doctor to his patient. They are also accountable to purchasers through the fulfilment of their contracts and to the public through internal and external auditors and their compliance with the law, such as health and safety requirements and equal opportunities. As the number of trusts increases so a growing proportion of the National Health Service may have less and less accountability to the centre.

The Management Executive is required to manage through purchasers (a tight relationship) and regulate the market through providers (a loose relationship). It must fulfil these tasks through a new method and style of working. It must, through general competence and clear leadership, gain increasing credibility in the eyes of purchasers and providers. It must exercise minimal regulation consistent with public accountability. It must develop a system of differential monitoring by exception rather than generality. It must enter into local partnerships with purchasers and providers, a partnership based on openness and equality of status. It must exercise discretion and prevent the 'suction pump effect' of pulling decisions to the centre.

If this is how the centre will exercise management in the market environment what will happen to the existing structure? Do purchasers remain health authorities with an element of representation in their constitution? Do they form purchasing consortia, with greater strength, to influence the services supplied by providers in the fulfilment of national policy? Do RHAs continue to exist or is it conceivable that at a future date ministers will have the courage to disband them and replace them with management outposts of central government? The direction in which we are travelling may be clear but it is a long journey in uncharted seas. The way to achieve this light but effective hand on the tiller to allow for unforeseen changes in wind and tide is to have a subtle, distributed system of central management, which is tight on direction and pace of change but loose on the means of getting there. The National Health Service needs national policies and priorities. It can no longer be controlled by a unified and simplistic management system. It must be allowed to develop through a network of local manifestations of central policy.

Footnote: However, on 21st October 1993 it appeared that the Secretary of State did take the courageous but foolhardy decision to do away with RHAs as public bodies. In future, she expects the market to be directly controlled from the centre by outposted creatures of the ME. So much for ministers' rhetoric on greater devolution.

REFERENCES

1. *Management arrangements for the reorganised National Health Service* (1972). London: HMSO.

2. Griffiths report (1983). *NHS management inquiry*. London: HMSO.

3. Department of Health and Social Security (1980). *Structure and management*. HC (80) 8.

4. Hansard (1986). *NHS (general managers), written answers.* 26 June, col. 298.

5. Sherman J (1984). Extra pay to attract outsiders. *Health Service J* XCIV: 662.

6. Ministry of Health and Scottish Home and Health Department (1966). *Report of the committee and senior nursing staff structure.* (Salmon report). London: HMSO.

7. Department of Health and Social Security, Welsh Office (1979). *Patients first: consultative paper on the structure and management of the National Health Service in England and Wales.* London: HMSO.

8. Department of Health (1991). *Performance related pay for general and senior managers.* HC (91) 10.

9. House of Commons Social Services Committee (1984). *First report from the social services committee session 1983–84: Griffiths NHS management inquiry report.* London: HMSO.

10. NHSME (1991). *A review of the functions and organisation of the Management Executive.* London: Department of Health.

11. Department of Health (1989). *Caring for people: community care in the next decade and beyond.* London: HMSO.

12

ADVOCACY

--------- ◆ ---------

INTRODUCTION

While government morale appeared to be high in 1990 for the overworked staff in the NHS it was at a particularly low point. It was proving to be an exhausting change, transplanting new jargon on to old attitudes. Morale was affected by confusion and uncertainty. Recent patients remained stoical, almost oblivious to the reforms, enthusiastic for the service, satisfied with their treatment, and uplifted by feelings of intense relief at having survived the system and returned home. Traditionally, patients admire the doctors and love the nurses into whose hands they are delivered when at their most vulnerable, and they will put up with much inconvenience, insensitivity and pain in order to escape from their caring clutches. Obtaining reliable data on patients' perceptions is difficult because very few people will tell the truth when they are in hospital, surrounded by their medical carers.

One of the permanent principles of the government's health policies since 1979 has been to provide opportunities for the views of the consumers to be made known to health authorities when planning and developing services. One of the key objectives of the reforms has been to offer greater choice and to make the service more responsive to people's wishes and needs. But balancing politics and policy at the macro level with consumer interests, however ill defined, at the micro level has always proved difficult, particularly when professional autonomy sits at the fulcrum and has the power to determine local priorities in treatment and the provision of care.

Is it possible to respond to all health needs and wishes, whether expressed by independent professional bodies with an axe to grind, individual clinicians with their widening definition of treatable morbidity, or by the rising expectations of the population as a whole? It is now clear that it is not possible. First, government after government has sought to meet rising demand and to protect standards by pumping in more and more money, which in recent years has clearly failed to stem the tide. Second, the Conservative government over the past 14 years has tried to make the money go further by continuously seeking greater efficiency and value for money. This has brought short–term benefits but there are limits to the amount of resources which can be gained from efficiency savings. Third, although rationing services has always taken place, usually behind the closed doors of the GP surgery or consultants' outpatient clinics, by the 1980s it had become an inevitable part of future policy. The question was how to involve the consumer in the rationing process other than through the ballot box and, therefore, make it appear more respectable and to give the patient a sense of greater involvement in the decisions taken and, if possible, of ownership of their NHS and, more important, its limitations. In the 1990s the aim is that the patient should have greater choice, including the ability to choose what society can and cannot afford. The intention is to replace the destructive party political slanging match of the past with wider and more informed public debate on choices in health care in order to achieve a more positive social consensus. Experiments in giving consumers influence over health care choices in the state of Oregon in the USA were put on hold by the Federal government in 1992. Maybe initiatives in the UK will learn from the American experience and, with positive support from the centre in pursuit of the Patient's Charter philosophy, have greater success.[1]

COMMUNITY HEALTH COUNCILS

The early years of the NHS saw the development of a number of specialist organisations representing consumer interests, such as the National Association for Welfare of Children in Hospital (NAWCH) and the Patients' Association, which concerned itself with general issues like the need for patients to have privacy in outpatient departments and the importance of informing patients of the implications of teaching and research. At first these organisations were not always taken very seriously by the professions, had few resources and, inevitably, a limited impact on improving patients' welfare in hospital.

In primary care very little happened until some experiments

in patient participation groups emerged in the early 1970s, usually based on health centres and large group practices. They consisted of progressive doctors, nurses and patients and were intended to provide an opportunity for a relaxed dialogue between patients and professionals. The aim was to develop mutual awareness of local issues and to break down professional barriers. In time these groups acquired the support of the Royal College of General Practitioners but never succeeded in becoming a major influence.

The first government sponsored system of consumer representation, the Community Health Councils (CHCs), was intended to speak with both the voice of the community and the individual patient in monitoring local health services and contributing to their future planning and development. A factor in the creation of these councils was the hope that ministers might be relieved of direct involvement in disputes over local hospital closures and changes of use, which was a political advantage rather than a positive development in consumer affairs. If a new consumer representative body could get close to health authorities and itself become involved in the necessary change process, the political heat generated by MPs and others about local management decisions might not have to reach Parliament and attract the attention of the national media. This motivation, however, proved a false hope over the succeeding years.

The 1974 reorganisation established one council for each health district to put the views of patients to area health authorities, which, because of the size of population served (in some cases one million) and the number of hospitals and clinics managed (often dozens), were somewhat remote from their communities.

Command Paper 5055 in August 1972[2] had made it clear that "Constructive interplay of ideas" would benefit both management and users of the service and would help "to make sure the public has a full say in what is done in its name and it helps the managing authorities by making them better informed on priorities, needs and deficiencies in the service." CHCs were "to influence area policy by contributing their own ideas on how services should be operated and developed... For their part, the AHAs will be expected to consult the councils on their plans for health service developments and particularly on pro-

posals for *important variations in services* affecting the public.
New services, closures of hospitals or departments of hospitals
or their change of use are examples." These expectations, however, were never fulfilled.

CHCs were under resourced by RHAs and undervalued by
managers in general, whose feelings were more nervous opposition than positive partnership. It was, of course, inevitable
that CHCs should be critical of local health services, but as half
their membership came directly from local authorities many
CHCs were politically hostile and sought openly to frustrate
government intentions. In the late 1970s, following the
financial stresses caused by the oil crisis, many health authorities were forced to alter the provision of health services and
undertake extensive 'rationalisation'. 'Rationalisation' was often seen as an euphemism for the apparent arbitrary closure of
small and uneconomic units to save money.

CHCs had been given the authority to refer final decisions
on closures through the RHA to the Department of Health and
Social Security. These delaying tactics caused irritation and
confusion all round. Ministers often took months to decide,
during which local MPs of all persuasions made representations, health authorities were harangued over detailed
procedural matters and the financial problem which had provoked the rationalisation in the first instance became a running
sore. This effective right of CHCs to halt closures became an
albatross around the neck of local management, who were
pressed by the centre to keep within the budget allocation and
at the same time by local MPs and other interest groups to
maintain the status quo. Eventually, circular HSC (IS) 207 (superseded by HC (81) 15)[3] clarified the issue. Health authorities
had the right to decide for themselves what was "a substantial
variation" and formal consultation extending over three
months was not necessary where action was "urgent." A closure was "temporary" if it was necessary to keep within
budget and it was in the interests of the service. Heated arguments often arose over the difference between a temporary
and a permanent closure. CHCs were not slow to realise that
the one soon became the other, because if the temporary closure of a small unit was followed by redundancies and
redeployment of staff how practical was it to prevent closure
from becoming a permanent fact of life? A health authority's

interpretation of the guidance and the 'urgent' decisions that it took often created mistrust among CHCs and in the local community. The Health Department made it clear that management actions could be challenged in the court of law, which they often were.

Ministers disliked the system but could do little about it. They continued to be dragged into making politically unattractive decisions and showed their frustration by blaming local management incompetence and insensitivity. This would take a line such as the health authority had not followed the closure procedures to the letter. Their target should have been to reduce apparently high management costs and to seek greater efficiency rather than to close a 'much loved' cottage hospital. Health authorities were advised that the closure of services should be seen not as 'cuts' (a political anathema) but as an opportunity to redistribute services and to offer better and safer care in the district general hospital. The reality was that closures were more often brought about by financial restrictions than clinical objectives and decisions were increasingly taken in an atmosphere of deepening cynicism.

It was not surprising, therefore, that as early as 1979, in his consultation paper 'Patients first',[4] Patrick Jenkin sought views on whether CHCs should be retained. The new DHAs would be closer to their communities and, with their membership including representatives of local authorities, surely they would act as both managers and monitors of the services provided? After all, he pointed out, it was important to justify the cost of separate consumer representation, which for the whole of the NHS had then reached £4 million. The response to the consultation was lukewarm but on balance was in favour of retaining the CHCs as a genuine attempt to bring the health service, or at least the hospital service, closer to the community. What was needed to make it work was imaginative management will, together with more positive and active members and better informed and resourced councils.

Management will to support and develop CHCs was usually lacking. Their resources were allocated by the regions and their staff were on the RHAs' books. This was intended to distance them from, and make them appear independent of, the local health authorities whose services they were expected to monitor. The management of CHCs by RHAs was theoreti-

cal rather than real. RHAs were expected to respect the CHCs'
independence and yet control and provide management development for the CHCs' staff. Each council elected its own
chairman, who was often at odds with his or her secretary and
nervous of the secretary's relationship with the RHA. The effectiveness of the CHC performance varied widely. At the
worse end of the scale some councils simply represented the
interests of pressure groups and, particularly in inner cities,
became more like political trouble makers than the consumer's
champion. In these circumstances it was hardly surprising that
the regional administrator/general manager came to regard
CHCs as a necessary management chore but a constant irritation and distraction from the core business of planning,
policy and strategy.

    All this meant inadequate resources and management iso-
lation for CHCs. When the future of CHCs was reviewed again
in 1989 the average annual budget was still only £35,000. This
had to cover the staff, usually limited to two, office accommodation, the cost of servicing the council and dealing with
consumer complaints. The CHCs' two relatively junior staff
were remote from their 'boss' at region and were situated in a
career vacuum. The CHCs' secretary's post was often seen as
a deadend job rather than a challenging role at the hotend of
NHS management. By the time the reforms were being introduced an imaginative concept had gone sour.

CHCs IN THE MARKET PLACE

The desirability of positive consumer involvement in the development of their own health services was, therefore,
reappraised in the run-up to the publication of 'Working for
patients'.[5] First, if "money travelling with patients" and better
"patient choice" was to mean more than mere rhetoric it was
a political necessity that CHCs had to be retained, however
restrictive their impact on the service. "Community Health
Councils are referred to in Working for patients only in pass-
ing," wrote Dr Tom Rathwell of the Nuffield Institute for
Health Service Studies, "and that is just to say they will be
retained—a bit like the chair of a football club saying the manager's job is perfectly safe."[6] Second, ways had to be sought to
overcome the problems created by smaller management bod-

ies with no representative element and the fears of secrecy in
decision making, particularly in NHS trusts. Third, there were
concerns about information on local health services being less
accessible in the future because of restrictions on a 'commercial
in confidence' basis. Fourth, to allay fears of what the market
place might mean in terms of winners and losers patients
would have to be given a new deal and new powers to protect
their rights and standards of care.

In December 1990 the Department of Health issued a booklet, 'Consultation and involving the consumer',[7] to summarise
existing procedures for consultation in the light of changes to
the CHCs' regulations and the introduction of a contractual
relationship between DHAs, as purchasers of health services
for their resident populations, and provider bodies. 'Consumer involvement' was at the heart of the reforms, had been
a strong theme in 'Promoting better health'[8] and would be vital
for the implementation of the proposals in 'Health of the nation'.[9]

This booklet made it clear once again that consultation with
users should be "an integral part of the management process"
and was necessary to respond "to the desire of the public to be
more informed about it and have influence in the design and
delivery of the services it receives." In the past, formal consultation with CHCs had made the public better informed but had
had a more destructive than constructive influence on the design and delivery of services. Why would it be better and not
worse in the market place?

The intention was to make consultation less formal, less
bureaucratic and less expensive. NHS authorities should develop "positive consumer relations policies" with the public
(note: not public relations policies with the consumer!). True
consumer involvement was to focus on meeting health care
needs and would have to be more than simply a rubber stamp
of decisions taken. It meant "developing a shared understanding of the DHAs' objectives for health and quality
improvements which will increasingly be expressed in terms
of outcomes; and the service strategies for achieving these objectives." Patients are interested in being treated individually
with dignity, care and concern. They are not generally motivated by service strategies.

Consultation in the new world of competition was meant to

cover only those services purchased by the DHA, whether provided by a DHA managed unit, an NHS trust or the independent sector. CHCs have been given no role "in the use by fundholding GPs of their funds to secure hospital services for their patients." It is clear that as the number of fundholders increases and as the proportion of total health care which they provide for the local community approaches or exceeds that of the DHA the CHCs' influence diminishes. In 1992, for example, more than a third of health services in Hertfordshire were already being purchased by GP fundholders. In time, consumer involvement, "an integral part of the management process," may come to concern only half the local health services.

On closing and altering services circular HSC(IS) 207 was cancelled and DHAs were required by CHCs' regulation 1985 (SI No. 304),[10] as amended by CHCs' regulation 1990(SI 1375),[11] to consult a relevant council on proposals for substantial changes to services in the CHC's own district, but not in those districts to which the local consumers may be sent through contracts. The DHA still retains the right to make substantial changes if it has "expressly decided that, in the interests of the health service, a decision has to be taken without allowing time for consultation... regulations 19(1) (2) do not distinguish between permanent and temporary closure—only 'urgency' permits closure without consultation." The definition of what is urgent and genuinely 'in the interests of the health service' has always caused problems and eluded the comprehension of most CHCs, and no doubt will continue to do so in the future.

To make life more difficult for CHCs these regulations apply only to DHAs and not to trusts. "Consultation on substantial changes in the pattern of services provided by NHS trusts as a result of major changes introduced by the contracts placed by DHAs will be the responsibility of the purchasing authority." But what about changes introduced by trusts that are implemented in expectation of new contracts not yet developed by DHAs? Unprofitable services can be run down and new money making ones developed without consultation with CHCs. Trusts may become a law unto themselves with only tenuous links with CHCs. This risk of isolation may have been foreseen at the time of drafting the provisions of the NHS and Community Care Act 1990,[12] which requires the RHA to consult the relevant CHC on the establishment of each trust. However, it allows the authority "to decide on the form, content, extent and timing of consultation" subject to challenge only on the grounds of reasonableness in a court of law, and, thereafter, the RHA is expected to have a "hands off" relationship with trusts. CHCs do not have a relationship with GP fundholders and a similar hands off relationship with trusts. No wonder some have felt marginalised in the brave new world of competition and consumer choice.

CHCs had started out as a bold experiment in local dialogue between managers and patients' representatives aimed at giving the patient at least some say in the provision of secondary, but not primary, care. In the 1970s AHAs included local authority councillors (elected representatives of the community anxious to champion the interests of their constituents) and local doctors and nurses (local practising professionals). Their chairman, although appointed directly by ministers, had always been required to live locally. There had been every hope and expectation, therefore, that a health authority consisting of local people would willingly engage in dialogue with a community health council similarly made up of people whose prime interest was in the quality of local health care.

But in the 1990s the market place changed all that. First, large health authorities, usually consisting of 16 members, became small management boards of DHAs and trusts, consisting of only five executive and five non-executive directors. These non-executive directors were usually businessmen, many of whom owed their appointment to the CBI's recruitment campaign, who had little knowledge of the NHS and only some of whom had close links with or experience of serving the local community. The requirement that the chairman should live locally no longer applied to the new boards, who were often viewed as comparative strangers by the local people.

The CHCs watched these changes with apprehension, fearing that they themselves might end up by knowing more about local needs and attitudes than the distant board members and yet be ignored by them. In these circumstances it appeared that the future of patient power might become a lottery. It would clearly depend on the priority given by non-executives to making positive efforts to move from the cosy and secret boardroom into the reality of the community. Would they be willing to hold uncomfortable meetings in town and village halls, in churches and in leisure centres to inform the consumers of what was available and then in turn to listen to their concerns and complaints?

THE PATIENT'S CHARTER

It has been suggested that John Major's most significant personal initiative and contribution to government policy has been the Citizen's Charter. On taking office he showed his determination to improve the quality of public services so that they would be more responsive to people's needs and wishes. He believed taxpayers had the right to demand high standards. It became a priority to make the public sector more like the private sector, which has always had to attract its customers to stay in business. The Prime Minister showed the importance he attached to this initiative by setting up the Charter Unit in the Cabinet Office in Whitehall and appointing a bright, energetic and independently-minded civil servant (Brian Hilton) to head it. The whole project was supervised at first by a tough minister with Treasury experience (Angus Maude) who made it clear to civil servants in other government departments that he meant business and would not accept excuses.

The Health Department knew that a Patient's Charter was imminent but believed that health was different and would prove too difficult to include in the charter. The concept of patients' rights, standards of service and targets, such as those for admission, discharge and waiting list time limits, were good in theory but what sanctions and sops were available to the NHS to enforce them? British Rail might offer money back to commuters if the trains were consistently late but how could you recompense a patient for long and painful delays on the waiting list or for being turned away from hospital on the day of admission because the empty bed had been filled by an emergency? Health was clearly different. While it was possible to offer a more personal service and improve the appearance of reception areas anything which appeared to criticise the long suffering caring professions or, worse still, required them to embark upon radical changes of attitude was unthinkable. The department, supported by the professions, began with special pleading and shroud waving. In time, however, this looked more like drowning than waving!

Early drafts of the charter winged their way across Whitehall over many weeks but all were below the Charter Unit's expectations. The need for radical change was made clear to all ministers, including those at Health. Evenutally, a new deal for patients was produced with real rights and standards. What emerged was a charter with teeth but they were, perhaps inevitably, like a baby's teeth—painful in coming, the first set to be abandoned after a while and replaced, ministers hoped, by a full set that could get stuck into the professional red meat and old bones of the NHS.

On 30th October 1991 executive letter EL (91)128 and copies of the Patient's Charter and guide[13] were issued by the Chief Executive to all general managers and trust executives. The charter and guide were sent to all general practitioners, dentists, opticians and community health councils and, subsequently, copies were pushed through the front doors of every household in the country. This executive letter thanked managers and staff for introducing the reforms quickly, effectively and politically painlessly. It explained that the charter dealt with rights and standards which staff "are already trying to deliver" and, therefore, placed no new demands on them. It called for staff identification with and commitment to the charter and said that regional general managers (the 'shock troops' of central policy) had been asked to lead the process throughout the NHS with the exception, of course, of trusts. Unlike DHAs, trusts were self-starters: they did not need leadership, monitoring or bullying and the Chief Executive expressed confidence that they would ensure the effective implementation of the charter. The letter also set April 1992 as the target date for operation, promised specific guidelines later, and enclosed an order form for nine ethnic language versions, including rather surprisingly Turkish— no doubt recognising that the NHS management was now in the hands of 'young Turks'.

The charter began with a foreword that reaffirmed the government's commitment to the NHS and the desire to "modernise" it. The Secretary of State, William Waldegrave, stated that he wanted a service that "always puts patients first", as professed since 1979; "provides services that produce clear measurable benefits to people's health", a new demand that would take years to achieve; "represents really good value for money", a permanent part of policy; and "respects and values the immense resource of skill and dedication" among those who work in it, a new and welcome appreciation of the workforce who in the past have too often been harangued and criticised by a succession of ministers.

It identified what it called seven patients' rights that were old and added three new ones: the right to be given information on health services, quality standards and waiting times; the right to be guaranteed admission no later than two years after joining a waiting list; and the right to have any complaint investigated and to receive a full and prompt reply. Apart from the reference to quality standards there was nothing particularly new or revolutionary in any of these 10 rights.

The charter also identified nine national standards and warned that where authorities made slow progress the Chief Executive would intervene. These national standards were based on good practice and were generally not new: respect for privacy and dignity; information for relatives; arrival time targets for emergency ambulances; nurses to wear name badges; and satisfactory arrangements on discharge. The one new standard dealt with cancelled operations, under which those who had their operation postponed twice would be admitted to hospital within one month, even if it was to a private hospital. These national standards were to be followed by local standards and district health authorities, in their annual reports, would have to compare their performance against their own pre-set standards. The charter set non-challenging guidelines (two years maximum time on a waiting list) and left local authorities to develop at their own pace. Some cynics regarded it as a damp squib. Others hoped that in time patients would learn how to 'light the touch paper'.

EMPOWERING THE PATIENT

'Empowering the patient' is a popular buzz phrase that stems from the reforms and the charter. It implies that it is time for patients to hit back at the medical system and to leave their mark on the body of professional opinion. It was something everyone could believe in and might change both the style and substance of treating the sick. It was time, according to the theory, that patients emerged as real people with feelings, fears, and social and psychological needs, which needed to be recognised and handled sensitively.

Who were these patients whom the charter wished to benefit? Did they only exist in acute hospitals? Did they include the elderly in nursing homes and sheltered accommodation, who were 'clients'? Did they include the mentally handicapped living at home, except for brief respite periods, or in old and tacky Victorian institutions? Did they include the chronically sick and the disabled? Could all of these, the most vulnerable in our society drifting in the stagnant backwaters of the enterprise culture, be 'patients' and 'consumers' waiting to be empowered by the charter? Or perhaps the charter was for the few educated, articulate and comparatively fit patients who made brief sojourns to acute hospitals? Was it not likely that even with the growth of health programmes on television the majority of patients would be too ill-informed about medicine to make value judgements about, and express preferences for, their own health care. Surely, sceptics argued, cosmetic changes, such as better food, more comfortable outpatient facilities and ward decorations, would help to meet these charter requirements while the hard questions of choice could be left to GPs.

Those who believed in the charter argued that it could change the very culture of caring institutions, create a mutual understanding of their proper purpose, and could transform the institutions from something separate from the community and something unfamiliar to be feared when at one's most vulnerable into being part of the fabric of the local community. Florence Nightingale's philosophy of doing the sick no harm still holds good today, although we should add that institutions should do their sick no affront, no embarrassment and no condescension. The sick must no longer remain second class citizens, whose rights, privileges and self-respect are temporarily abandoned while they are in the hands of the NHS.

This was the philosophy, but if patients are all those who come into contact with the health care system what can be done to give them a voice, strengthen their arm and enable them to influence the way they are cared for? 'Caring' must be

a permanent and pre-eminent value for the NHS and, like any
personal relationship, to care for someone is a two-way process of communication, with give and take. What has to be
given to patients to enable them to take their legitimate place
in the process?

Information is power. So the NHS needs to open up and talk
the language of the lay person. At one level, the institutional,
this means that purchasers, whether DHAs or GP fundholders,
must publish their service plans, contracts, and quality standards while providers, whether DMUs, trusts or GPs, must
publish their internal standards, complaints procedures and
practice profiles. All these publications need to be in user
friendly language and not an end to the process of informing
patients but the beginning of direct dialogue with consumers.
At another level, that of the patient-doctor, the breaking down
of professional protectionism, remoteness and jargon has to be
speeded up to ensure that patients are more involved in their
own care. There is some research evidence to suggest that
clinical outcomes improve when patients are actively consulted about treatment choices. The benefits might be shared.

At a third level, most consumers have never appreciated the
need to understand the complexity of the NHS—its jargon, its
acronyms, or its professional, managerial and constitutional
hierarchies. Most consumers have only needed to know their
GP's surgery, how to get into hospital and, more importantly,
how to get out of it. They have usually been oblivious to what
goes on outside their doctor's surgery, the hospital outpatient
clinic and the ward. But if they were able to express a choice,
if they were to know of the options available, and if they were
to have some influence on the organisation providing their
care then it was imperative that they begin to know how to
make their way round the NHS.

Population surveys by Gallup in the Trent region in 1989
showed an ignorance of the NHS organisation and of the proposals for reform. Consumer education has become even more
important since 1991 as the NHS has grown in complexity,
with new functions, new business jargon and new relationships. The internal market has deliberately introduced fluidity
into the whole bureaucratic system. No longer is the district
general hospital here to stay, with variations in services only
being implemented following some form of consultation with

the community health council that may appear in the local press. The new health authority contract, confusing to many of the public, requires patients to travel further afield for treatment and may change the range of services locally available. Would it be better for a patient to be sent to a trust hospital? Would that be like a free patient in a private hospital or would they be required to pay for food and television in the ward?

A nationwide information service is an essential prerequisite for empowering the patients. All citizens should have access to information about local services, GPs and consultants and it is to be hoped, in time, about relative performance—information like that of the Pensylvania Health Care Council. Consumers, as taxpayers, must be given the opportunity to understand the organisation, funding, management and political issues inherent in their own health service. Only through such understanding will the consumer stop being a puppet, whose strings are pulled by professionals, and become a 'living doll'.

The Help for Health Trust, a patient information service in the Wessex region, has been operating for some years and offers a model for the future. It is a regional phone-in for self-help and patient education. It offers a vast range of simple information about facilities, waiting lists, and where and how to get help for different clinical conditions and diagnoses. A comprehensive A-Z directory[14] has also been developed that offers everything you need to know about the NHS in lay language. It is the first user guide aimed at health promotion and education—how to keep well and make healthy choices about lifestyles, how to use the NHS and the options available, how rights and standards can offer consumers protection, how to complain and get redress, and how to have a say in the development of local services. This directory is aimed not so much at the consumers themselves but at those who advise them and who are independent of the system—CHCs, social workers, libraries, citizens advice bureaux—and should, with time, lead to more positive consumer advice at all levels. These are important first steps in the growth of people power.

To be forceful and effective consumers and their representatives need a nationwide network of health care information that must satisfy a number of criteria. It must be readily accessible due to the location of its premises, hours of opening and telephone service. It must be equitable by meeting the needs of all sections of society, particularly the under-privileged, the elderly, ethnic groups, and the disabled. It must also be self-monitoring by setting targets for user satisfaction and quality standards, and then monitoring publicly their performance against these targets. It must also examine the impact it may or may not be having on changes in lifestyles and in the pattern of use of health services. Ideally, such a network should pro-gressively be owned and run by the consumers through an effective system of representation, which reflects the demo-graphic pattern of the population.

ADVOCACY IN THE YEAR 2000

Advocacy literally means the function carried out by an advo-cate in pleading and defending the case of another. Patients' advocacy is a vital concept in any civilised society, but who is to speak out for the disadvantaged? Educated and articulate patients can, no doubt, take their complaint to their health authority, argue it vigorously and, if not satisfied with the outcome, refer it to the Ombudsman (Parliamentary Health Commissioner) or go to law to seek redress. But who is avail-able to help those who are less fortunate?

It is clear that so far statutory representative systems of ad-vocacy have not worked well and have had only a limited impact on the professional and management systems of health care. CHCs have had great difficulty in defining their own communities and in developing effective communications with them. They have also generally failed to overcome pa-tients' ignorance and feelings of apathy. They have been given grudging recognition by NHS management and have been under resourced by RHAs (some have felt deliberately). They have often had difficulty in comprehending the complexity of the NHS system and the information given to them by health authorities has often been either too little (cynics have sug-gested to keep them in the dark) or too much (to swamp them). It has invariably been in an indigestible form and full of health service jargon, which has had to be rewritten to make it under-standable to the public.

The constitution of CHCs has caused problems. Generally, there has been great difficulty in attracting the best local authority representatives because they have been too busy with normal council business. The complexity of appointing effective representatives from voluntary organisations has proved too much for RHAs, which have regarded CHC appointments as an extra chore and not part of their core business. CHCs have often relied upon people with a strong social conscience, ruled by their hearts rather than by their heads, and in some places they have been infiltrated by political activists for their own gains. On balance, they have not proved to be a success in social engineering.

But if CHCs have not proved very effective who else is there? What about MPs? Members of Parliament can make representations in the House of Commons but it is clearly impractical for them to frequently act for individual patients. What about health authority members? It is not possible for authority members of DHAs or trusts to be responsible for policy and management and at the same time be the patients' advocate. But why has the NHS not tried to develop its own internal system of advocacy? Surely it is important to know what 'they' think. Some health authorities have, of course, undertaken patients' opinion and satisfaction surveys, but most of these have avoided clinical areas and much of the data have proved unreliable. Complaints procedures have been improved but few patients (or for that matter relatives) will complain while in hospital for fear, rightly or wrongly, of intimidation or adversely affecting their treatment. Suggestions schemes have operated but usually involve staff rather than consumers. Could staff act as the patients' advocate? The lay administrator/manager was at one time seen as outside the professional system and was, therefore, more likely to be objective in the investigation of complaints by having no professional axe to grind. But with the NHS becoming more businesslike managers do not want internal conflicts and do not want their business to get bad publicity, because contracts might not be retained and the balance sheet might suffer.

Might it be valuable to learn again from the American experience, where patients' advocate or representative programmes have been operating in some 3,000 hospitals—70% of all hospitals with 500 or more beds. These programmes provide paid members of staff, usually social workers or ministers of religion, who try to remain outside the organisation so

that they may take the side of the patients 'against' the professionals and hospital management. What about the nurses who
are surely always the patient's friend and committed to tender
loving care? Could he or she, despite being employed by the
health authority, be an effective advocate to protect standards
and plead the patient's case?

Some nurses have tried this by speaking out against management and their health authority on ward closures,
understaffing and poor standards of care. The UKCC's code of
professional conduct[15] advises nurses to report "circumstances
in which safe and appropriate care for patients and clients
cannot be provided." The 'whistle-blowing' issue has caused
ministers to blush and produced many 'pink' faces among
managers. Should staff be 'gagged' and as loyal employees of
the health authority be expected to toe the line, or might they
be set free to speak on behalf of the patients under their care?
The first act of one RHA Chairman, who came from a big
business organisation, was to write to all his employees com-
manding company loyalty and warning them of the dangers of
stepping out of line. New Department of Health guidelines[16]
appeared to call for loyalty to the organisation until all else
fails to remedy a wrong.

What hope then for the hospital patient, charter or no charter? The patient cannot expect to look to NHS staff for pleading
and protection. The consumer cannot be reassured either by
looking back over the 20 year history of CHCs. The market
place presents new complexities and uncertainty and has not
worked effectively as a regulator in the United States where
President Clinton has sworn to protect the uninsured and
underprivileged in society. Educated and articulate patients
and past and potential consumers must become emboldened
and take matters into their own hands. Those in the NHS who
believe in the values of caring, equity and the dignity of the
individual must open their doors and welcome not just the sick
but the rest of the community, and must breakdown the professional and bureaucratic barriers to create a healthier NHS
and a healthier society.

What about advocacy for the individual who needs care in
the community? The NHS and Community Care Act[12] came
into force in April 1993 when local authority complaints and
inspections systems, and individual case management and as-

sessment procedures, were first put to the test. Many questions must be asked. Will the very elderly person have any real choice about the home into which he or she is being sent? Will local authorities manage to change their centralist culture, devolve their budgets and provide more varied ways of 'offering' services? Will the professionals welcome a new partnership with managers, users and carers to plan and deliver jointly across the psychological barriers of health and social services systems? In the financial year 1993/4, one of the worst for public sector expenditure, will the social security money transferred to local authorities, responsible for organising residential placements of people with long-term care needs, be adequate? In the years that follow can we expect the new integrated and imaginative systems to run into the buffers of the cash limit and on the ground lead to missed opportunities of greater choice and positive empowerment?

The Disabled Persons Act of 1986[17] addressed the issues of rights of advocacy and self-advocacy but slow progress has been made since. True empowerment implies the patient's personal involvement in his or her assessment and the right to self-assessment. But who holds the power now and how quickly and graciously will it be surrendered?

Community care is everybody's business, and to be effective and to comply with the spirit of the legislation care plans and systems must be developed not only between health and social services staff but with the direct involvement of local populations, patients and their representatives. The health service and social work jargon of purchasers and providers, of contracts and quality monitoring, must not be jealously preserved by professionals and managers alike but must be translated into everyday language so that the most vulnerable in our society can understand and make their voice heard. The balance of power must begin to shift through the development of 'coalitions of support'.

'Caring for people'[18] gave the categorical assurance that health authorities would "remain responsible for the health care needs of those people who also have a need for social care." But during the 1980s health authorities were put under increasing financial pressure, which led to major reductions in the number of hospital beds. It is a curious commentary on government policy that between 1978 and 1988, when the number of elderly and very elderly was rapidly increasing, the number of geriatric beds was, in fact, being reduced from some 58,000 to 53,000. The problem of the old was progressively being transferred to the rapidly expanding private and voluntary residential and nursing home sector. The costs of care were being progressively shifted on to the frail shoulders of the elderly themselves and their families.

There is much talk of 'grey power', the fourth estate – that ever increasing proportion of the community that progressively needs the NHS to provide tender loving care. Is it realistic to think that the best hope for effective advocacy in the future lies in the hands of the energetic and articulate few, who have free time to understand and learn how to use and change the system and to exert power not only through the ballot box but directly on social organisations, which were created for their benefit and that for far too long have acted independently and in isolation? At a time when we are all getting older, living longer and becoming more vulnerable surely there is an overwhelming moral obligation on all those who plan and implement policy and deliver services on the ground to change attitudes and relationships rather than just organisational charts? Surely we must all listen to the patient, the client, and the customer even though, or perhaps because, he/she may be ill informed, hard of hearing, frail, disabled, black or underprivileged? This new dialogue, this two-way communication, will undoubtedly be difficult but it is imperative for our future. If the 1980s were characterised by the survival of the fittest the 1990s and beyond must become a time of ensuring the survival of the weakest.

REFERENCES

1. Oregon Health Service Commission. *The 1991 prioritization of health services: report to the Governor.*

2. Department of Health and Social Security (1972). *National Health Service reorganisation: England.* Cmnd 5055. London: HMSO.

3. Department of Health and Social Security (1981). *Community health councils.* HC (81) 15.

4. Department of Health and Social Security (1979). *Patients first: consultative paper on the structure and management of the National Health Service in England and Wales.* London: HMSO.

5. Secretaries of State for Health, Wales, Northern Ireland and Scotland (1989).*Working for patients.* Cmnd 555. London: HMSO.

6. Rathwell T (1990). Stand up for patient rights. *Health Service J* 100: 88–89.

7. Department of Health (1990). *Consultation and involving the consumer.* London: Department of Health.

8. Secretary of State for Social Services (1987). *Promoting better health: the government's programme for improving primary health care.* Cmnd 249. London: HMSO.

9. Department of Health (1991). *The health of the nation.* CM 1523. London: HMSO.

10. *Community health councils regulations 1985.* S1 85/304.

11. *Community health councils regulations (amendment) regulations 1990.* S1 90/1375.

12. *National Health Service and Community Care Act* (1990). London: HMSO.

13. Department of Health (1991). *Patient's Charter.* EL (91) 128.

14. Help for Help Trust (1992). *The NHS A to Z.* Winchester: Help for Health Trust.

15. United Kingdom Central Council for Nursing Midwifery and Health Visiting (1992). *Code of professional conduct.* 3rd ed. London: UKCC.

16. Department of Health (1992). *Freedom of speech in the NHS.* London: Department of Health.

17. *Disabled Persons (services, consultation and representation) Act 1986.* London: HMSO.

18. Department of Health (1989). *Caring for people: community care in the next decade and beyond.* CM849. London: HMSO.

13

RESEARCH AND EDUCATION
———— ◆ ————

There is a long and successful history of medical and, in particular, health services research in Britain. John Simon, the first Chief Medical Officer to the Privy Council and Local Government Board, engaged in and commissioned research in the 1850s, when the priorities were the control of communicable diseases and an improvement in sanitation. Since then other organisations, which though centrally financed have been independent of the Ministry of Health and later the Department of Health, have taken an interest in health research. The most important of these has been the Medical Research Council (MRC), which was set up in 1913 as the Medical Research Committee to administer funds provided for medical research under the terms of the National Insurance Act of 1911. Given its present title by Royal Charter in 1920 the MRC is funded, as with other research councils, by the Department of Education and Science. It also receives funds for specific projects from other government sources, including the Health Department and the Overseas Development Administration.

The function of the MRC, as described in its handbook, "is to promote the balanced development of medical and related biological research in this country."[1] It employs its own research staff and is advised by about 150 scientists and doctors from a wide range of disciplines, who serve on boards, grants committees and councils. About 60% of the research funded by the MRC is through external grants. The basic research supported by the MRC is supplemented by charities and the pharmaceutical industry. The House of Lords Select Committee on priorities in medical research estimated that the MRC funded £121 million of research, the DHSS £17.8 million, charities £110 million and the pharmaceutical industry £490 million in 1985/86.[2] In fact, the research budget of the Wellcome Trust now exceeds the entire budget of the MRC. This demonstrates that the charity sector can now exert tremendous influence over medical research and British science. Wellcome has, for example, declared its determination to pay scientists what they are worth, which may have a profound effect on the pay scales of government agencies. The role of the MRC in supporting research in universities is complemented by the universities themselves. Until 1991 the University Grants Committee (UGC) supported the basic infrastructure for medical research in universities through their block grant, as it did for all university research under the dual support system, but was superseded in 1992 by the University Funding Council (UFC). We will not describe the details of the changes in support of research through the university system since this has been extensively detailed in recent publications.[3]

This Chapter will concentrate on research on the NHS and health services. The structure and functioning of research has been described by Holland and Fitzsimons[4] in great detail and will not be repeated here. It is, however, important to appreciate some of the factors that have influenced medical research and, particularly, health services research over the past decade. The origins and development of health services research and research conducted by the Department of Health have been detailed in a variety of publications, notably 'Portfolio for health one',[5] 'Portfolio for health two',[6] a number of Nuffield Trust publications and letters by Godber and Cohen.[7,8]

Dr RHL Cohen, who was also the Deputy Chief Medical Officer, was the first Chief Scientist at the Department of Health. He was both executive and advisory in commissioning research for the department. He was succeeded by Sir Douglas Black in 1974, who advised the Division of Research and Development within the department on which research should be commissioned rather than acting as an executive in that forum. This has been detailed in 'Five years after'[9] and in 'Positions, movements and directions in health services research'.[10] The 1980s began in controversy as Black was succeeded as Chief Scientist by Professor Arthur Buller, a physiologist. Buller and the department were concerned with the quality of some of the health services research being undertaken and attempted to remedy these deficiencies. Unfortunately, their knowledge of the complexities of health services research and, in particular, the need to develop interdisciplinary work was also deficient. Since this aspect of research had only been funded for the past

12 years very little training had been developed and, therefore, the dissatisfaction with the quality of the work was hardly surprising. Professor Buller was succeeded by Professor Desmond Pond, a psychiatrist, who acted as a part-time Chief Scientist for five years to be followed by Professor Francis O'Grady, another part-time Chief Scientist and microbiologist.

None of the Chief Scientists were expert in any of the major disciplines comprising health services research and it is, therefore, hardly surprising that the department and researchers encountered numerous problems. For instance, the commissioners of research, the Department of Health, had trouble in formulating research questions that required an analytical answer rather than ones which simply asked for a description of the problem. Those researchers who tried to meet the department's wishes had difficulty in interpreting their findings and those involved with the department, particularly in the Chief Scientist's office, had problems in transmitting research findings to their customers, which was partly because of their own ignorance of the subject. The Chief Scientist's Office was poorly regarded within the Department of Health, with the result that those commissioning research rarely knew of the direction in which health policy was being developed and were often only consulted at a late stage in the decision making process. Researchers who originally had ready access to department officials were later held at arms length, partly as a matter of policy but also because of the increasing politicisation of health policy decisions and the suspicion that researchers were not as supportive as the department would have wished.

When consulting researchers or asking them to develop appropriate research proposals the department was immediately deterred when informed that the time-scale for obtaining appropriate results would usually be a minimum of three to five years. A further problem was that civil servants often changed their posts every three years, making relationships between researchers and civil servants fragile and often nonexistent because when individual policymakers took up a new position they had to establish new networks rather than relying upon their old ones.

The department had recognised the need to develop a method of commissioning appropriate health services research. Advised by McKinsey's, a firm of management consultants, they had established a mechanism called research liaison groups (RLGs). These were initially chaired by assistant or under secretaries and staffed by a large number of officials with perhaps one, two or three research advisers, who were usually active academics. Some of these RLGs were able to establish an amicable and productive relationship, but others failed because of the changes in personnel and the effort involved in formulating appropriate and answerable research questions rather than vague administrative queries.

As the reforms of the health service have progressed so research has become even less of a priority. Consequently, decisions on health policy have largely been taken on the advice of external policy groups, politicians and the views of individual members of the department. Whereas the original Chief Medical Officer, Godber, had been supportive of the development of health services research his successors, Yellowlees and Acheson, did not share his enthusiasm. The Chief Scientist's office was itself considered of low status and thus failed to attract high flyers, while those who learnt how to commission research rapidly moved to other parts of the department to further their own careers.

The contrast between England and Scotland in the commissioning of health services research is stark. In Scotland there was a great deal of stability and the Scottish Health Department continued to have part-time Chief Scientists, who remained active within their own field, such as Drew Kay, a surgeon, and Pat Forrest, another surgeon, followed by Roy Weir, a Professor of Community Medicine. They retained the academic trust and responsibility of both the 'outside' and 'inside'. They were advised by a full-time medical officer with vast experience in the commissioning of health services research and who had a stable and experienced staff, the successes and possibilities of which are detailed by Kay and Ashley-Miller.[11]

One of the reasons why the Scottish Chief Scientist's office and the English, under Cohen, succeeded is probably because they had full responsibility for their department's research and development (R&D). The OCS was trusted by the respective departments and given the responsibility for financing and commissioning R&D. In England things went wrong when the finance and executive function was taken away from the Chief Scientist, who retained only an advisory function.

The neglect of research over the past decade has been, perhaps, even greater than has been outlined. Much of the research commissioned and undertaken in the early years, which could have been used and exploited, has been ignored, if not rejected. For example, health services research was initially concerned with considering the relevance and effectiveness of screening, particularly in general practice. A variety of investigations were undertaken in different situations and the results were presented and published. Despite this, the Department of Health imposed a contract on general practitioners, which included a number of screening procedures that had been shown to be both ineffective and inefficient. Similarly, there are many examples of the introduction of high-cost technology, such as the lithotripter, into the National Health Service even though the investigations commissioned and funded by the Department of Health had argued that caution was required and that there would only be limited benefits from the introduction of such procedures.

Sir Kenneth Stowe argued in his book[12] that health services research has failed to develop into a significant force in the Department of Health, in health care authorities or in the world of scientific research itself. Although the reasons for this are not very clear he suggested three possible contributory factors. First, was the diversion of effort required to implement the Rothschild white paper policy on R&D, under which the MRC funds for research were transferred to the Department of Health, which was then expected to act as a customer and to commission research from contractors operating under the controller, the MRC. Second, has been the constraint on resources, especially of high quality manpower, available for centrally commissioned health services research. Third, is the fact that while health services research is a science it is in reality more of a pragmatic analysis of effective or ineffective services to secure the best value for money and optimal use of resources. To achieve this the research programme has concentrated on issues that were not of immediate ministerial interest and then committed its resources so far ahead that it was unable to switch its efforts to subjects which were of importance to ministers. Stowe argued that "In the result, I know of no strategic issue with which Ministers were concerned during my time as Permanent Secretary which was illuminated by the Health Services Research Programme."

Part of the reforms of the National Health Service in 1991 were dependent upon the development of methods of health needs assessment. It is a credit to those who started health services research in the Department of Health in the 1960s that their first major programme of research was actually concerned with this subject.[13] Unfortunately, little, if any, notice was taken of this work by those involved in drafting the health services reforms and, even more surprisingly, it would appear that those involved in implementing it were mostly unaware of this endeavour. It is surprising that Stowe knew nothing of this work.

A further problem for health services research, which has been acknowledged, was the lack of involvement of the National Health Service in the funding, commissioning and application of research because this was the preserve of the Department of Health, which had few means to disseminate the research findings or impose their solutions on the NHS. Many studies have been conducted showing the lack of application of research findings within the NHS and the need for improved dissemination. Attempts had also been made to include representatives of the NHS on the RLGs. However, as we stated earlier these gradually went into disuse and, therefore, the effect of including NHS representatives on RLGs was small. The RLGs only covered a very small proportion of the research undertaken for the NHS and, therefore, their effectiveness in some areas would not have been great in any case. It was important in mental handicap and fertility control, although even in these areas it gradually began to diminish in influence.

Finally, the Health Department limitation of tenure on their research units and, as a consequence, the difficulty under civil service rules of providing a proper career structure for health services research workers in departmentally supported enterprises has undoubtedly had a major effect on both the quality and stability of the research.

The first significant external review of research on health was undertaken by a sub-committee of the Select Committee on Science and Technology of the House of Lords in 1987/88.[14]

The department had already reviewed its research activities on a number of occasions but their findings had never been published or publicly discussed. The sub-committee of the House of Lords was entitled 'Priorities in medical research' and it began by stating that "the Committee could not fail to be impressed, from the tone of almost all the evidence they received, by the atmosphere of despondency that reflected the low morale of those engaged in medical research. It is not only that funding is so inadequate that good research proposals are not supported; it is not only that career prospects in research are often dismal; it is not only that patient care frequently inhibits research activity, important as all these factors. The overriding cause of the collapse of morale is the impression, right or wrong, that neither the NHS nor the DHSS demonstrates any awareness of the importance of research nor is prepared to devote time, effort and resources to promote it, save only when either an immediate saving of money is in prospect or when public concern, as in the case of AIDS, forces its hand. Either the government considers that medical research does not matter or else it has simply failed to convey to the medical community and the public the fact that it thinks medical research does matter."

"Whichever interpretation is right the government must put this right now or it will have disastrous effects that will take years to rectify. Crucial if negative truths stand out," the report continued. "First, priorities do not announce themselves either in theory or in practice, and, second, it is by no means obvious what the needs of the National Health Service are." The committee continued, "better health for all is the goal but is not a clear one, evidence put to the committee reveals real differences to the approach as to how better health is to be achieved or even what it consists of. Should medical research concentrate on cure or prevention? Which approach will in the long-term yield greater benefits? Are benefits to be measured for the purpose of establishing priorities? These questions have complex answers and because of that complexity any form of mechanism for directing national priorities would almost certainly be inefficient and could stifle research. The committee thus considered that the present dual system for medical research was sound in principle and that the MRC was the right vehicle for funding basic and academic clinical re-

search and the UGC and the UFC should retain the responsibility for the funding of the academic infrastructure of medical
research."[2]

Much of the evidence dealt with whether medical research
should be science led or problem led. The committee
concluded that there was a need for a balance between the
two. The committee, however, was particularly concerned
with the difficulties of applied research or, as they wished
to call it, public health and operational research. They
regarded the mechanisms established by the Department
of Health as inadequate, both in asking those dealing with
the development of health policy to consider what research
was required and in applying the research findings. They
argued that health services research had been inadequately
supported in the UK and that the amount and organisation
of such research needed reform. They were, of course,
also concerned with the difficulties of clinical research
and the cut backs in both university and health service
budgets.

For NHS led public health and operational research it was
felt that a National Health Research Authority, which could act
as a central agency with the primary role of funding both
public health and operational research as well as having a part
role in funding clinical research, should be established. This
would demonstrate to both the Department of Health and the
NHS the importance of research, as well as involving the two
organisations in deciding what research should be conducted
and how its findings should be implemented. However, the
suggestion did not find favour with the government, whose
first response was to create a Research Directorate headed by
the Chief Scientist. After a great deal of lobbying by the House
of Lords the government revised its response and agreed to
create a Directorate of Research and Development with a full-
time Director of Research, who was graded as a Permanent
Secretary and was to be a full member of the Management
Executive of the NHS. They hoped that by making the Director
of Research a member of the Management Executive research
would now have a place at the top table with its concerns and
findings being taken into account by policymakers. It was
hoped that this would rectify some of the previous difficulties.
The first Director has been Professor Michael Peckham, whose

background was in cancer research and who was Director of the British PostGraduate Medical Federation.

The Directorate of Research and Development created a series of advisory committees, including the Central Research Advisory Group. Its aim was to make sure that in future 1.5% of the operating budget of the NHS would be spent on research activities, thus meeting some of the demands and hopes of the House of Lords Select Committee. In addition to the central Directorate of Research, the Director of Research and Development has spawned the regional directors of research and development who, within their own regions, are to be responsible for the development of research in the NHS, specifying what the local needs of research are and making sure that research findings, as well as central findings, are being applied locally. The degree of co-ordination between the regional and central research structure still needs to be defined and is presently being developed.

Although in some cases highly prestigious individuals have been appointed as either full or part-time regional research directors they are rarely members of the Regional Health Board. In most cases they report to the Regional Director of Public Health (RDPH), who serves on the Regional Board, and are therefore in second line positions.

Where the RDPH and Regional General Manager (RGM) have a good working relationship this system probably works successfully. There have been, however, situations in which the RDPH has been marginalised and has consequently lost most of his influence. The RGM is also responsible for the development of the regional strategy, with the result that it is likely that the Regional Research Director will have very little clout and might actually be used as a tool in the battles between the RGM and the RDPH. This is a common occurrence as the objectives of public health do not always match those of other groups in the NHS.

A further problem that arises in the devolution of responsibility to the regions is that the availability of information for the RDPH is extremely limited. This is a major problem for the health service as a whole and the responsibility for data development has rarely been under the control of those concerned with public health. This has meant that most of the data needs of the NHS are process rather than outcome oriented and, therefore, it is unlikely that the Regional Director of Research will be able to call upon the necessary information to enable him/her to develop an effective research programme.

There is a great difference between the House of Lords' recommendations for the development of public health and operational research and the research being developed by the new directorates, whose aim is simply the promotion of clinical and health research. The primary objectives of the directorates will be local and will, therefore, be expected to support clinical research and clinical units at the expense of the wider problems of assessing health care needs, of developing criteria for assessing priorities and the introduction of new methods of treatment and technology. This is a very worrying development. Although, there will still be a centrally led research effort, which will hopefully be concerned with the development of methods as well as training future researchers in the field, the central effort that was envisaged by the House of Lords should have been more closely integrated with both the health service and the urgent need to decide upon future priorities, rather than being dominated by local parochial interests.

Although the House of Lords Select Committee[2] identified the difficulties in determining priorities and the possibly time consuming nature of this activity, the central Research Directorate has spent its first 18 months trying to identify research priorities and stimulating research. So far, the only area which has been suggested for research has been mental health, in which a number of research proposals have been advertised. Most, if not all of these, could have been predicted and some either run counter to current health service policy or ignore contemporary research projects. Unfortunately, one of the major concerns of those involved in public health and operational research over the past 20 years has so far not been addressed, which is the difficulty of recruiting adequately trained researchers to the field and then to provide them with a career structure equivalent to those in universities or the NHS.

This, as Richard Smith argued in his review in the BMJ in 1987,[14] has led to the UK falling behind other countries in both the support of research and in the research being undertaken. The difficulties and needs of such research have been well documented on numerous occasions, such as the concern with the environment, with medical care provision and the technology of medical care itself. These aims may well be thwarted because the majority of the activities undertaken by public health research peer groups is controlled either by managers or scientists trained in biomedical research who have little, if any, knowledge of public health or behavioural research. Only a few outstanding biomedical scientists, such as Dollery, are able to comprehend and sympathise with the problems of multi-disciplinary research into applied activities.

Biomedical research involves the testing of scientifically verifiable hypotheses, either by individuals or a team with similar backgrounds. Such biological research is highly method-orientated and develops within defined methodological parameters, such as immunology or molecular biology. These methods largely result from the way in which the research problems are formulated by the scientist, such as the effect of aspirin on factors in red blood cells, the haematological characteristics of individuals with asthma or the biological mechanisms concerned with the transfer of saline across the cerebro-spinal membranes.

The aims and objectives of public health research groups are altogether more complex. In general, their problems are defined by the nature of public health policy, formulated usually by bureaucrats or politicians. The main goals, for example, of research into cigarette smoking are how to prevent people from taking up smoking or, possibly, the development of a harmless cigarette. The first would involve psychologists, educationalists and administrators, and the second epidemiologists, toxicologists and chemists. It is almost impossible for one discipline to provide for the array of skills and knowledge required to solve such problems. This need for interaction between separate disciplines in public health research has not been fully comprehended by the organisations responsible for supporting such research, in particular the need for appropriate team training and the establishment of coherent stable groups to undertake such work. A further problem is that by tradition research proposals are reviewed by peer groups. In public health research the groups' proposed methodology is often expressed inadequately to one or another discipline, or the method to be used does not adhere to the principles of good research accepted by one group of scientists. Scientists, for example, in the field of respiratory physiology consider that the peak flow meter is a poor instrument to measure lung function, merely because it only measures a rather difficult parameter of lung function that is badly understood. Other tests, such as mid-expiratory flow rates, are far more respectable. However, in the field situation of epidemiological public health studies sophisticated measurements of lung function are often difficult or impossible to apply, with the consequence that the peak-flow meter may be the only feasible mechanism to obtain an objective measurement of lung function.

In the classical model of funding medical research a principal investigator has an idea and the responsibility to devise a research programme. He may involve a research team but the project is essentially his and not the team's. This may not, however, be the most appropriate model for research in social science or in cases where biological, social science and mathematical disciplines are involved.

A further difficulty is the long-term nature of public health research. Whereas laboratory research can yield results in a week, a month or at most a year or two that is not often the case with public health and operational research, which can take five, 10 or even 20 years to show any worthwhile results. For example, the influence of cigarette smoking upon health was only widely accepted after a series of studies spanning some 15 to 17 years.

Clearly, there are alternative approaches to solving researchable problems, but members of peer groups reviewing research proposals are usually chosen from the basic disciplines and do not often appreciate the problems and needs of studies undertaken within the field rather than within the laboratory. The involvement of a number of disciplines in public health and operational research means that the structure of research units differ in important ways from that of basic clinical research units.

Finally, the application of results obtained in public health research groups often require changes in public health policy. In order to achieve such reforms there must be close contact and understanding between researchers and policymakers. This has been achieved only rarely over the past 20 years. It is necessary for those concerned with both political and managerial decisions to choose topics that require research and to use the available findings to illuminate the immediate question rather than to expect research to provide immediate answers. Weir, in his Queen Elizabeth Lecture, gave a superb description of the difficulties and methods of interaction between those concerned with commissioning research, those carrying it out and those using it.[15]

MEDICAL EDUCATION

In Chapter 10 the problems of nursing education and the changes that have occurred over the past 10 years were examined. Medical education has been discussed under a series of headings, particularly in Chapter 10.

During the past decade developments in medical education have been gradual. Following the Goodenough report in 1944[16] medical education became more scientifically based. The Royal Commission on medical education (the Todd report)[17] introduced major changes to the concept of education in medicine for future doctors. It outlined the need to have both undergraduate and postgraduate education.

The General Medical Council (GMC) in the late 1970s and 1980s reviewed the content of most medical curricula and emphasised the need for these curricula to become more general, rather than continually adding one subject after another to the curriculum.[18,19,20] A variety of medical schools, particularly the new ones such as Southampton, Leicester and Nottingham, pioneered experiments in medical education by introducing students to the practice of medicine early on and thus making the teaching of basic medical subjects more relevant. This gradually began to spread to other medical schools. However, the changes were not considered dramatic enough and in most of the schools in the United Kingdom the classical curriculum of preclinical sciences succeeded by clinical sciences continued to be taught.

Most schools added subjects as they came along, such as cardiology, radiotherapy and molecular biology, without being concerned about what actually should be taught in the undergraduate curriculum, what should be taught in the postgraduate period and what the medical student was supposed to know at the end of his period of training. The Todd report had already emphasised, some 30 years ago, that it was important to consider education in medicine as a continuum that needed to be fostered throughout the medical career.

In 1992 the GMC issued a further directive[21] and a series of articles in the BMJ by Stella Lowry[22,23] emphasised the need for change in the medical curriculum. This change, which is occurring in most medical schools, involves a greater emphasis on the social and behavioural sciences, communication skills, ethics and public health rather than the learning of all the minutiae of subjects, such as anatomy and biochemistry.

Whether this will produce different doctors is still to be seen. However, the emphasis on continuing education has also started. There is now far greater emphasis placed on the requirements for postgraduate education and for those who are entering general practice, the clinical specialties or public health medicine. This is reflected in the fact that at least half the salary of junior doctors is held by the postgraduate dean, who decides on the appropriate training qualification required by those in training posts. The possibility of recertification during a lifetime career has also surfaced in this country as in several others.

We have not attempted to deal in any depth with the problems of medical education since these deserve a volume on their own and many others have already dealt with this subject. However, one of the major changes that has occurred during the period covered by this book has been the publication of the report of the Tomlinson inquiry into medical services in London, which will have a profound effect not only on the clinical services and organisation of services within London but also on medical education and research.[24] The Tomlinson inquiry was set up by the Secretary of State, William Waldegrave, in November 1991 to meet the problems resulting from the creation of the internal market because it was envisaged that health services in London would not be required to continue to treat the population that was being cared for from outside the capital.

The Tomlinson report appeared in October 1992. It recommended a reduction in the number of teaching hospitals within London and that the teaching hospitals and medical schools should combine with basic university departments. For example King's College Hospital Medical School and

UMDS should combine with King's College; University College Hospital and Middlesex Medical School should combine with University College; and St. Mary's and Charing Cross should combine with Imperial College.

This change in attitude towards the concentration of medical schools with basic science universities re-emphasised the proposals that had originally been put forward by Todd in 1968. The reduction in numbers of medical schools in London may also have an effect on the total number of medical students educated within London.

The Tomlinson report will undoubtedly have a major effect on the distribution of research, education and services within London. At risk are the postgraduate medical facilities, which have grown so rapidly over the past few years, and their incorporation within the market mechanism, which is something that they have been able to avoid so far. This will have an effect on the amount, type and quality of clinical research in London and probably in the UK as a whole. What that effect will be is as yet uncertain.

A major emphasis of the report has been on the lack of community and general practice facilities within London. It is possible that this shift of emphasis will change the whole tenor of development so that medical education, research and health services in London will become similar to those outside the capital and will be concerned not only with acute care.

The future of health services research and medical research in the UK at the beginning of the 1990s does not look very promising. Pressures on researchers, restrictions on funds and short-term contracts are not conducive to good work. Unless there is an improvement in conditions for those conducting research it is unlikely that the best research will be achieved. The UK has a number of opportunities for undertaking important research and it would be detrimental to the health service in general if these projects were not fully utilised.

REFERENCES

1. Medical Research Council (1992). *MRC handbook 1992/93*. London: Medical Research Council Headquarters Office.

2. House of Lords Select Committee on Science and Technology: Session 1987–88 (1988). *Priorities in medical research*. Volume 1—report, HL54-I. London: HMSO.

3. Brown W (1992). A premier league for university research? *New Scientist* 1808: 22–23.

4. Holland WW, Fitzsimons B (1991). *Medical and health services research.* In: Nicholson R, Cunningham CM, Gummett P (1991). Science and technology in the United Kingdom. Harlow: Longman.

5. McLachlan G (1971). *Portfolio for health: problems and progress in medical care.* Sixth series. London: Oxford University Press and the Nuffield Provincial Hospitals Trust.

6. McLachlan G (1973). *Portfolio for health 2: problems and progress in medical care.* Eighth series. London: Oxford University Press and the Nuffield Provincial Hospitals Trust.

7. Godber GE (1992). The Health Department and research. *J Public Health Med* 14 (3): 339- 341. (Letter).

8. Cohen RHL (1992). The Health Department and research. *J Public Health Med* 14 (3): 341–342. (Letter).

9. McLachlan G (1978). *Five years after: a review of health care research management after Rothschild.* Oxford: Oxford University Press.

10. McLachlan G (1974). *Positions, movements and directions in health services research.* Oxford: Oxford University Press.

11. Ashley-Miller M, Kay AW (1985). *Initiating and supporting research—United Kingdom.* In: Holland WW, Detels R, Knox G. Oxford textbook of public health. Edition one, volume three. Oxford: Oxford University Press.

12. Stowe K (1988). *On caring for the National Health.* London: The Nuffield Provincial Hospitals Trust.

13. Cohen RHL (1971). *The department's role in research and development.* In: McLachlan G. Portfolio for health: problems and progress in medical care. Sixth series. London: Oxford University Press and the Nuffield Provincial Hospitals Trust.

14. Smith R (1987). All change for research. *BMJ* 295: 1177–1182.

15. Weir RD (1991). *Research in public health: who says; who does; and who cares.* The HM The Queen Elizabeth Annual Lecture. London: The Nuffield Provincial Hospitals Trust.

16. Ministry of Health (1944). *Report of the interdepartmental committee on medical schools* (Chairman, Sir William Goodenough). London: HMSO.

17. *Report of the Royal Commission on medical education 1965–68* (1968). (Todd report). Cmd 3569. London: HMSO.

18. General Medical Council (1977). *Basic medical education in the British Isles: the report of the GMC survey of basic medical education in the United Kingdom and Republic of Ireland 1975–6.* 1. General section and school profiles. London: Nuffield Provincial Hospitals Trust.

19. General Medical Council (1977). *Basic medical education in the British Isles: the report of the GMC survey of basic medical education in the United Kingdom and Republic of Ireland 1975–6.* 2. Reports on the teaching of the component

disciplines/specialties of the medical course. London: Nuffield Provincial Hospitals Trust.

20. General Medical Council Education Committee (1987). *The teaching of behavioural sciences, community medicine and general practice in basic medical education: report of a working party.* London: General Medical Council.

21. General Medical Education (1991). *Undergraduate medical education: the need for change.* (Unpublished discussion paper).

22. Lowry S (1992–1993). Medical education 1–9. *BMJ* 305–306; 6864–6873.

23. Lowry S (1993). Medical education—trends in health care and their effects on medical education. *BMJ* 306 (6878): 639.

24. Tomlinson B (1992). *Report of the inquiry into London's health service, medical education and research.* London: HMSO.

14

CONCLUSION

———— ◆ ————

INTRODUCTION

As we approach the mid-1990s health care has become a major social, ideological, ethical, political and economic issue. Modern society is facing a health crisis caused by, among other factors, the seemingly endless rise in costs, the increased burden caused by the growing number of elderly people, the AIDS epidemic, the lack of access to care for some members of the population, the increased complexity of the health service organisation, the increased expectations of the public, and further pressures on resources resulting from the unprecedented success of technological achievements in medicine. It is ironic that many of these factors are the result of the success of the modern health service.

The NHS faces another difficulty. As a consequence of its visibility, importance, power, the respect in which it is held, and its ever increasing costs it is being scrutinised and criticised as never before against a background of continuing belief that medical care should be universally available, with equal access regardless of income. It appears that it is now virtually impossible to supply such a comprehensive service mainly free at the point of use. It was against this background that the government decided to revolutionise the NHS.

The Conservative manifesto for the 1987 general election had promised nothing more specific than stronger management and greater efficiency—the same repeat prescription. Yet when Margaret Thatcher suddenly disclosed during an interview on BBC television in January 1988 that an internal government review of the NHS was underway everything changed. She was seizing the opportunity presented by a crisis of public and professional confidence in an underfunded NHS to initiate a programme of radical reform. The need and quest for efficiency and value for money in the public sector had been a prominent feature of government for the previous

decade but something exceptional was demanded to prevent
the NHS from getting out of financial control.

Until the mid-1970s there was no real debate about the welfare state. There were obviously differences between the main
political parties about what should be done and how quickly,
but there was near universal acceptance of the major role of the
state in welfare that had emerged in the early years between
1945 and 1950. However, this consensus broke down in the
1970s. Since 1979 the Conservative government has stressed
the importance of freedom, individualism, the free market
economy and the benefits of reducing the role of the state in
welfare services. Underlying this ideology has been the belief
that private provision is always better because: it is not damaging to the economy and will be more efficient than public
provision; it does not make government the creature of particular interests; and it does not make people dependent: it offers
choice and it makes providers accountable to consumers.

The NHS was changed out of all recognition by a public
sector policy which specifically attempted to:

(a) reduce the overall level of public expenditure and meet increases in demand by releasing resources through value for money intiatives;

(b) attack perceived bureaucracies through structural change;

(c) introduce an element of privatisation through next steps agencies;

(d) transform the administration of public services into business management;

(e) attack the power of the unions and the independence of the professions;

(f) devolve decision making from the central civil service wherever possible;
and

(g) extol the virtues of personal responsibility, freedom of the individual and
the opportunity to exercise choice.

Since 1979 the NHS has been subjected to the most radical
change in structure, management and style of provision since
its establishment. The urgency and pace of that change has
been stimulated by the publication of an unprecedented number of government white papers, which with supportive
legislation have succeeded in breaking through the NHS bureaucracy and in challenging 'sacred cows'. 'Working for
patients',[1] 'Caring for people',[2] 'Promoting better health',[3] and

'The health of the nation'[4] have brought about a virtual revolution in the way the NHS is structured and managed. They are intended, if successful, to transform the service towards the turn of the century from one that was centrally planned and run by institutional and professional hierarchies into one which it is hoped will be more efficient, more effective, more responsive to its customers, and hopefully no less caring.

At over £37 billion a year the NHS is still undoubtedly good value for money, as it is cheaper per head of population than health services in many other countries and its productivity is still rising. It has always been regarded as a success by the public and has succeeded in meeting most 'essential' health needs. It is now considered as also becoming an increasing success in business terms.

PUBLIC SERVICE AND BUSINESS MANAGEMENT

Perhaps the government's biggest success in the NHS has been in transforming the management of the service. In 1979 Patrick Jenkin was questioned by the House of Commons Social Services Committee about the implementation and monitoring of government policy on perinatal and neonatal services. Patrick Jenkin admitted that he was "trying to find an effective way of monitoring the service, hopefully independent of the people who administer the service."[5] By 1989 professional independence had taken a serious knock and the development of general management had apparently proved so successful that the government was willing to risk its reputation and its immediate future by introducing radical wholesale and unpopular change only two years before a general election. They succeeded because this new and confident class of general managers, with short-term contracts, paid according to performance, and directly accountable to the centre knew that their personal future lay in the successful implementation of the policies of their political masters.

The government proposal in January 1989 to introduce a market culture into the NHS was viewed by the professions and political opponents as a radical and dangerous tampering with a popular institution. The reforms were implemented 15 months later with limited political turbulence and despite a vigorous public campaign by the BMA against them. This remarkable success in preparing a market oriented environment, in separating purchasers from providers, in introducing hospital trusts and giving GPs their own budgets was achieved by a handful of general managers, whose allegiance to the centre was unquestioned. Indeed, the Health Service Journal wrote in May 1989 that managers were "under pressure to opt out [as trusts] or face sack."[6] General managers had taken the Secretary of State's £50,000 a year and implemented the government's policies, often fighting alone against the forces of reaction, entrenchment and professional shroud waving. In private meetings Kenneth Clarke claimed that managers "put their heads above the parapet" and surged forward often against the wishes of their legally constituted bosses (their own health authorities) and with unwilling troops (their staff), who expressed their opposition through unlawful ballots. Within a year, in the face of political pressure from the centre and against a background of apparent defeat for the BMA, the government's opponents waved white flags of truce, if not capitulation. Ten years earlier such a change, implemented by hospital 'officers', acting independently of their authorities and in opposition to medical and other local staff, would have been unthinkable. The government had succeeded in creating an effective tool for change that did not let them down when the going got tough.

However, the success and rewards were bought at a price. "Pay bill for NHS chiefs rises 900% in five years," wrote the Daily Telegraph in the autumn of 1992, drawing attention to the fact that in the same period nurses' and midwives' pay had gone up only 60%. "The health service spent £25 million on general managers pay in 1987, compared with more than £251 million in 1991" during which time "the number of managers rose from 700 to 13,200."[7] Ministers, who traditionally had treated administrators as political cannon fodder, came to the rescue of their new battalions. Virginia Bottomley argued that "We spend £35 billion of taxpayers money and still for every one pound we spend on managers we are spending £43 on professional staff."

Organisational instability was a deliberate aim of government policy to revive the NHS. A consequence of this, however, was the arrival of managerial instability. At a time when general management was still in its infancy, being only five years old, the new market environment required a new culture and new authorities with new roles, which appointed new managers with new titles. Once more it developed into a period of musical chairs when managers competed with each other for the most attractive and lucrative appointments. This meant that the time a good manager spent with one authority was measured in months rather than years.

This period of frenetic change came to affect even managers at the highest level. As a result of the lack of a clear long-term strategy for the structure of the internal market and the uncertain future of the regions, even RGMs came and went—from North East Thames to the Supplies Authority, from Oxford to help reform London and from South East Thames to run the Royal London/St. Bartholomew's Trust. All this occurred within a little over a year.

With the reforms came the ethics of modern macho management, which demanded that only the best was good enough. Those, therefore, perceived as not the best were sacked, passed over or let go. Short, sharp, shock treatment of managers of long and loyal service attracted so much professional and public attention that at the Institute of Health Services Management conference in Bournemouth in June 1992 Duncan Nichol made an unscheduled address to 1,000 delegates. He attacked "macho management which is spreading fear and despondency in too many places... in my book there is no place for the clear your desk tomorrow syndrome."[8] Managing health services has always been a sophisticated task and has required the highest calibre managers. The NHS has never had a superfluity of well trained, strong and effective managers and, therefore, at a time of fundamental change, when management skills were at a premium and when ministers' expectations were unrealistically high, the NHS could ill-afford the management bloodletting which occurred. It was clearly inappropriate, out of date and dangerous to believe that the body corporate would benefit from such treatment. Good managers were still too few on the ground, changed jobs too frequently, carried increasingly heavy burdens and were put under unnecessary stress. The bloodletting continued and the NHS got weaker, not stronger. Numerous managers practised macho management and in a few places effective management was conspicuous by its absence. Both attracted critical media attention. This was not surprising as the new breed of manager had to be visible to staff, to patients, and to the public. They were seen as personally accountable for the performance of their organisation.

The NHS market also needed accurate information for costing and contracting if it were to trade efficiently. National and regional information strategies had been developed during the 1980s and pressure had been exerted by the centre to invest in elaborate computer systems. A regional information strategy became one of many individual performance appraisal (IPR) objectives for all regional general managers. Progress with their development, however, was slow and proved to be extremely expensive. It was often characterised by weak management under pressure, poor in-house expertise, and outside consultants underestimating the magnitude and complexity of the development problems that were likely to arise, and when they did they naturally attracted national publicity.

Another new feature of the business culture in the NHS was the encouragement given by the government to corporate sponsorship in the public sector. Mintel, the market research company, predicted that corporate sponsorship, a business already worth over £325 million a year, would expand rapidly–particularly in education and health.[9] If this occurs what ethical issues are likely to be raised in the NHS? Trust status and the contracting process are bound to attract sponsorship to help stem the inexhaustible drain on limited resources. The Department of Health welcomed early schemes by BUPA to provide equipment for NHS hospitals, and Mothercare, for example, makes an annual grant of £100,000 to Great Ormond Street Hospital to support a clinical genetics unit. The food industry's keen interest in health education, however, may prove to be a two-edged sword. The National Consumer Council has issued ethical guidelines[9] but the question arises as to whether we need some kind of statutory system for sponsorship in health. The worthy intention is always, no doubt, to attract additional resources for a hardpressed NHS but one has to ask at what long-term cost to the standard of service is this being achieved?

Another side-effect of the introduction of business principles into the NHS is the fact that NHS executives have been given company perks and many may look for personal enhancement through the profitability of their trust. To what extent will their ethical standards be affected by the need to keep the trust's public image clean at all costs, the need to sell their services and increase their contracts, the need to keep within their budget, and the convenience of making unattractive decisions behind closed doors? Certain standards of honesty and integrity used to be expected. The new style business management may mean a more efficient service but it may also mean one which acquires a somewhat tarnished reputation for cutting corners, offering half-truths, and for bringing the talents of a door-to-door salesman to the handling of customer relations. In the past the patient has always trusted the doctor. With the internal market he must be able to trust the manager as well. Will this become too much to hope for in the 1990s?

TUG OF WAR—CENTRALISATION VERSUS DEVOLUTION

The past decade has seen a constant struggle to find the right balance between allowing local freedom for the effective management of services, the central monitoring of policy implementation and the control of the second largest section of public expenditure. This frequent and unsteady shift from a devolutionist to a centralist stance and back again has culminated in the conflict between the desire to leave health issues to be resolved by market forces and the reality of having to regulate the market for reasons of political pragmatism. The declared policy has consistently been one of devolution whereas the actual practise has often been highly interventionist.

Whatever the policy objectives, however, as the state of the economy has declined so central control has been tightened through a number of initiatives. First, cash limits were developed and became more effective in health than in any other government department: the national cash limit was not broken and the Treasury recognised it as an extremely powerful tool in the central control of the NHS. Second, the accountability review system held regional health authorities directly accountable and their chairmen, and later RGMs, personally accountable to the centre for policy implementation and total expenditure control. In time this system subjugated and subordinated district health authorities and their chairmen to regions and introduced some sense of constitutional hierarchy into what had previously been a network of semi-independent authorities. Third, the development of general management, which set out to ensure positive leadership, planning and control at the operational level, ended up by contributing to the centralist attitudes of those who wished to limit the increasing costs of the NHS.

Whatever the constitutional position of a general manager to his own health authority a direct line management hierachy was established whereby, de-facto, the Chief Executive in the centre had a strong superior/subordinate relationship with regional general managers, who in turn developed a similar relationship with district and unit managers through IPR and performance related pay (PRP). The theory had been that devolution of responsibility down should be matched by accountability up. But as time went on and as the financial situation worsened so the emphasis seemed to be placed increasingly on accountability up rather than on genuine devolution down. The gap widened between the rhetoric and the reality. Government policy papers still stressed devolution and decentralisation but the new management systems they had created ensured tighter political control from the centre. Although the cost of the NHS continued to rise, which was accepted as inevitable, it rose at a slower pace than might otherwise have been the case without these strong management systems that had introduced greater discipline into NHS operations. At the end of Norman Fowler's six years as Secretary of State for Health he could rightly claim that he was politically and managerially in control. The local management of operations and the central management of policy implementation was more effective than ever before.

It is always more difficult to manage on a devolved than on a centralised basis. Managing a decentralised market means promulgating objectives and expected outcomes, standards to be achieved, priorities to be addressed, and allowing the service and the internal market independence, subject only to these constraints. Such a decentralised system would make life harder for politicians, who would have to draw a clearer line between the role of management and politics and keep out of difficulties raised by the odd behaviour of local managers. But if there is to be the political will to loosen the structure and control systems could the market be managed by local managers and be regulated by the strategic managers in the regions and the Management Executive in Whitehall or Leeds? The Management Executive has developed enormously over recent years. It is acquiring an improved corporate identity and effective relationship with its lieutenants in the regions. The success that has been achieved in Richmond House owes much to the confidence of and contact with ministers. The unwise decision to go to Leeds is impractical because of the need to be inside ministers' minds and their offices. Much of what has been achieved will be put at risk. The 'them and us' syndrome will be redefined and the central responsibilities of management and politics will become more confused.

REGULATING A DECENTRALISED MARKET

It is now likely that whatever political party comes to power at the next general election, either through choice or necessity, they will retain a number of features of the internal market. The concept of the purchaser/provider split and the discipline of purchasing through contracts appear to be here to stay. During the 1992 general election no party spoke against the principle of greater devolution and the advantages of giving local hospitals more authority to manage their own affairs in meeting local needs. Under a Labour administration the providers (local hospitals) may in future be required to 'opt back in' but the purchaser/provider split should guarantee them greater devolved powers than before 1991.

There is general political agreement that there is now greater clarity of roles in the clear distinction between those who run clinical activities and provide services, and those who identify a local population's health needs and then commission to meet those needs through annual or longer term contracts. The purchasing authority is relieved of the responsibility of day to day hospital management, with its political and professional distractions, and can concentrate instead on the strategic task of buying better health. The risk of self-generating bureaucracy is clearly reduced because it can fulfil this task with a comparatively small number of staff with expertise in epidemiology, health trends, clinical advances, medical audit and contracting processes. It is in a position to step back from day to day issues, to survey health needs and community problems, to identify its objectives and then put them in the context of national priorities. Its role can best be fulfilled by taking strategic decisions affecting the balance of care and the direction of change. The theory is excellent.

Unfortunately, there are difficulties in turning the theory into reality. First, in the determination of need, in prioritising, in rationing, in defining and measuring health outcomes. Experienced and well informed directors of public health medicine are still rare and it will be years before the specialty comes to grips with the demands thrust upon it. Second, the purchaser/provider split has the disadvantage of distancing the assessment of current and future needs from day to day clinical practice. Clearly, the purchaser needs some means of forecasting clinical developments and future options available. An effective purchasing policy must look ahead over a number of years and be informed by advice from professional and technical experts. Some form of 'clinical futures group' is required to examine clinical changes and to assess the relative value, effectiveness and cost of alternative procedures so as to make informed judgements and to advise on clinical changes in strategy. This area of research and development has often been undervalued in the past as health authorities have traditionally concentrated on what is available rather than on what should be available. Technological and clinical advances can be rapid and it is vital that purchasing authorities try to keep up to date.

Another problem is that the DHAs only have five non-executive directors, almost all of whom are under the patronage of the Secretary of State, there are no representatives of practising clinicians and the majority of directors come from a business background. They know that successful businesses do not stand still but analyse technological advances in material usage and trends in customer needs and behaviour, and attune their business strategy accordingly. DHAs need to overcome this problem of representation to prevent a situation developing, as in the United States, where the provider determines what is on offer and the purchaser buys it. But the USA does have an Institute of Medicine, funded by the Federal government but independent of it, which commissions investigations into changes in clinical practice. To limit provider costs perhaps the UK internal market needs a similar experiment to assist purchasers with defining a better long-term clinical strategy. Perhaps the Clinical Standards Advisory Group, a national professional body, included in the 1990 NHS Act by Kenneth Clarke in response to the Medical Royal Colleges' concerns that the market would threaten clinical standards, will help define such a strategy.

But if purchasers improve their techniques of assessment of need, keep abreast of clinical advances, identify long-term trends, explain what rationing really means in terms of untreated morbidity, and identify the black hole between what we want and what we can afford, to what extent might they create a political time bomb? To what extent will they and the market as a whole be set free, how much regulation will be needed and who will do it? Ministers' rhetoric has often implied that the market will be self-monitoring and self-regulating. The theory is that strong purchasers will demand high quality standards and will scrutinise performance. GP fundholders will put increasing pressure on providers to improve their response to the needs of their patients. An inefficient trust will lose contracts and go out of business. 'Workloads' will transfer to more efficient trusts. However, this is pure dogma and politically unacceptable. Trusts will have to be monitored and regulated in the interests of ensuring that clinical and safety standards are maintained and comprehensive care is universally available. If the internal market were to decide its own pattern of services there would be unplanned and haphazard closures as trusts run out of money, with serious political consequences for ministers. In the winter of 1992/93 many hospitals exceeded contracted levels of care two-thirds of the way through the year. Health authorities asked them to postpone routine treatment until the following April. At many units only those patients referred by GP fundholders were treated for routine operations, which led to accusations of a two-tier service.[10]

Perhaps the government hoped that hospital league tables, supervised by the Audit Commission, might offer a partial solution. All trusts will have to publish details of waiting times and cancelled operations to help the centre monitor their effectiveness. But until these tables include such factors as infection rates, readmission rates and death rates following surgery, and until they impact directly upon the quality of clinical care and clinicians they will have limited value and may be dismissed along with league tables for schools and the police, in which crime clear-up rates are open to misuse and misinterpretation as guides to effectiveness.

Will trusts and GP fundholders capitalise on their new found freedoms? Will fundholders increase so rapidly that they become the predominant purchasers? Independent and opportunistic, will they in time replace the district health authorities, the official purchasers, through whom the government had hoped to act in delivering its 'Health of the nation' targets and policy objectives by means of national, regional and local purchasing strategies? Will the market take over so that the NHS becomes progressively fragmented without any overall central planning and control to ensure that the 1948 principles of equity and access are maintained? Or will the market become a mirage or chimera, with progressively tighter 'regulation', ostensibly to retain those principles and values but in reality to maintain political and financial central control? Is it likely that the Treasury will ever loosen its clammy grip and offer genuine devolution to the market place, where people are allowed to make their own decisions both good and bad (costly)?

Most people accept that there has to be some form of regulation of market forces. Perhaps, it could mean overall policy setting by the Management Executive, minimum political interference with the processes of implementation and greater devolution of strategic management to the service itself. But how might this be achieved when the NHS is still going through structural change, with different parts of the service either seeking to enhance new found freedoms or looking back and hoping to recover lost authority. Any regulation of the market might be undertaken by 'an intermediate tier', 'zonal outposts', or a 'local expression of the centre'. Might such a tier become an additional bureaucracy separate from the region but running parallel to it, supervising the performance of providers but leaving the RHA to do the strategic purchasing? Or might such a body replace the RHA, undertake both tasks and thus confuse management with regulation? Might it be constituted like other health authorities? Might it be made up of provider/purchaser representatives? Might it simply be the administrative tool of the Management Executive, comprised of outposted civil servants and inposted NHS managers?

Whatever kind of intermediate tier is chosen, a slimmed down RHA (a ministerial back watching bureaucracy) or a new executive arm of the Management Executive, it may be required to define both the local market rules and strategic purchasing objectives. It will become increasingly important to ensure that there is harmony between the two. For example, the number of GP fundholders allowed to operate in a section of the market directly affects the purchasing authority of the DHA and its role in delivering health objectives. If the funding system for GP fundholders remains the same and continues to be applied by RHAs the chances are that fundholders will multiply and DHAs will be progressively squeezed out. It appears that if a key priority is to guarantee the power of the major purchaser, which is essential for the implementation of national and local strategy, a tight control needs to be exerted on the number of GP fundholders in a locality and the funding of those GPs might with advantage be undertaken by the local and competitor purchaser, the DHA. If DHAs were to be allowed to allocate funds to GPs the criteria would be far more strictly applied in the interests of local planned purchasing so that national and local standards and priorities could be achieved. The control of their numbers and the trend towards consortia is one method and may be the only effective way of regulating GP fundholders' activities in the market to prevent major fragmentation of the service. In February 1993 Virginia Bottomley announced a review of the NHS structure above the level of local purchasers and providers. In May she extended this review to include "possible future changes in the configuration of NHS purchasers, including DHA mergers, joint DHA/FHSA working and the development of the GP fundholding scheme."[11] This suggests that the government has woken up to the serious risk to NHS strategic planning inherent in the 1991 reforms. Or might a cynic view it as Whitehall's attempt to claw back some of the power that had seeped away from it to a devolved NHS of independent trusts and free wheeling GP fundholders?

Maximum freedom in the market and maximum decentralisation means almost total provision being made through NHS trusts, with large numbers of fundholders contracting to meet the perceived needs of relatively small practice populations. It might mean the end of a planned service and could degenerate into a 'free-for-all', in which money talks and in which accountability by GPs for billions of pounds of taxpayers' money is little more than theoretical. A politically acceptable decentralised market could lead to local provider freedoms operating under the gaze of strong purchasers, whether they be DHAs or some new body to replace them. Although purchasers need to be in touch with and attuned to the needs of local populations, the larger the purchaser the less interference there is with provider freedoms for reasons of size and distance. Perhaps a future NHS market could consist of providers made up almost entirely of trusts protecting local freedoms and being regulated by large authorities, comprising DHAs and FHSAs subsuming and replacing RHAs as agents of the Management Executive. This would mean only one tier between the centre and provider level—one tier too busy enforcing strategic purchasing objectives to be able to engage in oppressive, detailed regulation of provider operations.

Whatever means of regulating the market is finally adopted one thing is clear, the Management Executive itself cannot do it all from Whitehall, let alone Leeds. It must act through agents and it is to be hoped that they will be as few as possible. It must be able to answer allegations of duplication of regulatory or strategic management and bureaucratic or political interference. It must preserve the principle of a free moving, decentralised service based on a network of competitive providers. The danger is that despite the rhetoric ministers tend to behave like centralists, particularly during periods of recession.

Footnote: On 21st October 1993, in order to help the beleagured chancellor with his budget cuts, Virginia Bottomley announced that DHAs and FHSAs would merge but also, very worryingly, that RHAs would be reduced from 14 to eight by April 1994 and be eliminated altogether as soon as primary legislation could be found parliamentary time. If it happens, this will mean both greater centralisation and control from Whitehall and a further serious loss of public accountability.

A NAIL IN THE COFFIN OF PROFESSIONAL INDEPENDENCE?

One of the effects of the reforms has been to offer major opportunities to GPs to redress the balance between hospital and community doctors. For decades the highest professional status and the greatest clinical power, not to mention pay, has been given to acute hospital doctors and within that select group to surgeons and physicians. Until the mid-1960s general practice was often second choice for successful and ambitious medical students. A decade later this was changing and by 1991 pressures were continuing to shift the balance through the development of primary care and improved rewards being given to GPs. The contentious new GP contract offered some unforeseen increases in pay and other benefits and was intended to act as a further stimulus to professional satisfaction by broadening the range of services offered within the community, such as health promotion and health education. The drawbacks were more bureaucracy and a bigger workload in general practice.

The reforms built on the positive developments and offered GPs the chance to become purchasers, with their own budgets and the ability to buy hospital services for their patients. An early and strong incentive was that they could keep any underspending and invest it in their practice. They would soon discover that hospital consultants, of whom many had often appeared remote if not superior, were most anxious to persuade GPs to refer their patients to the consultants' own hospital. The hospital's financial viability and the consultant's personal career were for the first time dependent on the volume of patient flow. This closer relationship, provoked by the reforms, had a two-way benefit for the profession and for patients. The consultant would have to increase the hospital's business, for example by sending discharge summaries quickly to GPs either by post or even by fax. He was also encouraged to undertake more work in the group practice or health centre, which meant increased pay for him and greater benefits for patients through an increase in the range of services offered to them at their local practice.

But were the reforms really of benefit to GPs and their patients? First, the new contract brought unexpected increases in

pay overall but it varied throughout the country. Immunisation and vaccination targets, if met, brought financial
rewards. But what were the chances of GPs in inner city areas
qualifying for extra payments? Could the new contract exacerbate previous inequalities? Second, it was part of policy to
encourage GPs to extend the range of services that they undertook through financial inducements. This would undoubtedly
provide a broader and more convenient local service for patients who would not have to travel to a hospital for minor
surgery. But would this encouragement lead to GPs undertaking new work for which they had not received the necessary
specialist training or to do operations which they would
undertake too infrequently to enable them to maintain the
desired level of skill along with inadequate backup facilities?
Might standards be affected and present additional hazards
for patients?

Would GPs remain unaffected by the development of general management? Practitioners saw stronger management in
the hospital service and hoped that it would pass them by.
They watched with concern as the family practitioner committees, which had been independent statutory bodies run by
doctors for doctors, were replaced by the FSHAs, which in turn
were to amalgamate with DHAs. These authorities were now
subordinate to and receiving their budgets from the RHAs. On
the introduction of the reforms the FSHAs, with a different
constitution and less medical influence, were urgently
strengthening their management to enable them to operate the
new contracts in a positive and pro-active way and to use them
to deliver national and local health priorities. Their new general managers had become part of the general manager
hierachy of accountability that led up through regions to
Whitehall. These developments augured ill for general practice.

What about the position of doctors in trust hospitals and,
particularly, trusts in London? Trusts were semi-independent
bodies and free from the control of RHAs, which had previously been accountable for, even if they had not managed,
medical manpower. Trust freedoms included fixing rates of
pay and conditions of service for all staff, including doctors.
The future meant new contracts, new and fuller job descriptions, closer monitoring and local accountability. Anxiety was

increased by the Tomlinson report on services in London,[12] which recommended what many had nervously feared for years—the closure of one or more of the oldest and much loved teaching hospitals in the country. The proposals implied the sacking, early retirement or displacement of some 500 consultant staff. If the government could implement this kind of decimation of undergraduate and postgraduate hospital services in London, on the assumption that they would invest in primary care, then consultants in the rest of the country must be under similar threat.

Doctors in London had always cherished the proximity of Harley Street and the opportunities provided for private practice. Did the recession and restrictions on NHS development mean possible growth of the independent sector and offer consultants a glimmer of hope? The reforms had been accompanied by the injection of additional resources to ensure 'smooth take-off' before the general election. Now that the government had been re-elected was the NHS about to feel the harsh reality of economic decline and the government's further attempt to restrain public sector expenditure? If the recession made deep cuts into the NHS would the independent sector grow?

Proponents of the internal market argue that the NHS will, given time, provide such an effective and consumer sensitive service that it will marginalise the majority of the independent sector. It is also possible that NHS providers, particularly trusts, will so expand and upgrade their NHS private facilities that the independent sector will find it hard to compete. Despite the government's continuing low key encouragement of the independent sector the probable outcome will be a steady if unspectacular growth. As purchasers, including GP fundholders, become more innovative the independent sector could offer stiff competition for the NHS. The independent sector is most likely to remain strong or flourish in areas such as elective surgery, pathology, fertility control, occupational health services, screening and, of course, institutional care of the disabled and the elderly. To achieve success, however, hospitals and units in the sector will need to provide full financial information and outcome measures on which NHS purchasers can base their decisions. This has not been widely available so far. The independent sector will also need to find a solution to their dependency on the NHS for their supply of skilled staff and may in the future have to amalgamate since their success in an increasingly competitive health sector could depend on their economies of scale, which is the NHS's strong suit.

THE END?

Since the Conservative party came to power in 1979 the NHS has seen unprecedented change and growth. The reforms have given the kaleidoscope a whole new shape by the turn towards the market. But will the hopes and promises be fulfilled?

The winter of 1992/93 proved bleak for the NHS. First, the market appeared to be failing to deliver the goods with hospitals having spent all their contract money, beds were closing, operations were postponed until the new financial year, and some hospitals were only treating patients from GP budget-holders. This scenario looked like fulfilling fears of the market becoming a two-tier system. Second, the market is a managed market and criticism of NHS management performance has led to some ministerial and public loss of confidence.

The most notable loss of confidence in management came through the scandals surrounding the awarding of huge computer contracts. The Wessex RHA sought to develop a regional information system plan (RISP)—a model for other regions to follow. This RISP strategy turned out to be a high risk strategy. In 1992 serious concerns were expressed in the district auditors report about the manner in which consultants Arthur Anderson and IBM had won a huge contract in September 1986 and the way that contract had been managed. The RHA itself investigated the situation and estimated that perhaps no less than half of the £43 million spent on the total RISP project over the years had been wasted. The Public Accounts Committee called the Chairman to account. The Audit Commission also produced critical reports on the West Midlands' systems of financial control, accusing one senior manager of a "cavalier disregard for the standards of conduct expected from public officers," and the award of a £2.5 million contract with an American firm, United Research Group, which was "improperly entered into and badly managed."[13] The PAC investigated, the RHA Chairman resigned and a new RGM was appointed.

Such changes in the standards of public sector behaviour augur badly for the prospect of the internal market proving to be a success in solving the health crisis. One might ask if an opportunity has been missed over the past 14 years. Is it fair to believe that too little attention has been paid to developing an integrated and holistic approach to total government policy, to defining essential health problems, needs and minimum services, to providing adequate resources to meet those needs and delivering monitoring and control systems, the sole purpose of which is to prove that it is all worthwhile? Has too little attention been paid to defining society's fundamental health problems and the reasonable expectations we can all have for improvements to come? Has the ever widening gap between rich and poor, the closure of asylums, and the growth in cardboard cities and unemployment to record levels all emphasised the importance of a reappraisal of fundamentals? Such a reappraisal has not taken place. Government belief in the individual and minimising the role of the state has created a society based upon the survival of the fittest.

One could go on: why is it that the chronic inequalities in health have been allowed to persist? Why is it that the mentally ill, mentally handicapped, elderly, disabled, and the diabetic still receive a second class service and can see few signs of it getting better? Why does rationing work ineffectively? Why are tattoos removed and vasectomies reversed while patients die waiting for life saving operations? The introduction of the internal market was intended to tackle some of these issues by transferring some difficult decisions about rationing, priorities and choices from politicians to the people whom it is there to serve. The money, we were told, would follow patients, who would be able to influence the pattern of services by exercising choice. The early experience, however, has suggested that money will determine choice in an unexpected way. Each winter, before the end of the financial year, hospital contracts are becoming exhausted and the money available from the commissioning district spent. At this point hospitals can only receive emergencies and those patients referred by GPs who still have money left in their budgets. In the old days there was equality of misery. Everyone suffered equally waiting in a

queue until admission was determined primarily by clinical
need. It now appears that the market will become a lottery,
where people suffer under the system differentially. If your GP
has money you can express a choice. If he does not you cannot.
Is the NHS stumbling towards a two-tier system?

The presentation of policy has been positive, but the reality
less so. The public might ask what has changed for the better,
why has there been so little progress? Who has failed us—the
managers, the professionals or the politicians? The medical
profession has spent too much time and energy protecting its
privileges and not enough on reviewing its purpose and effectiveness. It had near autonomy at local level for 45 years but
throughout this time had an uneasy relationship with management, government and civil servants. It has been too involved
with the centre over its contracts, conditions of service and
medical and management systems rather than determining
clinical priorities to improve the health of the nation. It has
failed to develop a strong culture of critical appraisal. Within
clinical practice professional attention has almost always been
focused on acute medicine with only token interest given to
the cinderella services. For example, it is estimated that four
million Britons suffer from depression and it is one of the main
reasons for visits to GPs' surgeries and yet its causes are not
perceived as a high clinical priority. Even in the glamorous
acute services, however, examples can be found of a failure to
offer the most appropriate care. One in three women undergo
dilation and curettage (D and C) and yet where is the
justification, the success criteria or evidence of healthier outcomes? Some have argued that D & Cs may frequently be used
inappropriately.[14]

In another example, over the past 20 years different options
for the treatment of renal failure have been available since the
development of transplantation skills. The best professional
opinion has emphasised the superior cost-benefits of transplantation over renal dialysis and yet to take advantage of this
clinical assessment it required a major shift in the balance of
services and the resolution of new ethical considerations over
the provision of donor organs. Yet priority still continues to be
given to dialysis through earmarked funding because politicians have been subjected to well established pressure groups
and because granting the authority to remove organs from a

dead person has proved to be a political hot potato. Where specialty centres have been established the organisation has proved to be insufficiently sophisticated to ensure that patients were attracted and treated on a basis of clinical priority rather than geography. Specialty centres have been notorious for treating patients from the immediate vicinity over those from further afield, almost irrespective of their clinical needs.

Even when doctors do look critically at their own clinical performance the necessary information upon which evaluation can be based is still poor, with little priority given to its formulation. This contrasts embarrassingly with the superfluity of information available to doctors about drugs, generated by the pharmaceutical industry primarily for the pharmaceutical industry and not necessarily in the best interests of the public.

The future of the NHS depends to a great extent on effective collaboration between an informed and critical profession giving a sense of direction and a sympathetic government providing the means to pursue it. Government has always had a love/hate relationship with the medical and other caring professions. The public holds doctors and nurses in high esteem (especially when they are sick) and all governments will more often than not go out of their way to avoid a public confrontation. The optimum arrangement would be for the politicians to set the priorities that are 'clinically informed' and 'politically obtainable'. The trouble is that such an arrangement demands mutual trust, respect and understanding. A unique opportunity for close collaboration presented itself with the publication of 'The health of the nation'.[4] The government feared the appearance of central interference and recognised that it might find itself in some difficulty in setting targets for improvement which might cause political embarrassment if they were not met. Nevertheless, both sides are to be criticised for not grasping a new challenge and opportunity.

Good NHS managers are increasingly effective tools of government and have come to exert strong influences on professional behaviour. They are, however, still rare and are struggling to maintain services and standards of care against a background of frantic change and organisational instability, which seems set to continue. Good management has helped 'to

make it happen' in the NHS, but the 'it' has always been determined and delivered by others.

So where are the politicians taking the welfare state in the
21st century? Will we be able to cope with the needs of relentless demographic change? Will it be possible to sustain the
present levels and standards of health and benefit provision?
Over the next 10 years will it finally destroy the economy? Will
the elderly, who only recently have had to move progressively
out of free NHS accommodation and into private and voluntary nursing homes, find that they cannot afford it and end up
either 'home alone' or on the streets? Will hospital hotel
charges finally become an attractive political reality? They
have always been avoided because of the number of exemptions and the cost of collection, but how long will it be before
charges become high enough and the exemptions few enough
for the collection costs to appear economic? How long will it be
before a visit to the GP costs the patient money? In all advanced countries a fundamental debate will surely be
inevitable between politicians and the public on seeking new
ways of containing costs and of limiting the provision of free
health care.

The public perception of its health service is changing. It
would appear that after some 45 years it is held in lower esteem than at any time since records began. A Gallup survey for
the Daily Telegraph published in February 1993 suggested that
pride in Britain and confidence in most British institutions was
significantly lower than 10 years before. The institutions which
the British people took greatest pride in were the armed services, the police and the BBC—with the NHS coming low
down on the list. Anthony King, Professor of Government at
Essex University, has suggested that this might be due in part
to a shift in emphasis to business values and away from traditional "aristocratic" values—"values relating to community,
continuity, disinterested public service and the pursuit of excellence for its own sake, regardless of profit."[15] Might it be
that the policy to turn the NHS into a business run by businessmen with business ethics and subject to market forces is one
which the public neither understands nor trusts? Is it time to
redress the balance and to regain some of the traditional values
of excellence and integrity in public service before it is too late?

This conclusion began by arguing that we face a health crisis. Although it is too early to judge it would appear that the health changes which have been introduced since 1979 will fail to provide the answer. The reforms have brought some successes and potential successes, such as medical audit, the purchaser/provider split, improved information systems and greater efficiency. What the reforms have failed to do, however, is to address how modern society can meet future health demands given the demographic changes, the advances in medical knowledge and technology, the increased expectations of the public and the fact that there is only a limited amount of money available for health care. As a matter of priority there is an urgent need for government to draw up a strategy for future health provision which is agreed and understood by the health professions and the public and which will inevitably involve some form of formal and open rationing of health care.

This strategy must take account of other worrying issues. First, the numerous problems that patients, carers, hospitals, GPs and local authorities are having to deal with as a result of the implementation of 'Caring for people'.[2] The consequences for the community of transferring the responsibility for 'purchasing' long-term care for the elderly, disabled, mentally ill and mentally handicapped to local authorities, with a probable reduction in state funding for these services, could have as profound an effect as the NHS reforms themselves, and will certainly affect the health service as well. Second, the dangers of increased secrecy now surrounding the health service following the formation of trusts, GP fundholders and contracts in a competitive internal market. Whistle blowers are just the most publicised consequences of this. Third, the change in style of health care, as patients now remain in hospital for shorter lengths of time but require more rehabilitative care. Already there is talk of the formation of bedless hospitals in London. Fourth, the fear that as devolution increases the NHS may become more fragmented while the need for long-term planning of health care becomes paramount.

This book is intended to provide the reader with a clearer insight into some of the motives behind, the implementation of and the consequences of the government's health changes since 1979. Let us hope that despite the apparently bleak future the NHS can continue to be the envy of much of the world.

REFERENCES

1. Secretaries of State for Health, Wales, Northern Ireland and Scotland (1989).*Working for patients.* Cmnd 555. London: HMSO.

2. Department of Health (1989). *Caring for people: community care in the next decade and beyond.* Cmnd 849. London: HMSO.

3. Secretary of State for Social Services (1987). *Promoting better health: the government's programme for improving primary health care.* Cmnd 249. London: HMSO.

4. Department of Health (1991). *The health of the nation.* Cm 1523. London: HMSO.

5. House of Commons Social Services Committee (1980). *Perinatal and neonatal mortality session 1979–80.* volume 4 evidence. House of Commons paper 663 session IV. London: HMSO.

6. Anon (1989). Managers under pressure to opt out or face sack. *Health Service J* 99: 557.

7. Fletcher D (1992). Pay bill for NHS chiefs rises 900% in 5 years. *Daily Telegraph* 5 September.

8. Anon (1992). Macho managers get a rough ride as IHSM seeks code of conduct. *Health Service J* 102 (5307): 11.

9. Willmore N (1992). Facts or propaganda? The government has opened the door to corporate sponsorship in the public sector. *The Times* 25 August.

10. Butler P (1993). Old whines and new battles. *Health Service J* 103 (5335): 11.

11. Beecham L (1993). NHS review extends to all levels of management. *BMJ* 306: 1364.

12. Tomlinson B (1992). *Report of the inquiry into London's health services, medical education and research.* London: HMSO.

13. Quoted by Anderson P (1992). Ackers and Watney to face MPs' probe of RHA finances. *Health Service J* 102 (5332): 8.

14. Coulter A, Klassen A, Mackenzie IZ, McPherson K (1993). Diagnostic dilatation and curettage: is it used appropriately? *BMJ* 306: 236–239.

15. King A (1993). A nation that thinks small is condemned to grow small. *The Daily Telegraph* 22 February.